ARCHAEOLOGY AND THE MICROSCOPE

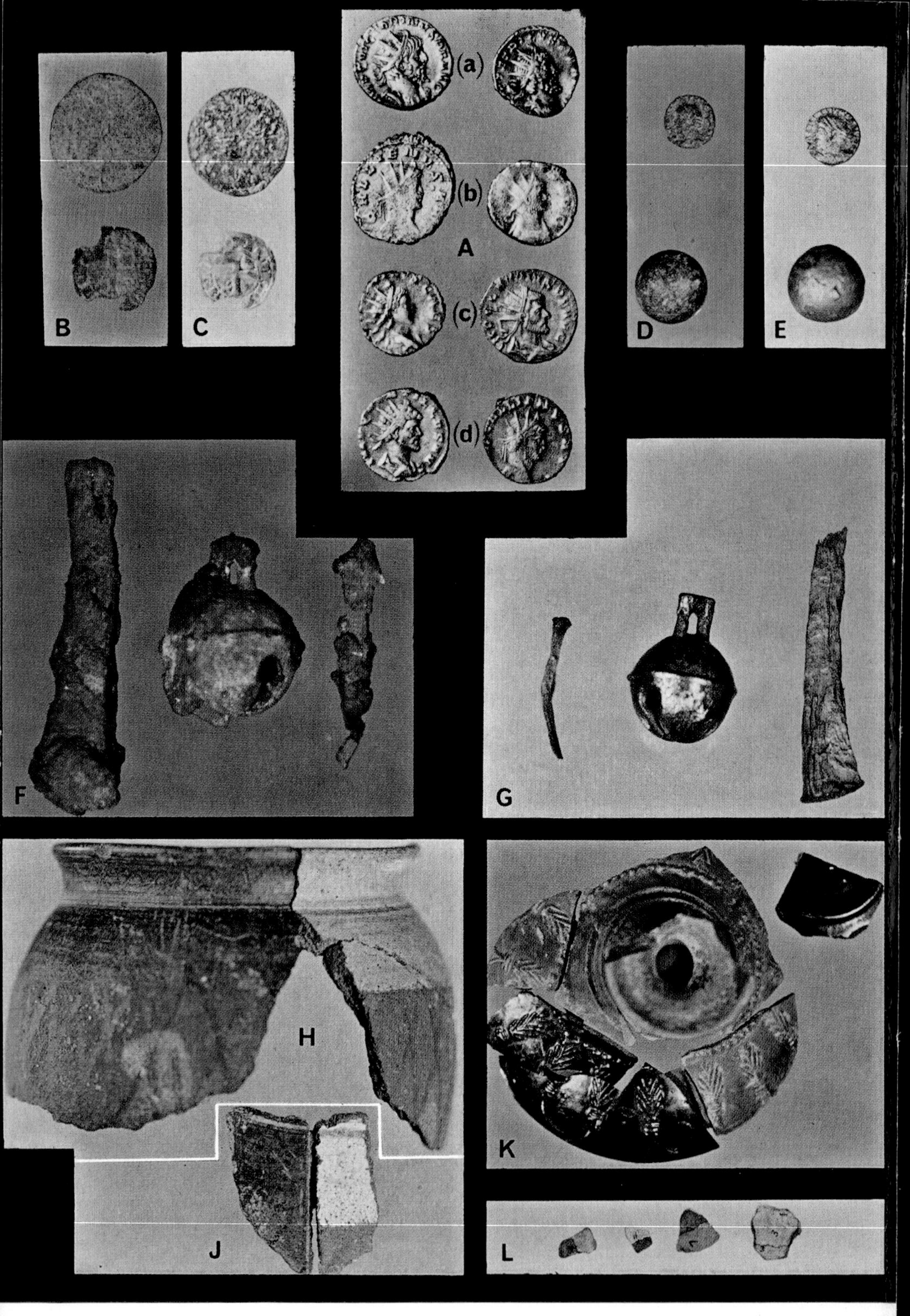

I–*A* Treated coins (p. 161): *a* Bath, *b* zinc/caustic soda, *c* gas reduction, *d* acid dip and *a*. *Left*, dipped (Birlon C); *right*, dipped, dried, flow-coated. *B–G* Bronze (*B–E* upper), silver (*B–C* lower), lead (*D–E* lower), iron and brass (*F–G*), before and after cleaning (p. 72). *H–L* Refired pottery (p. 167): *H*, *K* as found; *J*, *L* part refired in modern tests.

ARCHAEOLOGY
AND THE
MICROSCOPE

THE SCIENTIFIC EXAMINATION
OF ARCHAEOLOGICAL EVIDENCE

LEO BIEK

LUTTERWORTH PRESS
LONDON

First published 1963
Second impression 1965

To my wife

Made and printed in Great Britain by
William Clowes and Sons, Limited, London and Beccles

Foreword

by

SIR MORTIMER WHEELER

"If anybody calls say I am designing St. Paul's." But Sir Christopher might equally have been engrossed in the stars or the bones of the human body or the mystery of medicine. They were happy days of universal knowledge. Time passed and the fragmentation of knowledge set in apace. Even the word for knowledge was more and more narrowly focused upon the material universe; "science" ceased to comprehend the scientist save in so far as he was a few shillings-worth of chemicals. The *Philosophical Transactions* of the Royal Society forgot philosophy, and, not to be outdone, philosophy forgot science. Then in truth something like Two Cultures began to divide our thinking, or seemed to do so.

Consciousness of this apparent dichotomy was a slow growth, and it was not until the end of the nineteenth century that awareness reached the point of action. In 1899, at the urge of the Royal Society, the humanities and the sciences turned their (seemingly) different ways, the humanities shortly to be cloaked under the Royal Charter of the British Academy. It was not an easy separation, and as the years went by the divorced parties found themselves increasingly in each other's company again. Indeed from the outset the division was an administrative convenience rather than an intellectual necessity. Within our time, the President of the Royal Society has also been President of the Classical Association. Is there, after all, a Berlin wall between Greek and Gravity? Is Anthropology a science or a humanity? Are the Social Sciences social or scientific? And where does Archaeology come into all this?

Half a century ago an eminent university included Archaeology (then little more than a name) within both the Arts and the Science Faculties. I trust, though doubt, that it may still do so.

Archaeology has been defined as "an Art which employs a scientific technique". For what such definitions are worth, that may be regarded as an approximation. In so far as the archaeologist is labouring towards exact knowledge he is a scientist; in so far as he uses that knowledge to rediscover the involved workings of the human mind, he inevitably remains an artist. His judgement in the last resort is a subjective one; the defendant has been put into the jury-box.

But year by year the scientist is finding new ways of helping the archaeologist in his pursuit of exact knowledge. Nor is this entirely a one-way traffic. "The need for permanent co-operation between archaeologists and scientists can be seen to be vital and urgent for both." Those are comforting words from one who knows his archaeologist almost as intimately as he knows his laboratory. With a wide range of first-hand examples, Mr Biek shows how this profit-sharing process works. His book is full of information though it is not in primary purpose a technical manual; it is above all a serious and expert contribution to public relations. It demonstrates to the archaeologist the sort of results which he may expect from his scientific colleague, always including the unexpected; and it demonstrates with the controlled, all-round enthusiasm which is a proper basis for effective co-operation.

In so doing it makes nonsense of Two Cultures and restores to "science" something of its universal meaning. If for that reason alone, I welcome the invitation to introduce it to the younger, and indeed the less young, practitioners of a branch of the humanities which, within my lifetime as an archaeologist, has entered more than most into the astonishing technological advancement of the age without ceasing to be a humanity. Here is a discipline in which the dichotomy is nearly healed, and scientists such as Mr Biek are contributing daily to the healing of it.

Contents

List of Illustrations

COLOUR PLATES

MONOCHROME PLATES

FIGURES

List of Tables

Life travels upward in spirals. He who takes pains to search the shadows of the past below us, then, can better judge the tiny arc up which he climbs, more surely guess the dim curves of the future above him. . . .

If the natural sciences had been developed in Socrates' day as they are now, all the sophists would have been scientists. One would have hung a microscope outside his shop in order to attract custom, and then would have had a sign painted saying: "Learn and see through a giant microscope how a man thinks" (and on reading the advertisement Socrates would have said: "That is how men who do not think behave").

Kierkegaard

Is it altogether too fanciful to suggest that the study of world prehistory may even help to nourish the solidarity of mankind on which our well-being, if not our very existence, depends?

J. G. D. Clark

Introduction

WHEN I was nine and my father shaving, I remember telling him the story of Robinson Crusoe. Suddenly I found the hero in a situation from which he could escape only by firing round a corner. A moment of agony—then I plunged forward, but stopped when I saw my father's musing eyes twinkling at me from the mirror.

Today this vivid impression seems to me significant in two ways. For one thing it may be possible soon—or even now—to shoot round the corner. Intellectually, on the other hand, such a temptation to act desperately will always remain. Indeed it persists into adult life, where we can be made to yield to it quite easily by obstacles in the way of our stories—especially those about the nature of the heavens or the history dug from the earth—stories to which we stick however preposterous they may appear to a sane view of life here today.

The conjunction of these two aspects seems to me as symbolic as the binocular microscope, through which I have tried to turn the total view on our human situation.

This book is not about microscopical techniques applied to archaeology, nor is archaeology as such under the microscope. At heart, it is a tale of two citadels—archaeology (in humanism) and science—told by a go-between, about the changing boundaries of imagination. The microscope both enlarges and confines them.[S9] It can clarify and terrify. The power of the principle, which includes telescopy, has been immense for centuries and its potentialities are limited only by the speed of light. The Renaissance is unthinkable without it. Yet just over a hundred years ago Goethe, that most universal of all men, preached fervently against it. He warned us of disaster if our understanding did not keep pace with what the microscope revealed. Today, our first reaction to his sermon might be a cool surprise—but was the warning not prophetic?

All this enters into the background here. There are other

symbolisms. My stereoscopic binocular microscope mixes different views and clues, dimensions and declensions, and makes sure the left eye knows what the right is up to. Even as it comes down and gently explores the outlines of the different brass tacks it keeps them all in view together. Is this leather? What was that stain in the soil? Why was this iron key preserved? How old is that bone? The most important question, as always, is: What is the connection between them?

With apologies to Clemenceau—and you may read "science" for "archaeology", too—*archaeology has become too important to be left to the archaeologists.* The time has come to make quite sure in every case that something really could have been a spade before calling it one. After the Reform Bill was passed we had to educate our masters. A hundred and thirty years later we must seriously set to and *civilize* them; and we simply cannot do so unless we get all our facts absolutely straight. We need, quickly, to develop a third culture[D4]—an ultimate culture—or we shall fizzle out between our present two.[S20]

Today our diurnal metamorphoses are too well washed over by mere existence. We should all be nervous wrecks if we thought about our every change from one kind of statistical unit to another. So we roll out automatically from sleeper to soap user, bus fare and insurance number, back to member of household and part of audience. . . . The danger of over-specialization in any one guise appears ridiculously remote. We care only when our individuality is offended. Yet the pattern is there, not only in the minds of advertiser and clerk and clippie, superficially; for the specialist, too, in a deeper and more disturbing sense, this kind of fragmentation is precisely what has taken place.

As we follow the archaeologist in re-creating past activity—and the archaeo-forensic scientist, at his side, in reconstituting the technical evidence—we incidentally bestride this little world of compartmentalization.

With a few exceptions, I have taken for granted the theory and practice of archaeological field work, and in a sense also the overriding *humanity* of it all—I am concerned with precision of scientific detail. And yet my main purpose is to demonstrate that the meticulous salvage and reconstruction of man's past is an activity of supreme importance to humanity—not least because in the collaboration of different individuals it holds the key to general understanding, to the proper study of mankind.

To present a really complete picture one would have to add, to what I have said below, a systematic list of requirements, and to develop in greater detail than I have done the main theme against the background of life on earth today—even to prepare seriously for lunar archaeology and beyond. (Such preparations would be typical of my argument. Only the trained digger would be able to discover traces of activity; yet he could not move, without a swarm of specialists.) But sketchy outlines alone are possible here. Our needs are, in fact, quite simple; they can be put into one word: MORE . . .; more awareness, specialist time and equipment. The connection between our work and the modern world will be equally plain: CO-OPERATION . . .; ours is a microcosm, crying out like the whole world for the collaboration of all men in all fields of endeavour. The two words together, in both senses, make a plea that applies most clearly of all.

Specialists are inclined not to take archaeology very seriously. As laymen they are often attracted by its utter lack of "usefulness" as much as its intrinsic fascination. Explanations are difficult and could be dangerous; feelings run high in the wide gulfs that separate the various peaks of attitude. Yet all misconceptions are quite washed away by a week in the trench. Basically it is an intellectual need. Or one may simply get bitten. The most superficial discovery can tap hidden reservoirs of interest. But even if we do not care at all, can we really afford just to bulldoze straight through the accumulated practical experience of millennia? The urgency of rescue digging in the river gravels has recently been demonstrated in a striking manner. It is only a *Matter of Time* [R18] before all the evidence is systematically destroyed. On the other hand, of course, excessive zeal and *laissez faire* can produce exactly the same results.

Professionally, we need a first degree course in materials—*all* materials, with special reference to deterioration and conservation—based and developed on a broad appreciation of the whole range of human experience. Tactically, qualified archaeologists in strategic positions—for instance, with the Soil Survey and the

Ministry of Transport—would greatly reduce the loss of valuable information.

Above all, the digging archaeologist has to be "materialized". This is best done by experiment, and by demonstrating how the constant interplay between hand and head and heart that he knows so well—between toil and hypothesis, tape and hunch—extends right through the whole of human activity. But we also need to accept as a matter of principle that a non-material outlook is of very great importance to the technologist,[A15] and that the scientist is actually an emotional being—this appears to be rather more difficult. Even in practice the divergence of attitude and approach—between pure and applied, humanist and scientific—is real enough, still, to invite a great deal of constructive criticism.

There is wide and growing support for the broader curriculum[A9, B27] and for a more intensive integration of humanities and sciences.[A7, H14, H19] After all, as we parade the whole of science,[N2] history[B1, T10] and philosophy[R20] before us, each separately, they merely drift away into doubt, the greatest single factor in life today. But if we may no longer be quite sure of anything we can at least fix definite limits of confidence, organize our facts and co-operate as individuals. The true scientific attitude envelops all aspects of human thought and activity. It is the real mark of man, man the maker of tools for the communication of experience. To operate this our "second mechanism of inheritance"[M3] we must educate ourselves into education. We must learn that "we are much more likely to be able to improve our performance by learning how to learn than in any other way".[Y1] We must also accept that, with the advent of historicism, "the greatest spiritual revolution western thought has ever undergone, . . . historical conceptions have come to dominate . . . all other . . . mental activity".[B4A]

For the moment, we need to shout "more science" and "more humanities" at the same time, and just as much—but not in the same direction, or too much. . . . Still, if there is cause for alarm there is none for despondency. The dynamic view, the notion of changes taking place in an object even as we are looking at it, is coming to be accepted not as a necessary evil but as an integral part of our experience.

For the broad understanding in depth which is of primary importance, archaeology—most human of sciences, most scientific of humanities—provides the only firm common ground for all the infinite variety in size and shape of feet. Luckily the practical details of arranging communal perambulations are easy enough—they return us to the baptismal week in the trench. At the same time, the fundamental validity of archaeology itself, as an independent discipline, is questioned[S16] and established, indeed reinterpreted and enhanced, from every point on the perimeter of this scientific collaboration, which in the process benefits everything and everybody else as well.

In the end, the fresh dimension which archaeo-scientific work contributes to human experience is vital in two ways. It gives true perspective to our view of ourselves. No one need now be unaware of the sheer immensity of ancestral savagery, in time as well as in detail of action. This is surely as important to our understanding of nations as childhood is in fathoming the individual.[C9] But perhaps even more valuable, as something positive and progressive, is the opportunity of getting to know one another, on the best and easiest of terms—of establishing a total view where all conflict is resolved.

This is inevitably a personal book in many respects. It is micro-autobiographical in reflecting the development of professional experience, in post-neolithic Britain, at the Ancient Monuments Laboratory of the Ministry of Public Building and Works. The Ministry cannot of course be held in any way responsible for my remarks, but I am grateful for formal permission to publish them, including as they do in some cases details in advance of full publication.

At the same time the frequent occurrence of "we" clearly speaks for itself. Where appropriate, this is intended to acknowledge with gratitude the great help and constant support I have received from my many friends and colleagues, in particular the staff of the Laboratory: earlier, J. W. Anstee and K. J. Barton; now, W. E. Lee and C. W. Burgess; and E. S. Cripps throughout.

Well over a hundred scientific and technical specialists have kindly helped me to get my facts straight but, again, cannot be taken to task for the manner of presentation. It is to them that primary credit is due, and gratefully given in one way or another, for the fine detail of identification and interpretation in many cases.

Terminology presents great problems. For the sake of simplicity I have used "bronze", "soil" and other terms in the usual archaeological sense except where specific, critical comment seemed appropriate (e.g. pp. 163 and 222).

A difficulty at the very nucleus of writing has been not only to cater for two widely differing outlooks—broadly the humanities and sciences—but also, in presenting science to archaeology and archaeology to science, to take account of a more fundamental dichotomy.

Even as they observe the same phenomenon—in the same field, at the same level, and from the same angle—different specialists see different things. Some are concerned with the purely static aspect, the morphology and taxonomy of what they see. Others follow the dynamics involved; and though they can only study an instant frozen for examination they look at it as just that, and are for ever conscious of changes in equilibria. It is like the difference between architecture and music, painting and poetry. The two approaches are separated by a whole dimension—time. Their stereoscopic fusion may sometimes be more urgent even than the evolution of our ultimate culture which could not, in the end, cohere without such dynamic unity.

I have been further embarrassed by the spontaneous recurrence of cyclic arguments, and the consequent frequency of *Leitmotive*. Yet this is inevitable here—and also encouraging, as it underlines the essential unity of the subject which, moreover, is developing so rapidly that some phases of its progress have overtaken the writing of this book.

It was never intended as a primer—at best, it can only point to the great need for one; though *Science in Archaeology* [B32] is a brave attempt, a comprehensive textbook on the scientific examination of archaeological evidence is not likely to be possible for a few years to come. On the contrary, the book was meant to be a personal reaction to the whole fascinating and colourful spectrum of possibilities latent in such work. I am grateful for this opportunity of looking at it as a whole, and hope that the result may be found at once coherent, progressive and challenging.

Acknowledgements

THE undermentioned friends and colleagues have very kindly given of their time and trouble in reading through those parts of the book which concerned their speciality or contributions. In the many cases where institutions have so helped, my sincere thanks are due to the Principals and Staff, especially to those individually named.

J. Alexander, J. W. Anstee, P. Ashbee, R. C. L. Ashbee (née Disher), T. A. Bailey, J. C. Belshé, M. Bimson, G. H. Booth, H. H. Coghlan, C. D. Cook, N. Cook, P. S. Coston, E. Crowfoot, D. H. Dalby, N. Davey, H. R. Ellis Davidson, R. T. P. Derbyshire, G. W. Dimbleby, R. Emmerson, V. I. Evison, the late T. W. Farrer, S. B. Gilroy, R. Gilyard Beer, H. Godwin, E. Greenfield, L. V. Grinsell, W. R. C. Handley, A. J. Hatley, S. Hawkes (née Chadwick), H. Helbaek, E. W. Holden, J. G. Hurst, P. A. Jewell, M. U. Jones, E. M. Jope, G. M. Knocker, J. F. Levy, J. Lunn, L. Murray Threipland, L. R. Moore, A. Ozanne (née Furness), P. A. Rahtz, S. Rees Jones, K. M. Richardson, E. Salin, A. D. Saunders, D. J. Schove, J. Shipley, F. W. Shotton, I. M. Stead, N. E. W. Thomas, F. C. Thompson, M. W. Thompson, E. G. Turner, R. F. Tylecote, the late E. Voce, J. S. Wacher, J. W. Waterer, F. J. Watson, G. Webster, T. White, A. H. Williams.

Associated Lead Manufacturers' Research Association
T. A. Read, W. W. Robson;
British Glass Industry Research Association
R. G. Newton;
British Hat and Allied Feltmakers' Research Association
T. Barr, D. Haigh, J. A. C. Watts;
British Jute Trade Research Association
T. H. Soutar;
British Leather Manufacturers' Research Association
M. Dempsey, B. M. Haines, D. E. Hathway (then on the Staff), A. Moss;

British Museum (Natural History)
D. R. Brothwell, G. F. Claringbull, F. C. Fraser, M. Glemser, J. E. King, K. P. Oakley;

British Non-Ferrous Metals Research Association
H. S. Campbell;

Building Research Station, D.S.I.R.
B. Butterworth, D. B. Honeyborne, J. F. Ryder;

Department of the Government Chemist, D.S.I.R.
C. F. M. Fryd, E. I. Johnson;

Forest Products Research Laboratory, D.S.I.R.
J. D. Bletchly, R. H. Farmer, the late R. C. Fisher, J. G. Savory, B. J. Rendle;

Fire Research Station
L. A. Ashton;

Geological Survey and Museum, D.S.I.R. and Ministry of Education
P. J. Adams, E. A. Jobbins;

Low Temperature Research Station, Agricultural Research Council and D.S.I.R.
E. C. Bate-Smith, T. Swain;

Leeds University
R. D. Preston, R. Reed;

London University, Institute of Archaeology
I. W. Cornwall, S. S. Frere, I. Gedye, W. F. Grimes, H. W. M. Hodges, F. E. Zeuner;

Morganite Research and Development Company
D. W. Brown, J. B. Nelson;

National Gallery Laboratory
M. Hey, J. Plesters, G. Thomson;

National Physical Laboratory, D.S.I.R.
W. E. Carrington, W. J. Callow;

Oxford University, Research Laboratory for Archaeology and the History of Ari
M. J. Aitken, E. T. Hall;

Paint Research Station
T. R. Bullett, C. P. Cole (then on the Staff);

Royal Botanic Gardens, Kew
C. R. Metcalfe, F. Richardson;

Shirley Institute, Didsbury, Manchester
B. M. Abraham, G. G. Clegg, A. Heckels, A. H. Little, C. Malpas;
Soil Survey of England and Wales
C. Bloomfield, C. L. Bascomb, G. W. Cooke, D. C. Findlay;
Wool Industries' Research Association
H. M. Appleyard, A. B. Wildman;
Tin Research Institute
S. C. Britton, E. C. Ellwood (now at Royal College of Science, Glasgow), W. R. Lewis, D. A. Robins;
Zinc Development Association
P. Dolan (then on the Staff).

Special thanks are also due to David Lowe, sixth-former at St. Marylebone Grammar School, who commented on the manuscript, and to Betty Carvajal who patiently retyped much of it.

Both the colour plates, and most of the other plates (excepting those from X-radiographs exposed in the Ancient Monuments Laboratory) were made from photographs taken in the normal course of work by the Photographic Section, Ministry of Public Building and Works, almost exclusively by Mr. J. H. L. Bloomfield, with the exception of pl. 1, *lower right*; pl. 4, *lower*; pl. 5, *lower right*; and col. pl. II *J*, which were made from photographs taken by the architect and excavators, respectively, who were directly concerned with the work on behalf of the Ministry. Other photographs were kindly made available by Dr. J. K. S. St. Joseph, the Cambridge University Committee for Aerial Photography and the Air Ministry (pl. 1, *upper*), and the Department of Scientific and Industrial Research (pl. 3, *upper left*, and pl. 4, *upper*). *All these photographs are Crown Copyright*, and I am grateful to H.M. Stationery Office for permission to publish.

For the rest, I am greatly indebted to the following for photographs and/or permission to publish illustrations: Messrs. Aerofilms Ltd. (pl. 1, *lower left*), the Tin Research Institute (pl. 2, *lower*, and pl. 14, *lower*), the late F. W. Jane (pl. 3, *upper right* and *lower left*), R. D. Preston (pl. 3, *lower right*), J. F. Levy (pl. 5, *upper right*, and pl. 23, *below right*), the British Hat and Allied Feltmakers' Research Association (pl. 7, *upper right*), S. Rees Jones, by courtesy of the Director, Courtauld Institute of Art (pl. 7, *lower left*), the Shirley Institute (pl. 7, *lower right*), E. Salin (pl. 10, *lower right*), the British Non-Ferrous Metals Research Association and the Zinc Development Association (pl. 15, *lower right*), the Royal Botanic Gardens, Kew (pl. 19), and Messrs. Westland Aircraft Ltd. (pl. 20, *upper*); the Commonwealth Scientific and Industrial Organization (fig. 1), the Paint Research Station (fig. 3), R. M. Cook, J. C. Belshé and M. J. Aitken (fig. 9); W. E. S. Turner (table 1, previously published in *J. Soc. Glass Tech.*[T12]); Lady Aileen Fox (pl. 14, *upper*).

I am also grateful for permission to publish information based on material supplied by R. H. Farmer, Forest Production Research Laboratories D.S.I.R. (pl. 11), and M. U. Jones (col. pl. II *O*, and fig. 10).

CHAPTER ONE

What it is all about—Background

SCIENCE IS systematic practical curiosity. It is one of man's many organized attempts to apprehend the pattern of the perceptible. In it, as in other forms of learning, the rough desire to know is consciously restrained and soothed by reflection; the innate energy is canalized by planning, and intuition is cooled by the necessity for experimental proof. From it emerges a balanced judgement of the nature of the particles of material phenomena and their relation to one another, and of the limitations to our knowledge of them.[B6]

Applied science harnesses these results for man's benefit. Nevertheless, it is inevitably more concerned—and must be, if it is to be successful—with the influence of Nature on the works of man.

Archaeology is a science in that it objectively examines, draws conclusions, and then tests them in field work. But, although it studies, of course, the same material as applied science, it does so from an entirely different point of view. It is interested far more in position than in condition, and even in relationships in space—where they are not purely structural—largely because they mean relationships in time. It is fundamentally more concerned with the influence of man on the works of Nature.

In its systematic search for material remains it is really after the spiritual values. However meagre the residues may be, they are the results of motivated activity. The detailed and imaginative study of earthworks, barrows and field systems gives us a direct insight into the mind of prehistoric man, his fears and tribulations, customs and beliefs. In Sir Mortimer Wheeler's challenging words, "the archaeological excavator is not digging up things, he is digging up people; however much he may analyse . . . and desiccate his discoveries in the laboratory, the ultimate appeal across the ages . . . is from mind to intelligent mind, from man to sentient man".[W11]

The approach being thus primarily "human", the subject is taught almost exclusively within the Faculty of Arts. But it is significant that archaeology may be read at some universities for a B.Sc. degree. Recognition of its nonconformist outlook is here established from the start. The unfortunate division of knowledge into two separating streams is also shown up for the arbitrary artifice it is. And yet, one of the germs of the solution to this problem, whose urgency today reaches out beyond mere academic polemic to strike at the very roots of survival, lies dormant at the centre of this very situation; it is the enormous unifying potential in archaeology, in a past that is real and live, for bringing together minds caught up in the current pattern of diverging humanities and sciences.

For the appeal of archaeology is universal and it provides common ground for people with the most varied interests. Everyone is interested in people, and the fascination of the past provides an effective counterpoise to speculations about the future. Moreover, the study of primitive man quite naturally involves the study of his environment and is, in fact, becoming increasingly dependent on it; so there is really something for everybody. Whatever the helper's experience—or motives, provided they are sincere—and whether he comes to dig or makes a spectrographic analysis in the laboratory or gives of his time and knowledge in discussion—so much help is needed that he can be quite sure his contribution will be of enormous value.

Some come for one reason and stay for another. Their routine field of activity may be a very narrow specialized one far from archaeology, on the face of it, and they may choose digging as a complete change or for a holiday. But as they become initiated and realize the possibilities, entirely new vistas of exploration are opened up for them and they begin to see their subject in a different light. This enriches not only their own experience but also that of their fellow diggers, not least that of the supervising archaeologist; the scope of the excavation widens as a result of the interplay of ideas springing from different attitudes to the same problem, and the general technique of field work benefits all round.

On a small excavation recently, I found a pathologist, an entomologist, a pedologist and a bacteriologist entering archaeology the hard way, with spades and buckets. They had not been at it very long, but already they had found a multitude of things in which they took a specialized interest, to the extent of taking samples away for examination at their laboratories. Some of the results which they brought back touched on points the archaeologist would never have dreamt of considering—nor for that matter would they, either.

Obviously one cannot expect an immediately or invariably relevant return. There are many red herrings, some real, some apparent, and only a great amount of work over a period of time will show the true value of such fragments of study and information. But a start has to be made—and has been made—and the first fruits are already beginning to develop. The important thing is the attitude of mind.

Help often comes from an unexpected quarter. The chance remark in a pub, a casual glance from the train window, a shaft of sunlight falling at an uncommon angle, a sentence in a forgotten book—all have played their part in touching off that sudden illumination. Or, again, one of the labourers employed on the heavy digging may be familiar with local conditions and traditions. His knowledge of a particular custom or craft—no less than a specialist's quick appraisal of conditions from the shell finds [W3]—may be decisive in determining the course of an excavation—quite apart from adding to his own interest in the work.

"Indeed, it is always interesting," an eminent metallurgist said to me, when we had been discussing the condition of a Saxon metal object and had decided that it was of no direct value to him in his work. There was an air of disappointment in his voice and he was almost apologetic. For he had heard of my association with some research for modern industry which had arisen directly from an archaeological find. "Something may come out of it, or it may not. But it is always interesting."

Whatever the reason, or the angle of approach, there is this underlying partiality. It may start with a trickle of curiosity, and it may spill over in a torrent of fanatical disregard for everything and everyone else—but at any level, once archaeology has been recognized for what it is, everybody can be charmed by some aspect of the fascination. There is an absorbing quality about it all, shared in some ways by detection and discovery in the widest sense. I believe this to be so because it provides an outlet for the creative urge, in the vital "reconstruction of man's past achievement".[W11]

At the same time, the steadily increasing amount and complexity of this work—coupled with the general advance in technique in all other fields of inquiry—has made it both possible and necessary for the archaeologist to rely more and more on specialists in all spheres, from the finest art to the most mechanical science. Not only is there something for everybody—there is also plenty for everyone to do.[A10]

Long before the dig begins, the ground has to be prepared in many ways. There is the search for records, and the appraisal of the general geographical situation of the site. These are normally tasks for the supervisor of the excavation and he receives much help from the local museum. But there is usually someone elsewhere who has made a special study of these very aspects and a great deal of time and labour will be saved if he can be found.

There may be an economic historian interested in a particular period, or method of land cultivation, or system of property transfer, who knows where many of the existing documents may be found. In Britain it is often possible to get a fairly comprehensive picture, starting with the Domesday Book, or even earlier, with the Romans. An archaeologist working in a limited area will usually be familiar with his beat. But in London and other cities so many things have happened on a particular plot of land over the centuries that documentary evidence may often be a vital factor. The level of Roman occupation in such cases can be at a depth of thirty or forty feet below present street level, and while this raises special problems due to mud and waterlogging the stratification is fairly clear where the different layers are thick and easily distinguishable. It is where a series of similar activities have followed in rapid succession, as in the case of medieval wells, drainage schemes and rubbish pits, that the interpenetrating disturbances which are visible in the section of a trench may be so confusing and misleading. Grimes, rescue-excavating during the rebuilding in the City of London, devised ingenious techniques to overcome this difficulty,[B33] but he was greatly helped by the relatively good records available.

Then there is almost certain to be a geographer, or perhaps even a geomorphologist, who has concerned himself with the relation of the prospective site to near-by coalfields, mines, quarries, sources of timber and water, etc.; also with accessibility and climate, both now and at various periods in the past. There are many instances of rivers changing course and coast-lines altering even in historical times;[S25, V6] earlier modifications—particularly when associated with changes in climate—although less may be known about them, are usually even more pronounced and important.[G11]

There are many other ways in which specialists can assist the excavator before he begins field work, as with advice on defensibility of fortifications, navigability of waterways, and so on down to the smallest detail. Wherever occupation right up to comparatively recent times is suspected, interest in deserted medieval villages[B10, B33] and even eighteenth-century pottery industries has greatly enhanced the value of first-hand knowledge of local traditions almost within reach of living memory. Finally it is important to know what modern disturbance there has been, and that includes anything from a nineteenth-century "excavation" or deep ploughing to temporary works or Home Guard trenches.

Apart from these lines of attack there are others which may appear, at this stage at least, to be less obvious but are nevertheless often more generally applicable; where they are, their usefulness remains great throughout the excavation and even beyond. Preliminary inspection of the site with a geologist and an ecologist is always valuable to the excavator. He learns the nature of the undisturbed rock formation, what the ancients might be expected to have found in it, how it would have weathered and affected the type of soil accumulating on it. Directly dependent on this, but also influenced by other factors, is the kind of vegetable and animal life to be found there, now as well as then.

Again, he can then see his particular area in relation to the surroundings. This may be particularly important where the locality has been affected by glaciation, or lies on a junction of different types of rock. The insight so gained complements what has been described earlier. To some extent the various fields of view are bound to overlap, but there is never any harm in illumining a subject from several angles, even if some of the light sources are very close to each other.

Finally, there are two "mechanical" ways of obtaining information before field work begins. One is aerial photography whose application in this context has been extensively described in recent years.[C21, S2] Its usefulness is based on two fundamental observations. First, slight differences in ground level due to the remains of ancient ditches and banks, indistinguishable from the ground, may be visible from the air. Secondly, ground plans of earthworks, buildings and field systems, which have now completely disappeared from the surface but whose construction has disturbed the soil in some regular pattern, may show up as crop marks in areas that are now under cultivation. This observation was in fact recorded as early as 1541.[F2]

The method is sensitive in several ways. Much depends on the angle of both sunlight and photography, on the time of year and the kind of season, and even on the distribution of any fertilizers in the past (pl. I, *lower left*). Yet its results are often strikingly successful (pl. I, *upper*). Not only does it provide a basis for excavation where something is known to exist; frequently it also brings to light new evidence. Some progress has been made towards a more systematic use of this extremely valuable tool.[R18, S2]

The other kind of technique involves the measurement of some geophysical property of the soil, such as resistivity. "Meggering" (p. 207) has been employed for many years in the study of soil physics and mechanics, connected with the earthing of electrical installations, location of water tables and foundations for buildings. Its usefulness depends on the fact that the resistance of soils to the passage of electric current is determined by the amount and nature of substances like water and salts which they contain; this in turn reflects the type of soil down to a chosen depth.

The application of the principle to archaeology was first described by Atkinson,[A16, L2] and fully discussed at a recent conference.[B9] By carrying out a resistivity survey on selected areas, or even extensively all over the site, a remarkably accurate picture of soil disturbances, in the form of filled-in ditches and pits, etc., may be obtained quite simply and rapidly.

Again, the method is sensitive to changes in the weather and the general ground mass, and there are about it a number of things whose archaeological significance is not as yet properly understood. This may have contributed to its comparatively limited use so far. But when employed in a relative way to indicate changes in subsoil structure from one point to the next, this underground surveying can produce ghosts of ground plans in much the same way as aerial photography. Another similar type of survey, producing in some ways more spectacular results, uses differences of magnetic susceptibility in the soil (p. 208).[A3]

I have drawn attention to these lines of inquiry because, with some notable exceptions, their importance is usually underrated. All the approaches have this in common: they can be made at any time, within limits, and without scratching the surface. In that respect they are akin to "non-destructive analysis" which has in recent years been so successfully applied particularly to the study of priceless archaeological material. The preliminary surveys are also independent of the constraints of the excavation itself; once this has started everyone is far too busy and survey teams are usually in the way, although some overlap is clearly vital.

The main value of such initial work clearly lies in its function of predicting what is likely to be encountered—more, even: of suggesting what the excavator might with advantage be on the look-out for, and what would require the immediate attention of a specialist. It could be argued that this is a bad thing, that the excavator should embark on field work with an open mind, and that in any case he has enough to think about already. But on reflection it should be clear that any such disadvantages are completely outweighed by the danger of destroying or missing evidence whose existence is not suspected.

It is as well, therefore, for the supervisor to be prepared in this respect—no less than in all the other, more usual, ways in which he knows he must make ready as excavation becomes imminent.

As far as organization goes, an archaeological site is very much like a simple building site in its first stages. All the Ministry's specialist advice in this respect and, within the inevitable financial limits, all necessary equipment is automatically available to an archaeologist on a Ministry dig.

But then there is the weather. Unfortunately most of the Ministry's undertakings of this nature are rescue work. The Minister is empowered by law to delay development work which threatens archaeologically important sites, but the period of delay is often insufficient to allow a really adequate excavation to be carried out unhurriedly and may moreover fall into the most unsuitable time of year. Hence the weather is a more than usually important factor. Normal meteorological services are extensively used. Promised improvements in long-range forecasting would be most valuable and are eagerly awaited.

Apart from the obvious physical hardship involved, the archaeologist's chief concern in this connection is that the delicate features of evidence which he has carefully exposed during the day should not be obliterated by wind or rain overnight. After all, every action in field work is irrevocable and cannot be repeated; it produces a change which is liable in turn to give rise to further changes. In the limit, significant traces of a chemical sensitive to oxygen or light, which have lain for centuries protected by waterlogged soil or in some other way, may lose their identity within a few hours or even minutes (p. 131) of being exposed to the air. This refers back to the need for immediate specialist assistance, and for awareness on the archaeologist's part of what he might come across. Since everything he does is in that sense destructive he must be able to record it properly at every stage. The effects of natural destructive agencies must therefore be kept to an absolute minimum.

At present the means of protection against them are limited, in general, to boards, roofing felt, tarpaulins and corrugated metal sheets. Although these can be adequate in many cases, valuable evidence has been lost where they have proved ineffective. Moreover it would be a tremendous advantage if at least some detailed work could be done, during prolonged spells of bad weather, on one or two important sections. Cost has so far prevented the provision of suitable cover for this purpose, but it should be possible in the near future to develop the idea of a transparent plastic dome or some simple mobile roof of synthetic-resin laminate for use in this connection,[L5, M4] and polythene sheeting is just beginning to come into its own.

Water rising from the ground can be an equally great nuisance. High water tables and natural springs may even be a menace, especially in unstable ground or during the excavation of deep wells where they can cause not only confusion but even sudden collapse. This is a difficult problem because archaeological techniques must here diverge from building practice. You cannot simply sink a coffer dam or concrete-in a trench. So far excavators have felt their way slowly and patiently towards the limit of safety, pumping and shoring up as efficiently as circumstances and equipment would permit, and have then quietly given up in the face of superior forces. But again it ought to be possible within a reasonable time to adapt some of the standard methods of soil mechanics into an economic technique of temporary soil stabilization, and to provide safe and dry working conditions. Recent work in a 100 feet deep shaft at Wilsford, near Stonehenge,[A14] has indicated what is possible even within a six-foot diameter: from hoist and air supply to closed circuit television.

Where a rescue excavation involves the rapid survey of a large area, earth-moving machinery can be a great boon. It must, of course, be used only with a full knowledge of its potentialities, otherwise it will reveal and destroy concurrently and indiscriminately. Bulldozers are already being used to shift topsoil and modern rubble and level the site conveniently for excavation. It is also possible, under suitable conditions, to search for significant features very efficiently with a long scraper blade drawn by a tractor. Although this can remove soil at the rate of foot-acres per hour, and yet can be safely adjusted to take off as little as half an inch at a time, the method is attended by obvious hazards. But against these must be set the very real possibility of exhausting a rescue dig in a small insignificant area, while the truly valuable evidence in another is then destroyed, and with ironically unfailing certainty, by the very development works which were so laboriously held up in order to search for it.

Heavy machinery can also be used in other ways. An application to what might be called constructive archaeology, in its most literal sense, was the use of heavy cranes to raise some of the fallen trilithons at Stonehenge.[B2] Heavy equipment is, of course, widely employed in many capacities for the exacting task of preserving standing monuments by the Ancient Monuments Architects of the Ministry of Public Building and Works. The technological basis of this work is very similar to that of modern building techniques and here again the help of the Ministry's other appropriate branches is a great asset.

In view of the multiplicity of uses which have currently been found for helicopters, for instance as at Coventry in the attachment of a finial to the top of a spire, it is tempting to consider their potentialities in excavation work. A number of applications immediately spring to mind. For the careful removal of heavy stones they would appear to be ideal, and where the ground is inaccessible to heavy machinery they might provide the only means of dealing with this and many other problems. But cost has so far limited their use to low altitude photography. For this purpose small captive balloons, with remotely controlled cameras, can now be used with advantage.[A1]

Cousteau has made possible an entirely fresh approach to underwater exploration.[D12] The methods employed at present limit the work to comparatively shallow and quiet waters, but research which could be carried out in this way off the Mediterranean coast alone would keep several generations of archaeologists very busy indeed. Some aspects of the technique are moreover directly applicable to the exploration of waterlogged underground caves. Speleological research, which has brought to light much useful evidence about the life of very early man, has therefore benefited directly from developments in Cousteau's work and similar improvements made in Britain in association with the Royal Navy. It is interesting to note that Cousteau's activities also provide an example of the reverse process, of a technique evolved largely for archaeological purposes being applied, as this has latterly been, to another field of scientific investigation: the geological survey of the bottom of the Persian Gulf in the search for oil. "Rocket" surveys,[M2] such as that of the bed of Lake Windermere, provide further exciting possibilities of application.

But to return to the archaeologist preparing for an excavation on firmer ground. The elementary surveying required in the layout of a site is an essential part of archaeological training. Here the use of nylon cord for datum levels, as pioneered by P. A. Rahtz, particularly in trenches where complicated sections have to be studied over a considerable length, and in wet weather, is obviously a great improvement on the conventional string.

As in all branches of scientific inquiry photography has become indispensable. In the first place it provides a continuous record of the general progress of the excavation. Until the use of balloons or helicopters becomes an economic proposition, anything from a ladder to a platform on scaffolding will of necessity continue to serve as a means for getting the camera sufficiently high above the site to take in enough of it. There are on the market mobile platforms which can be raised to a height of twenty feet or more, but again cost has so far prevented their general use in the field, although they would surely be invaluable on a site of any size.

There are innumerable other applications of photography, from features, sections and other significant details to small finds, both in the field and in the laboratory, and at all stages.[C17] As a rule, excavators have to be their own photographers, at least in the field, and in general that is a pity. For one thing they cannot be expected to have the specialized knowledge which is necessary in many cases to bring out to the best advantage the particular feature they wish to demonstrate. For another, they could utilize the time and energy spent on photography—and these can be considerable—better for work which they alone are qualified to do. Clearly, also, they would be wasting their time developing and printing; and yet in many delicate cases this should really be done by the man who takes the pictures.

The number of good archaeological films, expertly made, is as small as the need for them is great, and films on technique are practically non-existent. The obvious advantages of colour cinematography, at the rate of its present development in other fields, should become generally available to archaeology in a few years' time. Colour photography is already extensively used. 3-D colour has been tried in museum work and proved a magnificent asset. Its application to complex features and stratifications would open up exciting new vistas in archaeological recording.[W14]

Finally all the multitudes of small ways in which, as each excavator's personal experience has taught him, the loose ends must be tied up materially speaking, have to be prepared for. Particularly where access to the site is difficult, even the transportation of heavy, friable objects or unwieldy structures to the laboratory or museum can assume the proportions of a minor engineering problem.

Special arrangements had to be made when it was decided to transfer to London, in one piece, a substantial fragment of a Roman mosaic floor, found during the excavation of a villa at Downton,[R4] near Salisbury in Wiltshire. The fragment measured 10 feet by 8 feet, and by the time it had been undercut, lifted, boarded up and packed with sand for safety it weighed several tons. It was loaded on to a lorry and driven at 20 m.p.h. to London where it received treatment. When mounted it was returned in a similar manner to Salisbury Museum where it is now on permanent exhibition.[H11] The salvage of the Swedish warship *Vasa,* lost at the start of her maiden voyage in 1628, has recently provided a most striking example of complexity and ingenuity.[O2]

From the time the first spadeful is turned everything that is exposed is important. Even if not immediately recognizable, or indeed visible to the naked eye, with a bit of luck foresight will preserve it, patience will reveal it, and skill may be able to develop it into a piece of information that will fit into the general jigsaw. Having primed himself properly with recorded information of all kinds, and drawing on his practical experience in the past, the excavator must be ready for anything.

Once digging has begun there will be little time for deliberation. He will have to decide quickly whether he should call in a specialist to inspect a freshly exposed feature in the field. Or if he thinks this is unnecessary he must know how to take his samples and what to put them in, how to keep them and where to send them, and how quickly.

Sometimes a tiny stain may have to be sampled with a cork-borer, tightly packed into a specimen tube which is quickly and securely corked—all this to keep out the air—and sent off at once. In other cases a pound or more of a pit filling may be required, together with a similar quantity of the undisturbed soil into which the pit had been dug; and the samples can safely wait for months before they are examined.

In general the use of polythene bags, squeezed free of air, with the open end screwed up and secured with a rubber band, is proving most effective. In this way soil samples, and even wooden and leather objects, can be kept virtually as found until they can be dealt with, provided there is nothing about them that will puncture the bags and the whole is handled sensibly.

Correct packaging is always most important.[N5] All the care bestowed on accurate sampling or on excavating a delicate object may so easily be brought to nothing. Although in most cases crumpled newspaper or cotton wool is sufficient protection, some particularly tricky instances may require much thought and ingenuity. It would seem so easy on the face of it; there are only two principal requirements: a robust outer cover or case that will withstand rough treatment, and a means of protecting the vital inner core against contamination and shock. And yet these simple aims are often quite difficult to achieve. Moreover other complications are likely to arise.

Imagine, for example, a large funerary urn expertly made some 3,000 years ago but none too well fired. After all that time in the ground, during which the pottery has been softened to some extent back on the way to clay, the vessel is found upright, somewhat crushed under the weight of soil, and crumbly, but with its contents intact, protected as they have been by a slab of stone. It is just possible to lift the urn, together with some surrounding soil, out of the ground in one lump. It is vitally important to get it to the laboratory without further disturbance or delay, so that the contents can be examined as they were found and the urn can be consolidated and restored.

How, now, to prevent the pottery from collapsing either outwards or inwards, to keep the contents damp and in position, although they only half-fill the urn, and yet not risk contamination with anything that might affect the analysis—all at the same time and intended for transport? A pretty problem in mechanics and materials (p. 93). It must be admitted that the ordinary parcel lives a most precarious life anyway on its journey from the field to the laboratory. All the same, a great deal of damage can be avoided by a little forethought. But sometimes even common sense is not enough, and one must consult the Printing, Packaging and Allied Trades Research Association.

The excavator's primary concern has been and probably always will be, in the laboratory as in the field, with recognizable objects. In most cases they form the solid skeleton of the evidence on to which the archaeologist grafts his interpretative flesh in order to give life to the whole body. More often than not, unfortunately, objects other than pottery are found in Britain in a poor state of preservation. The excavator must therefore be prepared to impregnate or otherwise to consolidate any finds that may be too fragile to be lifted without support, avoiding contamination where possible (p. 243).

Most laboratories are mobile enough to be able to help out in exceptional cases, but ideally, of course, the excavator should be relieved of *all* worry about objects (and indeed samples too) to devote himself to his own special task of revelation in the field. Moreover, the laboratory worker could then keep in direct touch with field conditions and this, quite apart from enriching his experience and adding to his interest enormously, would enable him to do his job properly: to see all the finds through, in a material sense, from the trench to the museum.

For it is now widely recognized that the skeleton of evidence can be filled in very considerably by the application of scientific techniques to work on small finds. Analysis and cleaning can throw valuable light on their nature which, after all, most clearly reflects the cultural status of their makers and users. Proper preservation will ensure that they will continue to remain, for enjoyment and research, even after we have gone.

What is not generally appreciated, however, is the extent to which all the other material circumstances can be made to help in filling out the general background. The real skeletons are already becoming as important as the metaphorical one. We are passing from the motionless exhibit in the glass case of the Anatomy Lecture Theatre, as it were, to watch the farmer sowing in the field by the stream, at the edge of the forest.

CHAPTER TWO

What it is all for—Purpose

FUNDAMENTALLY a knowledge of the past is desirable to consolidate the foundations on which we are building the future. In certain ways our activity is already and inevitably conditioned; in others much is unconsciously accepted as traditional in the best and widest sense, as well tried and proven. But it is only by consciously exercising his individual powers of judgement and selection to the full, and learning from the total experience of the human race, that man can hope to mature into fulfilment.

Particularly at present, when science tends to blind us, at first sight, with the significance of a limited truth which we are tempted to revere, it is necessary to remind ourselves that beauty is just as important and the appreciation of it as ancient and as easily suppressed—if not more so. By its preoccupation with the material present and future, science is in danger of cutting us off from our spiritual roots.

The importance of archaeology as of history lies in its ability, by reconstructing human life in detail, to reveal eternal human values. Most of our ends and means have been handed down to us but, in Orwellian terms, some have been handed down more than others, and first-hand knowledge is an invaluable asset in discriminating between them. The most salutary effect of the development of nuclear fission has been to sharpen into an acute question man's random musings about his fitness to survive. We are enjoined most movingly in many ways to consider this seriously before it is too late. Archaeology must play a vital part in helping to provide the answer.

Although like science it acts by placing man today in perspective, archaeology does so not coldly against the vast, empty spaces of the atom and the universe, but against time, the mainspring of life and full of the warmth of human activity. In that way it induces humility without a sense of overwhelming isolation or insignificance. And then, at a time when the very nucleus of science is developing some unsavoury interference fringes, the casual manner in which archaeology strides across all artificial boundaries is truly magnificent.

It is immensely heartening to know at first hand that other beings, essentially similar to ourselves, have been faced over scores of millennia with the same fundamental problems of controlling nature, each other, and themselves. By projecting ourselves into their minds, in the nearest approach there is to a time machine, and studying in detail how they worked out their individual solutions, we are suffused with a feeling of solidarity and continuity that is infinitely restful. As a reviewer of *The History of Man* has put it, speaking of "the unique and almost incredible epic that comprises human history": ". . . the lessons to be drawn from it affect us to the very core of our being". But the review begins, significantly, by saying that any good writer on archaeology has an exciting story to tell, provided he keeps to the facts.

Now the Scientific Attitude demands a continual re-examination of all evidence, and a rigorous control over its acquisition and acceptance. Where its power over men's minds is both hidden and great, as in history and archaeology, it is vital that such evidence should be correct, precise, complete and balanced. There are many other things it might be, with advantage, such as imaginatively developed and persuasively presented; but such aspects, although they may in many cases come very near it psychologically, are not fundamental from the philosophical point of view and must be kept separate. Only by resting securely on those four essential attributes can a knowledge of the past inspire the confidence which is necessary if it is to contribute in full measure, as quite clearly it should, with all the other streams of experience, to an integrated philosophy of life.

For over a century now, historians have systematically been trying to re-check known sources and to find new ones, to speak more simply and broadmindedly. Aware of their tremendous responsibility, they have been at pains to turn upon themselves the full force of their professional interrogation and integrity, in order to discover objectively how objective it is possible for them to be. Butterfield[B35] regards this "history of historiography not as a branch of the history of literature but as, so to speak, a subsection in the history of *science*" (my italics). Our knowledge of the past, he goes on to say, is seriously affected if we learn how that knowledge came into existence and see the part which historical study has played in the role of the human race. "The historian who survives" (as opposed to his "outmoded" colleague who suffers a death "more complete and pitiful" than that of an ordinary mortal) "seems to be the one who in some way or other has managed to break through into the realm of enduring ideas or gives hints of a deeper tide in the affairs of men."

Although the beginnings of the modern method of historical study are associated with a group of professors at Göttingen University in the late eighteenth century who, "in a system of combined operations, achieved what amounts to a creative act", the first great names to appear are those of Niebuhr and Ranke. In 1824 the latter began his preface in a companion volume[R8] to his monumental works on the history of the Renaissance with these words:

> In writing this treatise . . . my intentions were threefold: first to justify the manner in which I have utilised my sources; the second, to indicate to those who would instruct themselves on the beginnings of modern history the books from which they can do this, and those from which they cannot; a third, the pre-eminent and purely scientific, to contribute, as much as I may, to the collection of genuine material for modern history, to a thorough assessment of the nature and value of the available sources.

It is both instructive and refreshing, if somewhat unsettling, to see him demolish the principal source, Guicciardini, point by point, and then to watch, in the remainder of the two hundred pages, a whole galaxy of European chroniclers being subjected to a withering scrutiny. And yet even Ranke, in discussing what remained to be done, did not go beyond advocating a more intensive search for, and examination of, documentary evidence.

The fundamental questions are still with us. A reviewer of UNESCO's *History of the Western World* asks: "Has history a pattern? What is the criterion of significance for selecting historical facts? Are moral judgements permissible in history?" Whatever answers might be given, and however history might be used or abused, there would probably be broad agreement that "its final justification is as an added dimension of human experience". In order to fulfil this function properly, history must surely be supported by a framework in which the human experience is at some points literally tangible.

Trevelyan, one feels, is perfectly right when he says that "the impelling motive of historical study is poetic". For that reason, the best initiation into it may well be "the stories which have become the common saga of all mankind—Moses . . . Leonidas . . . Alexander . . . Mahomet . . . Columbus . . . Napoleon . . ." for all that the last regarded history as an "agreed fable". (Ranke, who wrote a long appendix in his defence, would have included Macchiavelli.) Whether or not one agrees that "this is much better history"—after all "it is how Gibbon began"—one feels instinctively that it might well be, as an introduction, "more helpful to a sensitive international understanding than the onward march of the human family from the palaeolithic caves to the Universal Postal Union". And yet it is vital that the route of this march should be clearly defined at all points. Wherever the meandering path of a casual inquirer, even, should happen to cross it, he must find the milestones correctly placed and accurately inscribed. Signposts are a different matter, as progress might not always be in the same direction.

Progress was Baudelaire's *bête noire*. As Sir Herbert Read reminds us,[R10] "we may not now be so confident of ourselves, but we still live in the same age"—Baudelaire's "arrogant age which believes itself to be above the misadventures of Greece and Rome" —the age of "steam, electricity and gas—miracles unknown to the Romans—whose discovery bears full witness to our superiority over the ancients". There is great power in the poet's passionate rejection of the concept of progress: "this modern lantern throws a stream of darkness upon all the objects of knowledge; liberty melts away, discipline vanishes. Anyone who wants to see his way clear through history must first and foremost extinguish this treacherous beacon." Even modern science would agree.

Imagination is the cardinal faculty. "It is both analysis and synthesis. . . . In the beginning of the world it created analogy and metaphor. It decomposes all creation, and with the raw materials accumulated and disposed in accordance with rules whose origins one cannot find save in the furthest depths of the soul, it produces a sensation of newness." But whatever echoes this may stir within our furthest depths, even imagination cannot work in a vacuum. It must have the raw materials to feed on. And while it might, and indeed must, transmute them in art, it must not in history.

Plato must have had a similar process in mind when he made Socrates examine concepts, "observing how each of them is split into many and torn apart, and then collecting each of them into one again: and so try to discern in what possible way each of them is in fact both a one and a many". For "there is a gift of the gods" which "the men of old, who were better than ourselves . . . (*sic*), passed on . . . in the form of a saying"—and "it is indeed the instrument through which every discovery ever made in the sphere of the arts and sciences has been brought to light"—namely: "all things . . . that are ever said to be consist of a one and a many, and have in their nature a conjunction of Limit and Unlimitedness." If one were to develop this slightly out of its immediate, but not its general, philosophical context, one might say that Baudelaire's "imagination" would soar into the unlimited sphere, having seized on the limited nucleus as raw material, from which it can take off, and to which it must return. And Butterfield is surely thinking in the same terms when he speaks of the "critical point" (Plato's "conjunction") "on which historical explanation depends" as "the possibility of maintaining the unique in every individual, event and moment, at the same time subjecting movements of masses and processes of centuries to analysis and generalization."

It is plain that history, like philosophy and indeed all forms of experience, must in the end be presented imaginatively, in terms of the general and the "unlimited", in order to be intelligible. But it is equally clear that the point of "conjunction", at which such a presentation becomes significant, must never be lost sight of—otherwise imagination becomes a fugitive balloon, at the mercy of freak and fancy. And it is precisely at this point that archaeology comes in. For it studies in minute detail the exact nature of the "limited" historical unit: the raw material—the individual, event and moment—and it studies them independently and at first hand.

History, modern—Lord Acton jotted down—begins by getting behind historians. The way in which historians are tackling the problem, by checking up on their predecessors and at the same time on themselves, has been described. But there is this other more literal way of getting behind the chronicler at the event itself, by digging up the material evidence. When some years ago UNESCO, in its concern to promote the "teaching of honest history", to get away from Napoleon's "fable", sent an invitation to Croce, he attacked its "dilettante optimism, its ready-made solutions for the profoundest of human problems, its attempt 'to solve the most delicate questions of the life of the mind by the method of majority votes.'" This seems a little hard when UNESCO was only trying to get the facts straight. Now that some of the fruits of this labour are beginning to see the light, they might indeed perhaps be criticized for a certain lack of imagination, for being too concerned with "the highest *common* factor of human experience" (my italics). But no one would deny their brave attempts at accuracy and objectivity. Yet they faithfully reflect the "majority" conception that because prehistory, of necessity and by definition, belongs to archaeology, archaeology therefore belongs as inevitably to prehistory.

Now this is of course manifestly untrue. The fundamental distinction between history and archaeology is in method and not in period. Excavation has probably done as much as contemporary record to elucidate the Roman era, the Dark Ages—which have recently been illuminated quite considerably—and the Early Medieval period. And yet, while distinguished archaeologists have contributed to *History of the Western World* on prehistory, the debt to archaeology for knowledge of the later periods remains unrecognized.

No doubt this is partly the archaeologists' own fault. In their preoccupation with the earlier periods they have tended, at least until fairly recently, to neglect the later, historical ones. In a way this is understandable since it is more worth while to explore, by the only available method, where no written records exist. And that has continued to lend support to the general classicist belief that archaeology ceases to be conjectural, and indeed becomes truly profitable, only when it uncovers a fresh text or, to a lesser extent, when it produces some tangible material illustration or confirmation in detail of what is already known from, or suggested by, documentary evidence. It is true that the imagination is fired more readily by the way in which excavations in the Mediterranean have served to turn Homer's epics into history[K1] than by the discovery of an obscure Pagan Saxon settlement on the north bank of the Thames. But the latter, the first to be found in that area, may well prove intrinsically to be more significant.[B4B]

The general misconception seems to be due mainly to the magic power of the written word. Such magic can be very black, even in purely literary criticism.[B24A] In actual fact, archaeology has lately been pushing forward in time, with the help of history, as much as history has been penetrating backward, with the aid of archaeology. In both cases the results have been of great mutual benefit in many ways. For various reasons discrepancies between records and events can be considerable, even in comparatively recent times. There is nothing as objective as the concrete material evidence.

For nearly a century also, archaeology has been moving away rapidly from its initial treasure hunting attitude towards a scientific consideration of what Glyn Daniel calls the "totality of evidence". Once the principle of stratigraphy had been established and its importance had been fully recognized, accurate recording became an absolute necessity. Remembering once again that excavation is here synonymous with destruction, one can see that the supervisor must always have a clear picture in his mind of what precisely he is doing. While the field work is in progress this is important because it enables him to go back with confidence to a section he may have abandoned, in order to re-examine some detail in the light of something that may have been found in the meantime on another part of the site. Also, in working through the day's notes when the light has failed, he may suddenly see a connection that was not obvious in the field but is just beginning to emerge on the general plan, and he can modify the next morning's work accordingly. After the dig is over, when everything that seemed worth removing has been taken out of the earth, and the site has been filled in again, it becomes more important than ever for the excavator to be able to tell exactly where an object was found or a sample was taken, under what conditions and in what surroundings. He still has the finds but he can no longer study the soil profile except from his records. So much varied and sometimes conflicting evidence will have been revealed that he cannot possibly rely on his memory in any detail when he begins his exacting task of imaginative reconstruction.

Three principal trends may perhaps be selected as having contributed most, in a purely material sense, to the development of analytical archaeology, that is to say to the branch of the discipline primarily concerned with extracting the maximum possible information from the evidence. All three grew out of a sharpening of the excavator's powers of observation. Two of them evolved together, side by side, being dependent on one another to some extent and encouraging each other for that reason. The third was an offshoot in a slightly different direction, but making use of the other two and complementing them most effectively. In all the three trends, keenness of observation and usefulness of analytical results have been linked by that happy reciprocal relationship which, as in other lines of inquiry, is governed by the law of increasing returns. The more is noticed, the more is recorded, the more rewarding become the results of specialist examination; and that in turn has the effect of making the excavator more observant.

The first of the three developments was an extension in the number of materials in which the excavator took a particular interest. By its very nature pottery reigned supreme in its importance as evidence until quite recently, and even today it occupies a position of pre-eminence. Objects might be fashioned more easily from wood or leather, but in Britain, at least, such articles are likely to be found in a useful condition only where they have been buried in exceptional circumstances. Metal artefacts might be discovered in a slightly better state of preservation, but their manufacture required much greater skill and they were therefore precious to the ancients, particularly as the metal could be re-used. Even metal objects are thus comparatively rare finds.

Early investigators were admittedly interested in early periods.

For the ages before pottery began to be made, flint implements and stone tools furnished practically the only remaining evidence, and must of necessity continue to do so. Where, from later deposits, pottery began to appear it was seized upon as an obviously more satisfactory touchstone. In any case, even much later when metal had become plentiful, pottery continued to be far more generally used; it also got broken very easily, became useless and was thrown away. And from the archaeologist's point of view it was particularly valuable because it could nearly always be depended upon to survive.

It is therefore not surprising that such a reliable and ubiquitous form of evidence should have been regarded as of prime, and even overriding, importance. Unfortunately, however, its appraisal depended (and still does, almost) entirely on a superficial examination of the ware and a comparison on stylistic grounds. Where different types of pottery were found neatly stratified in layers, a sequence in time could be established easily enough. But when there was only one kind which had to be related to similar finds in other parts of the country, the results were far less satisfactory. Although there is a great deal of comparative material available nowadays, this situation still remains much the same for certain periods and some areas. And sometimes, if rarely, no pottery is found at all.

The excavator was thus forced to look for other evidence. Strictly speaking, of course, he did not have to look very far because it was all there for him, such as it was; only he had omitted to notice it in some cases—in others he did not yet realize its significance. Gradually metal articles began to receive greater attention, the foundations of buildings were studied more carefully, and earthworks were excavated in such a way as to permit a detailed examination of their nature and construction.

The rewards were immediate and exciting. Like metal artefacts, objects made of other materials had, of course, been recorded and reported, where and when they occurred, from the first, but rather for the sake of completeness and almost as curiosities. Compared with the abundance of pottery, their isolated and as yet unrelated appearance seemed unlikely to make them of direct use to the excavator. But as they became more plentiful, and it became possible to associate them with certain periods and regions—still on stylistic grounds, and in conjunction with pottery—all kinds of finds, from shale ornaments to glass beads, from wooden wheels and buckets to leather soles, bone combs and whetstones, became increasingly important. All the same, it was still possible for Coghlan to complain in 1951:

> Up to the present pottery and lithic implements have received more intensive study than have the metal objects; but there can be no question that the metals form a most important part of the material culture of a prehistoric people, as they indeed do to a greatly increased extent in our present civilisation.

After stressing that "we cannot afford to neglect [a people's] advance, or degeneration, in the metallurgical field", he urges that "the archaeologist should not rest content until he knows exactly the composition of the metal, and by which process the artefacts were made; it is far from sufficient merely to know the typological and chronological background to the object."

And that is precisely the second trend I mentioned earlier: an extension of the interest in objects to include a detailed knowledge of their material nature. It was, after all, only natural that the archaeologist, as he came to take notice of these other objects, should begin to wonder what exactly they were made of and how. For various technical reasons this line of inquiry has been rather slow to develop, and from a systematic point of view, as Coghlan pointed out, the position is still far from satisfactory. Nevertheless, as will be seen later, tremendous advances have been made in the analysis of ancient materials and methods, recently even in the somewhat laborious examination of stone implements and, to some extent, pottery.

Most is now known, perhaps, about metal articles; and that is not only natural but also appropriate since they form a universal and important part of the evidence, next to pottery and stone. With the help of specialists, every step involved in the passage of the metal from the ore to the finished axe-head, sword or coin came to be studied in detail. In the process a great deal of valuable information has been obtained, not only about ancient methods of metal-working but also about trade routes and other signs of mutual influence linked to the development of technical skill.

The same applies, *mutatis mutandis* and to a lesser extent, to all the other materials from which articles have been made. As a result of the more or less systematic botanical examination of remains, on the all-too-rare occasions when enough had been preserved, it has been found that certain types of wood were preferred for certain purposes already by the ancients. The petrological matching of stone implements with their parent rocks has made it possible to establish the existence of certain centres of primitive stone-working industries. The presence of a particular chemical element in a fragment of glass, even of a minor constituent in a pottery glaze, has suggested or confirmed a foreign import or influence.[T3A]

Finally, the excavator could not fail to realize that man stood in a definite relationship to his natural environment, far more rigorously than he does today. Just as the development of his skill was limited, in the last analysis, by the materials that he used, his whole life was ultimately dependent on the climate and soil, the fauna and flora with which he had to contend, and on the resources and security offered him by the area in which he lived. In order to understand him properly one must set his achievement against this background to his existence. To judge him fairly one must learn how he controlled his surroundings and took advantage of his opportunities. And for that purpose it is essential to recreate in detail not only his life and works but also the totality of his environment.[J3C]

Thus the archaeologist began to train part of his observation on features that were outside the immediate field of man-made objects and structures. This third line of development, the offshoot into the sphere of indirect evaluation, concerned itself first of all with the minor evidence of daily routine and the waste products associated with it: a patch of fire-reddened sand, some charcoal, a heap of animal and fish bones, oyster shells, a lump of slag. With the increasing interest in the precise nature and significance of the materials of fashioned articles went a correspondingly closer scrutiny of such less obviously useful clues. The results were again immediately fruitful and encouraging. In discovering what animals primitive man hunted and ate, what trees he felled and used for firewood among other things, we can form a picture of the wild life that shared his environment and of the forests that flourished where he lived. The slags not only throw additional light on his status as a metal-worker but also indicate the kind of natural resources of which he was aware.

As the "natural history" aspect of excavations developed, human remains also began to come in for more detailed attention. Specialists interested themselves, often of their own accord, in the stature, type of skull and other physical characteristics which could be determined from the skeletons—more recently also in evidence of disease and even primitive surgery. As more material became available it began to be possible to treat the results statistically and make comparisons as between different areas and periods. This, and similar work on the flora and fauna, is proving remarkably significant and thus increasingly valuable to the archaeologist.

As an inevitable result of the improvements in technique which took place in other, more purely scientific, fields during the past half-century—and it always strikes one afresh how little time they have taken compared with development during the millennia they are now being used to study—investigations were gradually extended to include, first, the minor states of life such as snails, insects and worms, and eventually the minute forms in which evidence of life is preserved, such as seeds and pollen. Together with the appropriate study of the soil which holds the precious grains, pollen analysis produced something like a revolution in the methods of this "environmental archaeology". For the examination of ancient soil surfaces which lie buried, for example, under a Bronze Age barrow can now yield precise information about the types of tree and even herbaceous plant which grew in the immediate vicinity at that time, as well as about the climate which controlled them, even something about the date[D9] and of course the activities of man.

I have tried to indicate in a general way how and why the archaeologist has come so largely to depend on, and profit by, specialist assistance. The main burden naturally still falls on the excavator. It is he, after all, who conceives, plans, organizes, directs, digs, correlates, interprets and reports. But he has taken on human life in all its complexity and there will always be many others, as he will be the first to agree, who have made a special study of some particular aspect of this fascinating phenomenon or its relationship to the rest of the world.

The precise delineation of the significant features of the buried past, many of them no longer clearly visible on excavation, and some only ghosts of shadows reflected or even refracted in the background, can be attempted with any degree of certainty only if the combined power of all the available techniques is brought into play. Although it is left to one man to draw the actual line in each case, he must be guided by the experienced eye of the craftsman and by the automatic pen recording atomic radiation. The resources are fully mobilized in their own fields. It is merely a question of adapting them for an unusual purpose. For various reasons, among them the very human nature to whose study all these efforts are bent, this is not always easy. But possible it is—in most cases already, in others likely to be proved so within the next few years.

The task is made easier by a circumstance which at first sight might appear unexpected, irrelevant and even incongruous. In fact it is none of these. Experience has shown, particularly in recent years, that the scientific examination of archaeological evidence, apart from its fundamental importance, can be of direct and considerable value to the specialist examiner in his own field. In principle, it provides him with material which is not available to him from any other source. There are difficulties but they can be overcome and, when they are, the mutual relationship of increasing returns becomes operative once again, and in a multitude of ways. The general, if gradual, recognition of this state of affairs is bound to advance such work and enlarge its scope enormously.

From the purely scientific point of view, interest is primarily focused on an aspect with which the archaeologist is least concerned: the condition of objects as found after prolonged burial in given circumstances. The excavator has tended to accept the state of preservation, good or bad, virtually as providential and of little or no significance. Actually an understanding of the processes which were responsible for it can be vital, both for the successful conservation of the object and as circumstantial evidence.

But the scientist's concern, systematically curious, is at once more fundamental and more generally practical. He is interested to know exactly how it happened that the material (rather than the particular object) came to be so weakened and disfigured as it is, or more especially why, in some cases, it did not. If he can find out, the answer will help not only to conserve the particular object, and others like it, but also in general modern practice to protect the material, as such, when it has to be buried as part of some installation, and thus to prolong the latter's life.

This can be a very serious consideration. It has been estimated that some five million pounds are spent in England and Wales every year on replacing corroded water mains alone. A proportionate amount of money and labour is thus devoted to research into the mechanism by which iron corrodes underground. But however encouraging the results may appear in the laboratory, only field tests and ultimately the behaviour of the actual pipe in service will demonstrate the usefulness of such research. During the past forty years or so innumerable testing sites have been laid out all over the world in order that the phenomena might be observed under controlled conditions.[R17]

When therefore well-preserved archaeological material comes to light that has, in effect, been under test not for years but for millennia, the event is of paramount general importance. Sometimes such a find can be of immediate use to modern industry and an example is given in Chapter Six. But even evidence which appears to have no direct value may hold the germ of an idea, furnish a missing link later when its full significance comes to be appreciated, or give an impetus to research in another field with which it has no obvious connection.

Similar considerations apply to other materials. The condition of wood, leather, glass and even fabrics, where they have been preserved or decayed in some particular fashion over a long period of burial, is of considerable fundamental and practical interest. The very corrosion products which have formed on metal articles during archaeological time provide the mineralogist, in his search for the mechanism of geological formation, with an intermediate stepping stone between ideas which cannot be verified in the laboratory and the evidence that confronts him in a rock (p. 188[W10A]).

Then there is the case of a certain beetle, which was discovered in a deposit of the first century A.D. at Stanwick in Yorkshire, but is now no longer found north of Lincolnshire[W12]; or of the worm species evidently persisting only where buried deep in a Roman ditch.[D11] Even such tiny scraps of information, when they become sufficiently numerous, and can be taken together with reliable evidence about general conditions during the period to which they belong, may be of great value to the ecologist studying the way in which climate and environment affect animal populations. It has already been possible for the forester to show,[D10] by examining the tree pollen and soil which were found buried under Bronze Age barrows in Yorkshire, that extensive forests flourished at that time where the moors are now, and that there is therefore no very good reason why they could not do so again.

Returning to consider the actual articles made and structures built in antiquity, both from the technological and the more purely human point of view, one is always struck afresh by the thorough familiarity with properties of materials and principles of mechanics. From the use of bitumen in Babylonian mortars, and of pozzolanic cement which has outlived the bricks on the Roman pier at Naples,[D2] to Roman pattern-welded iron swords (p. 165) and the magnificent workmanship that went into the finest Jutish jewellery, it was all there, the knowledge and the skill, a thousand years ago and more. And quite recently irrigation engineers were helped in the most direct fashion when the excavation of an ancient canal system in Egypt showed quite plainly the shape which its modern counterpart should take.

In these different ways and to all of us, by no means least to the technician and craftsman, the achievements of antiquity are a comfort and delight, a lesson and a challenge. In our various ways, and whether we profit directly or not, we can all contribute in unravelling the details of the material record which, again, is all there, under our feet—in making the interpretation correct, precise, complete and balanced.

What is the present state and scope of this contribution? What, in effect, does it all amount to? This book is an attempt to indicate the answer. But I have chosen at this stage an illustration which is very near the mark; it is a good example of the kind of statement which, as a result of scientific analysis, it is now possible to make with increasing certainty:

> I don't really like using technical words . . ., but from the evidence of Anglo-Saxon burial sites, I should say that the chances are they were made of some cereal mixture (*triticum vulgare*) and some kind of coarse oatmeal gruel, coagulated with bran-mash and left for some time to solidify on a peat hearth.

The one peculiarity about this statement is its context. Without in any way affecting its validity as an example in the present instance, the circumstances in which it was published naturally leave the quotation open to a great variety of interpretations. For it is preceded by the following paragraph:

> This is the ninety-ninth session of *Archaeology for the Million.* Fortunately we happen to have two old friends in the studio, Sir Mortimer Wheeler and Dr. Glyn Daniel, who chanced to come along this evening. The first question comes from Mrs. Donkey of Mildew Green, Suffolk. She asks "What do the experts think King Alfred's cakes were made of?" Well, Sir Mortimer, what do you say to that? (*Punch*)

CHAPTER THREE

What can be done—Possibilities

MATTER IS indestructible. That holds good even in the H-bomb era; the definition of matter merely has to be modified. After all, it is possible to describe an atomic explosion thousands of miles away from the type and amount of radioactivity that is present a few days later in the upper air.

It follows, fundamentally, that nothing vanishes without a trace and no change occurs without leaving some record. The difficulty, equally fundamental, lies in detecting the trace and interpreting the record. Nevertheless, as Rowe says,[K5] "not even the most 'perishable' organic matter is entirely annihilated in the ground; even though it becomes so altered as to be invisible to the naked eye, its former state may be detected by suitable chemical means." He virtually annihilates the ground under his own feet in the very next sentence: "The present survey indicates that this field remains almost entirely unexplored." All the same the claim is at once large enough, and sufficiently justified already, to require that it should be examined and substantiated in some detail.

The extremely complex nature of the material evidence makes it necessary in this connection to consider it from various angles. There is first of all the classification according to type, outlined in Chapter Two (p. 45): one distinguishes the remains of structures and smaller, movable artefacts; of waste products in the widest sense and other minor indications of human activity; and of the natural environment.

Although these distinctions are archaeologically by far the most important, from the standpoint of scientific examination they matter very little. This may appear rather surprising but is really quite reasonable and indeed inevitable. There is here a fundamental difference in approach, whose full implications must be recognized before any co-operation between archaeologist and scientist can become truly effective.

The specialist does need an exact picture of the circumstances of the find wherever relative methods of analysis are involved. But as soon as the question has crystallized in his own terms, he is no longer concerned with this other aspect until his examination has been completed and the results have to be interpreted.

For the next angle from which archaeological evidence may be considered scientifically, and which is of primary importance to the specialist, the whole apparatus of observation is, as it were, swung round through ninety degrees and trained along lines that cut right across the previous classification. Distinctions are drawn as between different materials and not according to the type of evidence. Wood, in this sense, is basically the same substance, whether it appears as a beam or a bowl, as a heap of charcoal or a pile of twigs. Similarly, lead may be found in the shape of a water-pipe or a loom-weight, in a slag or an ore. Fundamentally the same considerations will apply in the examination of any given material, whatever its form.

On the other hand, the remains of a building may contain different kinds of stone, bricks and tiles, timber, mortars, painted wall-plaster, mosaic floors, etc. A pattern-welded iron sword inlaid with brass may carry residues of a wooden scabbard lined with fur. A rubbish pit may produce various kinds of slag and charcoal, animal bones, snail shells, insect pupae, leaves, nuts, seeds and pollen—as well as showing significant features in the adjacent buried soil profile. In every case each different material aspect of such an archaeological unity will require a separate specialist investigation.

Furthermore this does not mean that there is only one kind of specialist for any particular material. On the contrary, there are many instances of successful collaboration even on a single, simple find between a number of scientists each concerned in his own work with a different aspect of the same material. The field of metals probably furnishes the best examples. Starting from the end—with the condition in which, say, a prehistoric bronze dagger has been discovered—the corrosion worker can infer the circumstances of burial; the metallographer can say how it was made, and how well, perhaps also something about its subsequent history. Chemical analysis will determine the major constituents precisely, spectroscopy reveal characteristic minor elements. From these data the extraction metallurgist might be able to indicate the smelting activity which produced the raw material for the dagger, and the mineralogist suggest likely types and localities for the ores.

Although such a case history could stand on its own, other evidence will usually be available to confirm or modify the various details. We can begin to make a more generally useful statistical analysis as the number of comparable daggers increases. A stone mould and hammer head, crucible fragments and remains of a furnace indicate methods of production. Traces of a wooden handle attached to the dagger prove that it has not been burnt. The nature of the soil around it sets the limits of inference possible from its condition. Finally, a heap of charcoal mixed with ash, slag fragments showing various degrees of extraction, lumps of metal-bearing rock and some crushed crude ore will fill out the picture.

So it is not really necessary to consider a case in isolation, and its ultimate value will lie—and indeed be enhanced—in its contribution to the evidence as a whole. All the same it is useful to contemplate it separately. When only a few apparently disconnected finds appear on a potentially important site, one must know how to make the most of them. Then again, in any correlation each individual part should pull its weight as much as it can. But I have chosen such an example mainly because it shows the need for yet another angle from which the evidence must be considered—for a third dimension of observation.

So far we have been looking at the remains from two sides, as it were horizontally, classifying them according to type and material. Now a vertical approach is necessary and the distinguishing criterion becomes one of focal length. It is clear that different kinds of information may be obtained from any one object or material, depending on the magnification at which it is studied.[S9]

The available aids can be related to the different points on the focal scale, but there are three general considerations. Several techniques may often be used at any one point. Our dagger could be photographed by ultra-violet, infra-red or X-rays, each exposing a different aspect of its condition, but all the films comparable at natural size. Or one method may be carried down the whole length: optically, magnification remains the same from the three times of the jeweller's eyeglass to the 300,000 times of the electron microscope. Finally, a technique may be used at one level specifically to describe the situation at another. Thus chemical tests may be carried out with large amounts in a flask or with traces under the microscope, but the result in either case will give information about the disposition of atoms in molecules.

Some analysis of the vertical approach is essential for a proper appreciation of its characteristics; two of these are combined: as we approach more closely there is, at the same time, a reduction in the field of view and a resolution of one material into several. In the most literal sense, we come to know more and more about less and less.

As the area of immediate observation diminishes, the result may become less representative. This sharpens the need for care, in sampling or choosing the point of examination; it also requires a minimum of such points or samples before a significant picture of the whole can begin to emerge. Thus the composition of our dagger may vary considerably from one area to another, owing to uneven distribution of various components in the molten metal during casting; and even the hammered edge may differ in structure over its length according to the number of times it has been re-softened by heat and then worked again, at any given point. Similarly the mortar in a single joint of masonry may vary from the surface to the heart of a wall because of differential weathering, or even at the same depth owing to incomplete mixing. But, if properly taken into account, these difficulties can be turned to advantage, as evidence of the skill at the disposal of the community behind the process.

At the same time there is a change in material outlook. We start with a bronze dagger encrusted with dirty bluish-green warts all over. By way of magnifying glass and microscope we approach crystals of green malachite and blue azurite, among others, interspersed with sand grains and clay particles, overlying deposits of ruby-coloured cuprite, with pockets of white stannic oxide powder. Then colour becomes less and structure more important.

At about × 100, after polishing and etching, we can see the real nature of the metal—comparatively large aggregates of chemical units fused and crystallized into an alloy with definite properties—and at higher magnifications a more detailed picture of one of the dendrites of alpha-bronze against the background of inter-dendritic alpha-delta eutectoid (pl. 2).

Next, each of our entities is multiplied into various combinations of more fundamental chemical units. In malachite and azurite, copper, carbon, oxygen and hydrogen are joined in slightly different ways that may perhaps be even archaeologically significant. The properties of the metal reflect the multiplicity of ways in which copper and tin atoms can associate and such associations may be modified by lead and other atoms. Finally we reach the heart of matter, as the finest distinction is made between different isotopic forms of these atoms—copper, tin, lead. In each case, significant sets of atoms—though chemically identical with the bulk—differ even from each other in mass; ultimately the proportions of copper and, perhaps, tin isotopes in bronze daggers may become as vital as radiocarbon in wood.

If we now consider wood, just as, in the sense of forest, it is resolved into individual trees when close enough to us, so as a material it comes to be subdivided into many different components. First comes appraisal as timber, according to original size, density, strength and durability, in other words its fitness for the presumed purpose. Under the hand lens certain characteristics appear which in most cases enable the specialist to split up each functional class into representatives of the botanical genera. The very structural details he uses are in themselves another multiplication of "wood" into growth rings, rays, resin ducts, vessels and fibres.

Other evidence may be found, directly relevant though not actually part of the original wood: holes and tunnels made by woodborers or strands of fungus; in each case there are again a number of different possibilities. Under the microscope the whole situation is clarified and resolved: fibres become threads of cells, in one of which, say, the central of the three layers that make up its wall may appear completely destroyed by fungus. Higher magnifications in the electron microscope show the cell walls as

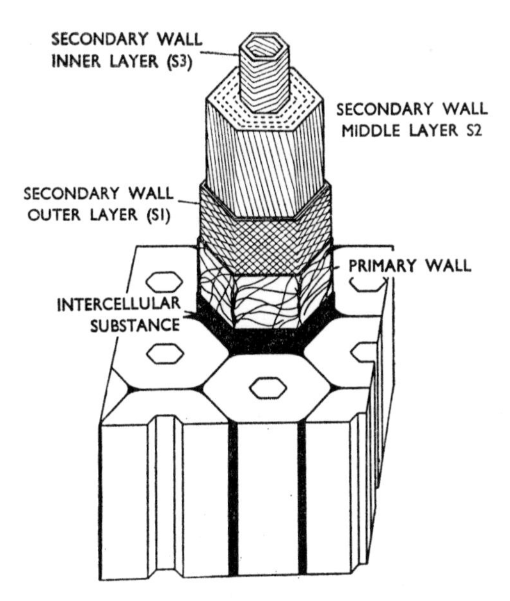

FIGURE 1. A diagrammatic representation of the structure of a cell wall of a fibre or tracheid.[H13]

spiral bundles of microfibrils, consisting mainly of the basic vegetable substance—cellulose (pl. 3, fig. 1).[N6, P11, S5]

Next, this and the other chemical compounds in the wood appear as different arrangements of the same types of atom, mainly carbon, hydrogen and oxygen. There are also crystalline and amorphous forms of cellulose. Finally, once again, each kind of atom can appear in the same structure in several isotopic forms. One of these may be radioactive, and it is this property of carbon-14 which has made the use of wood for dating possible.

These brief outlines will have clearly indicated the immense complexity of any rational approach to the material record as a whole. Yet the possibilities actually increase with ramification. Each avenue that branches off the main route of investigation leads, so to speak, not into the wilderness but to another observation post, usually set up for a different, non-archaeological purpose, it is true, and perhaps not fully manned, but at least well-established.

If we now reconsider, against this background, the bold claim with which the chapter began, the crucial question becomes: at what focal distance does scientific examination cease to be archaeologically significant? How near can we get to the tree without losing sight of the wood?

Often the choice will be dictated by the limitations of evidence and available techniques. In any case one has almost always to decide between alternatives. It is a great help if the archaeologist can suggest some. But even when he can only ask, "What is this?" the question is automatically translated by the specialist into "Is it this or that?" Unfortunately, where the distinction is a fine one, "this" and "that" may by now have changed into materials which are indistinguishable or even identical. Thus it is not really a matter of survival, but rather of persistence near enough to the original location, and in a form which can be detected and related to what the material was in the first place, at a level that is archaeologically significant.

Such a distinction might well seem absurd in practice; after all, evidence must be capable of interpretation to be worthy of the name. But in principle it is of the utmost importance because it fosters a certain attitude of mind. There are different degrees of evidence, as well as various kinds. If one accepts the distinction one looks not merely for the kind of evidence that is visible or is known to be detectable; whether there is a particular archaeological problem or not, one is continually and almost unconsciously on the alert for fresh possibilities. Instinctively one works down the vertical approach until *something* comes into focus, becomes determinable.

It is then a question of matching it with what is already known. Such an identification may not be directly significant; if the positive attitude prevails the evidence is not simply discarded. At worst the information is stored, but it is usually possible to make something more of the evidence straightaway. It needs a taste for obscure similarities, perhaps mainly a delight in sliding up and down the vertical approach; for the closer we have to be the less we can see—so we must back away regularly.

Where it is only a matter of relative size,[W13A] there is little danger (pl. 4) but at a critical limit heterogeneity may become dominant.

As we so approach the proverbial wood we first lose sight of it for the trees—and then of the tree for the wood substance that occurs in any tree. Beyond that, we can only say "vegetable"; then only "carbon, hydrogen and oxygen joined in a certain way", and so on, down to the final limit of detection.

Unfortunately the isolated trace often does not lie within the relevant limits of identification. It all depends, of course, on what the archaeologist wants to know. He may not be interested in the kind of tree and may be concerned to establish merely that there had, in fact, been timber in a presumed sleeper trench. This is a question of great importance right through to the Late Middle Ages. Wood has always been an extremely popular building material. The archaeologist profits, if obliquely, by the fact that nothing can be spirited away without a trace, and evidence of stone robbing is usually fairly clear in the disturbed soil. But sometimes one cannot be quite sure. Then, and also when there clearly never had been any stone, it might be vital to know whether there had ever been any wood.

In general, archaeological experience has shown that in places where one can presume wood had once lain the soil differs from the surroundings in colour or texture, often in both.[R16] Such distinctions grade from imperceptible to sharp and the question does not arise at all, of course, where the wood has been continuously waterlogged and thereby preserved (p. 142).

Sometimes wood and masonry may have disappeared completely, but the "stain" carries an impression of woody grain either in the soil or in remnants of mortar. From this alone one might be justified in the inference that such a stain means timber even in the absence of any grain impression. In fact there has recently been a most remarkable instance of the validity of such inference. The Jewel Tower in Westminster, now flanked by the House of Lords and the Abbey, was built in the fourteenth century on marshy ground, and was therefore stood on wooden piles. In the course of repair work, excavations showed that the piles were very well preserved at one end, where completely in clay, but progressively deteriorated towards the other end where, completely in gravel, they had only left a dark brown powdery stain (pl. 5).

However, such a phenomenon is not simply translatable to a

different set of conditions where a similar stain may be due to another cause; or the stain may be there but not easily distinguishable from the undisturbed subsoil. There may be no stain at all where, archaeologically, one might have expected it. Most important of all, timber may have been and left no stain, where the excavator may not have been looking for it. After all, such detective work must ultimately pass beyond what can be seen with the unaided eye to suggest things that might otherwise never have been suspected.

Clearly, then, close scientific scrutiny is always most desirable even where it may not seem essential. There are not enough specialist-hours to go over the entire excavation with a fine toothed scientific comb; but that is the ideal, and as we near attainment it will become easier, in turn, to answer the isolated questions that are asked today. Even so, far more can already be made of the available evidence than is usually thought to be possible.

Isolated traces of fibrous structure in the ground—or on a sword or bucket hoop—especially if charred, may be identifiable, or perhaps characteristic of softwood, or at least "wood". When the largest surviving structural unit could once have been equally well part of a tree, herbaceous plant or modern root—and roots can be very troublesome indeed (p. 123)—it might seem that further investigation would be fruitless. After all, it is no longer possible to tell the excavator what he wants to know, namely, whether there had been any wood about.

But wood does not decay uniformly: knots and neighbouring areas tend to outlast the other parts, or corrosion products from a chance bronze object might have rot-proofed some significant trace. Also the particular deposit in the field may still be accessible to further search. There is then quite often a reasonable hope of finding something useful. Besides, an "irrelevant" aspect of the search continues almost automatically. Not content with "vegetable remains", the botanist will track them as far as he can, irrespective of the original question about wood. Quite unsuspected features may come to light—such as fungal spores (p. 188) indicating the burial, some 3,500 years ago, of cereal leaves that are now unrecognizable.

Such oblique evidence is not uncommon. As with wood, the various components of any system may differ considerably in their resistance to decay—indeed leaves and seeds clearly must, to ensure propagation of the plant. Vegetable tenacity should be matched with human perseverance in the search for it—incidentally turning the difference to advantage for distinguishing possible ancient from (impossible and thus) modern survival.

When no structure remains, chemical tests may help. Woody and plant materials are usually detectable as "humus" residue for some time, and under certain conditions a significant humic feature might be referred back to wood. In other circumstances a replica may be found, almost devoid of organic matter but perhaps comparatively rich in iron or manganese compounds (p. 181). Similar stains are then also caused by materials of animal origin so that detailed chemical checks and care in their interpretation would be necessary.

In the absence of all visible traces the present position is not at all promising; but there is no reason why it should remain so. Thus aluminium, which is not visible in the soil, may behave like manganese and future work might make it feasible to "develop" the invisible ground plan of a timber dwelling from a suitable chemical plot. Similar phosphate and trace element plots can already be so used under certain conditions to delimit areas of occupation.[D1, L9, S21]

Or one might follow the original organic compounds through their metamorphoses. Studies of the fate of humus or more fundamental carbon compounds might indicate suitable "tracers"; failing them, differences in organic-carbon content as such could be significant.

How far will such traces have been removed into the background of soil and plant metabolism and thus lost to interpretation? It is at this level, for all materials, that research is particularly needed. At present the vertical approach is usually limited by the very practical relationship between archaeological value and specialist time. Quite often, the importance of wood remains might already make such expenditure here worth while. Ultimately it may then become possible not only to plot invisible remains of vegetable origin, and to check on their antiquity by refined radiocarbon measurement, but even to decide whether they were in fact due to timber or not.

Such an argument applies equally to other materials. In the search for buildings, for instance, we may come upon wall foundations in various ways. The stones may have remained intact and in position. When only fragments are found because the stones have flaked, from decay or on robbing, it is still possible to identify even the bed and perhaps the quarry, if the rock is distinctive and the piece large enough. The soil may be stony, robbing or other disturbances may have produced confusion, so that even small fragments of material suitable for building, and not immediately local, might be valuable in confirming the ground plan.

Very much smaller particles will at least allow broad distinctions—as between limestone, sandstone, granite and flint—and under suitable conditions even a stone dust may help. In a fine flour the microscope often reveals enough characteristic structure to distinguish limestone from mortar, chalk or fertilizer. Where one has to resort to purely chemical criteria, say in developing an invisible ground plan from a calcium plot, the difference between "foundations" and surrounding soil would have to be accurately measurable and consistently large. Such work is possible, and other helpful indications may appear: thus in certain soils crops may grow better where limestone walls have once been, although these may be no longer traceable just by chemical means; or efflorescence of salts in drying ground may even provide such a development spontaneously.[L1]

A similar vertical approach to leather shows a different but complementary picture. Under specially favourable conditions, either waterlogged or extremely dry, preservation may be so remarkably good that an object can be described completely. In smaller fragments, first the object ceases to be determinable and then only the kind of animal can be identified. Beyond, unless some structure is preserved by bronze or rust, any traces can be no more than "of animal origin, possibly leather". Closer still, as with wood remains, a stain in the ground where a "belt" has lain might be due to manganese. Only where wood, textile and bone have also been and left traces of structure, might one suggest by comparison that the belt stain did in fact represent leather.

Next, the fate of protein and its component amino acids is not accurately known. Also some of the decomposition products of vegetable litter can become bound in the ground in aggregates containing protein. In looking chemically for leather or other animal remains one therefore needs to distinguish between different kinds and amounts of protein. Nor is nitrogen helpful in marginal cases, except where strictly localized by controls, because it plays an important part in the metabolism of a completely natural soil. But methods of detection have recently been much refined and might in time prove adequate even for the development of invisible leather remains.

Aluminium residues may be detectable where tawed leather had decayed away.[W19] Vegetable tannins might also modify conditions permanently, but at present no direct method will detect them even in buried leather that is well preserved.

The reason for this is important and in a sense typical. The tannins are a variety of complex mixtures of organic compounds. Partly owing to their vegetable origin, their basic structure is similar also to that of various other materials irrelevant to leather, such as are found for example in humus.[P8] Recent work has used the subtle differences to distinguish and isolate them. However, only some of the tannins introduced into hide will remain chemically locked into it for any length of time. During use or burial, the rest would be leached out and then degraded quite quickly.

Unfortunately the portion fixed in the leather cannot be recovered either, as the tannins are broken down by the very process of separation for analysis. On degradation, here, "this" and "that" change into the same thing; but in the process they may modify their surroundings in slightly different ways. It might thus become possible eventually not only to plot invisible leather residues but even to identify the plant which provided the tannins.

Several features of all this work emerge as important: archaeology of all sciences comes nearest to detection in the popular sense precisely because it is the most human. It is concerned with all aspects of the activity of man, and motive is thus a cardinal factor in the inquiry. It follows that good guessers—necessary everywhere—are here essential. The intuitive element in scientific research has been unjustly minimized. Yet all progress is made best and most rapidly by a combination of intuition and experiment.

The severity of specialist training and its objectivity in presentation are proverbial; reduction of the human factor to an absolute minimum tends to increase an inherent isolation from colleagues, life in general and popular appreciation. All the same, despite mistrust of human judgement resulting from discoveries about the limitations of the human body and counter-distrust for that reason, even scientific specialists are essentially human. Most of their important ideas and actions begin by being irrational. This is a manifest advantage in the study of the behaviour of man, prehistoric or otherwise, and specialists usually adopt a more "human" attitude when examining archaeological material.

Yet intuition is not enough by a long way; by itself it only rarely escapes being governed by the law of probability, and then only as a result of previous—perhaps ancestral—experience. In archaeological work as a whole, it is followed as a matter of course by objective comparison with relevant material. To help with such confirmatory work, as I said earlier, is one of the primary functions of specialist analysis, just as in crime detection—indeed the methods are identical.[N3] The other is to suggest new possibilities. If both are to be properly fulfilled it is important for *all* the evidence to be seen by specialists, from the general environment to the most insignificant find.

In a particular sense, it is the business of archaeologists to recognize where and how soil has been disturbed. Certainly this will in many cases be at once apparent to the experienced eye, and it is said that native workmen employed on excavations in Egypt seemed to show almost uncanny powers in this respect—no doubt born of a familiarity with the soil that was, more than in most areas, a matter of life and death. But there will always be many boundary cases where one cannot be sure. Soil specialists may not yet have the answer, but they will never be able to help to the full unless they can measure reliable instances in the field where, from the archaeological standpoint, it might seem unnecessary. Only after such routine work will it become possible for them to go over from the confirmatory to the suggestive, clearly more important in the long run, by indicating disturbance where none might be visible or even suspected.

In general, with all he uncovers, the archaeologist faces these fundamental questions: What is it? What does it mean? If due to human agency, what was the nature and skill of the activity? If due to natural agency, what light does it throw on the environment? I have discussed, also in general, the theoretical possibilities of trying to help with the answers. It is now necessary to consider the particular nature of the various practical limitations.

CHAPTER FOUR

Exploring the Limits—Reconnaissance

LIMITS ARE inevitable. However we regard them—as walls that make us change direction or as illusions to be ignored—it is as well to study them.

Here, straightaway, another imaginary rift threatens between the humanist and the scientist. The one refuses to admit any limits to man's spiritual adventure—his whole attitude rests on belief in the eternal and illimitable. The other cannot work without limits—where there are none he makes some. Or so it might seem.

The truth is again dichotomous—rather, there is one truth and there are many. First, limits exist but must not be mistaken for limitations. As for the rest, *Quot homines* . . ., and these limits will always be personal. To that extent they must, in the last analysis, be conditioned by the final uncertainty:

> So long as men can breathe, or eyes can see,
> So long lives this . . .

And only so long? Shakespeare had no doubt—he accepted the limit and thereby freed himself of the limitation.

The rift is quite patently bogus. For the first thing the artist accepts is form, and form like all order is a limit. Within such limits he is free. Exactly the same applies to the mathematician to whom the permutations of the symbols, conventions and laws he accepts may give an astronomical number of degrees of freedom.

In turning limits inside out and back upon themselves, abstract science differs little from abstract art.[D8] Perhaps the mathematician might seem to be at greater pains to establish the number of degrees of freedom before he starts. The sculptor would probably not understand the meaning of such activity, being instinctively concerned with three and yet unaware of any limit, having no less and needing no more. But the distinction is unreal, being based on over-specialization of language. Clearly the concept behind "harmony" is common ground to mathematics and sculpture, as it is to music and biology.

The only real difference lies in the emphasis: one aspect is more concerned with measurement, accuracy and reproducibility, with objective statement, logical induction and deduction; the other more with delineation, suggestion and variety, with subjective, selective interpretation, emotional development. But both have to deal with the same phenomena, problems and limits. Both require integrity, imagination, patience and skill if they are to be useful, and where they are, both are universally valid—and wholly complementary.

For some people a palpable limit will always be a challenge, whether it be space or the atom, time or a proportion. Others will be attracted sometimes, and some will almost always be repelled. But all must agree that limits exist. Certainly early man proceeded by exploring the limits, as the child does today. It is the natural way even when not the only one. Civilization has brought to many, directly or indirectly, the opportunity of refining the senses and making possible an immediate experience of reality. A few rare spirits have been fortunate enough to avail themselves of it. For the rest of us, the exploration of limits may be an adventure, or it can be a necessity—or even an attitude to life.

The archaeologist conceives, plans, organizes, directs, digs, correlates, interprets and reports. The responsibility is entirely his, but if only for this very reason he has to make quite sure that the maximum of information is extracted from all he uncovers. A good archaeologist will be the first to realize his own limits as a human. Most of them are his affair, but there are a number of a more general nature. These can be considerably and constantly extended, as of course they normally are, by the use of other people's experience and skill, with or without the aid of specialized instruments and machinery.

There are financial and climatic limits, and others due to time and also to those incredible miscellania which restrict the liabilities of transporting companies. Here he has no control and I have nothing to say. The kind of help that could be given to an excavator with the first five operations listed above, down to the digging part, has already been outlined. It is with the last three, and particularly with interpretation, that I am concerned here and indeed, in essence, throughout the whole book.

The scientific examination of archaeological evidence is, in effect, the extension of the excavator's powers to interpret what he exposes. The idea itself might seem obvious enough, and so might the corollary, that the process means transcending the immediate limits of the excavator's senses. Yet at once difficulties appear. The archaeologist in the field, relying as he does so completely on the evidence of his five unaided senses, not to mention the sixth, will not readily be persuaded of their inadequacy in certain respects. Even as he comes to realize the necessity, and appreciate the value, of scientific aids he remains suspicious of them and their application.

The attitude is by no means peculiar to this aspect—it is typical of the layman in science; not uncommonly, it forces itself even upon one scientist with regard to another. The tendency is inevitable, like that of personalities to conflict. But rational beings are capable of being convinced by argument and demonstration. Tension gradually relaxes into a mutual, sceptical watchfulness tinged with respect.

Sometimes, of course, deadlock remains or even deteriorates into active mistrust and fear, as (unfortunately) between the man in the street and the atomic scientist. Then the business may become dangerous in proportion as it gets out of hand. Normally, however, co-operation breeds confidence and understanding of one another's aims and obstacles. It is the scepticism, now, of which only a tinge remains; and it is entirely healthy that a little should remain. Imperceptibly, mutual respect unfolds to admit and accept the other's point of view. The conditions are made right for something new and exciting or even great to develop. This tendency, also, is in the nature of things.

Quite recently it has become possible for Aldous Huxley to link, in this sense, such very different persuasions so easily, and mix paradoxes so palatably, that one has swallowed the lot before realizing what an unlikely combination they make:

> Knowing as he does (or at least as he can know, if he so desires) what are the chemical conditions of transcendental experience, the aspir-

ing mystic should turn for technical help to the specialists—in pharmacology, in biochemistry, in physiology and neurology, in psychology and psychiatry and parapsychology.

This is even more relevant than it might at first appear because the archaeologist is something of a visionary. When he takes Huxley's advice he does so with a vengeance. In consequence the poor scientists are not only overwhelmed, sometimes, by the quantity but also embarrassed, more often, by the expectations. Why not a magic box, flashing out the answer to any poor archaeologist's problem? It is on the way, and indeed some instruments already look the part.

But such a machine would still have to be told in great detail not only what the problem was but also how to work it out. Although the thinking part can already be done in a flash it would be quite wasted except on long series of the same type of problem. Since every archaeological problem tends to be slightly different from all similar ones, we should be little better off.

It is only a more complicated version of our present difficulty of thinking round the job. In most cases the specialist needs time not only to do the job but also, often predominantly, to think it out. Usually the problem, or at least its origin, will be out of the common run and he will have to readjust his mental focus.

First of all he will need to understand it, against the background of the archaeologist's other evidence and difficulties. Then he will have to translate it in terms of his own outlook, of the quantities that he can measure and compare with his standard values, and to formulate the more mechanical part of the analysis or examination in such a way that it may best and most quickly yield a significant result.

When the practical part of the work has been done the results must be interpreted, and that can often take up more time than all the rest of the thought and activity together. It involves much discussion, both with the excavator and with other specialists—inevitably with long gaps between the occasions on which it is possible—sometimes also repetition of an analysis to check a particular point, not infrequently some research into a novel aspect, and possibly an independent confirmatory test.

Finally a report has to be written and this—quite apart from having to be fitted in, like the rest, as and when the routine work permits—meets with a basic, psychological difficulty: the disinclination of any specialist to commit himself within the limits of the evidence—limits that may be too wide for him but are, archaeologically, the only ones possible, and without which the results may be virtually useless to the excavator.

In comparison the time needed for the actual analysis may often be negligible. Still, when practical as well as theoretical preparation is involved, such as setting up a piece of apparatus or modifying a routine run, this aspect of the time factor may also assume a magnitude out of all proportion to the original problem.

Even when accepted, the job is likely to be much delayed for such reasons. This is important from the start because, all else apart, it may hold up the excavator's report. Also there are instances where the work is both tedious and really time-consuming, however one looks at it. Then it is a serious decision for the specialist to embark on any particular project and usually impossible to consider doing so unless the investigation bears some direct relation to a general research problem.

One must therefore discourage extravagant hopes. At the same time it is unfortunately necessary to undeceive the excavator to some extent about the evidence of his senses.

It may not be generally realized that all of them can contribute. Sometimes bosing[A4] or even the sound heard on tapping a certain part of the section (as noted in 1658 by Sir Thomas Browne), or the taste or grittiness of a given layer, may give a useful clue. Smells are often very strong, especially in deposits that have been sealed by water and where slow decomposition in the absence of air has produced the kind of informative organic complex described later (Chapter Six). But deposits of this kind may have similar smells even though they differ in origin. Also, many common odours seem not to be caused by the actual process with which they are linked in our mind and, even where characteristic, can be masked by irrelevant traces.

Colours can be equally misleading (col. pl. I). In some of the examples the primary association is actually correct; it is the corrosion process which has distorted the superficial reflection, as we see it, of the balance of materials present. In a base silver coin, the copper will be preferentially corroded and form a green skin. Similarly, a leaded bronze coin will contain more lead in the patina than in the metal below. We are right to expect copper and lead from the colours we see—and they duly appear on cleaning—as also iron in the bell which had an iron pea though this cannot be revived. But in the original objects the subsidiary metals would not be noticeable. In many of the examples even the association is confusing, particularly for iron.

This may not seem to matter much as the finds will on cleaning be revealed anyway for what they are. The examples were chosen to illustrate the general approach to materials; yet on occasion such a view would also have a practical value, and sometimes it could be vital. Faulty diagnosis can lead to wrong treatment and produce cases of mistaken identity which tend to be perpetuated. If, for instance, green silver coins are cleaned electrolytically, they may emerge with a complete copper coating which it is very tedious to take off.

By contrast, it is very easy in cleaning to remove evidence which now exists only in the corrosion products. Dark brown spots may be all that remain of iron rivets in a piece of brass mail (p. 162). Or there may be signs of fire—perhaps hidden between the immediate surface and the remaining metal (especially iron, p. 133). Such signs could be valuable even in the field, and impatience over cleaning may destroy not only them but also the object itself.

Still more valuable is the advance warning, given by those unusual states and colours of metal objects (col. pl. II, p. 142), that an extremely rich deposit lies below, full of organic material that deteriorates rapidly on exposure to the air.

Perhaps most unfortunate is a direct archaeological deduction with far-reaching consequences in time and space. Two otherwise similar types of Mediterranean neolithic pottery, differing only in colour, were thought to be culturally distinct until it was recently shown that the red could be turned into grey, and *vice versa*, by refiring in a reducing or an oxidizing atmosphere, respectively (information from A. Ozanne). Several instances of this phenomenon, well-known to potters, have been described (p. 166). The red-and-grey transformation is due, again, mainly to iron but there are other colour changes caused by other materials.

Iron is further responsible for much of the colour—and confusion—in the soil. A dark, greyish-brown band, which runs more or less horizontally along the soil profile may represent the organic humus residue of an ancient, buried surface; or it may be no more than a "natural" iron "pan". The distinction is often of decisive importance, so it is unwise to be guided by colour—or texture—especially as a simple laboratory test will provide the answer readily and unequivocally (p. 223).

The texture of different materials may also be deceptive. Plate 6 shows a provocative selection and the reader is invited to guess. A slight deterioration in condition will change appearances yet again. The complementary aspect, the feel of weight, hardness, smoothness and compactness, while most valuable, can often be equally misleading. Nor will it be safe to assume that the "greasiness" of a soil is characteristic of occupation, until some connection has been established in measurable terms.

Textural evidence may sometimes be unambiguous and can be accepted, with experience, in its own right. Yet in similar cases further examination—sometimes just deeper digging—can show human activity to have been quite impossible. This illustrates a particular and important form of problem—a combination of our four basic questions: We know what this would mean, had man made it; but can such things occur naturally, and is it possible to say definitely in this case?

Three examples came up in as many months a little while ago. The problem in each case concerned a timber structure, or rather the dotted ground plan of postholes. If the soil overlying the structure's floor had been different from it, postholes would show up clearly because the new soil would fall and partly fill the space provided as the wood disintegrated. In a more compact soil, holes may remain largely empty[R2] (pl. 5).

A Middle Bronze Age structure under a barrow at Swarkeston, in Derbyshire,[G12] had left no distinct colour difference in the ginger-brown gravelly soil. But while the normal living surface was virtually impervious to a steel pin, this sank easily and deep into the posthole fillings which were made up of finer material from above.

At Downton,[R4] near Salisbury in Wiltshire, it was an altogether different story. Under the normal clayey sand an irregular but solid mortar floor suddenly appeared, containing a scatter of postholes that seemed somewhat aimless. This is not unusual, since consecutive structures can produce a confusion of superimposed ground plans.

But the "mortar" was shown by further digging to be at least several feet thick and any idea of floor and postholes had to be abandoned. Broken and washed-down chalk from an adjacent spur had evidently intruded here to produce an underground mirage of human activity, and the "posts" responsible for the holes had never been more substantial than ground-water with mineral salts in solution.

The third example was provided by a mound near Litton Cheney in Dorset.[W2] With just a thin spread of gravel and dark soil over the chalk, every feature in this area shows up quite distinctly on excavation. The mound itself seemed to have been constructed along standard lines, but there were numerous stake or postholes under it, in the chalk surface.

The excavator thought they could not be what they seemed but wanted confirmation. I told him what I had just seen at Downton. Clearly such things did happen naturally; there seemed to be no pattern about the holes nor any difference at all between their filling and the overlying soil. On this basis alone, we "inclined to the view" that the things were "more likely to be" solution holes than stake holes (pl. 1).

The current part of my tale seems to have grown a sting. Having set out to show that we must not trust our unaided senses, I appear to have demonstrated that it is in many cases unnecessary—indeed it is often impossible as yet—to do anything else. The two notions are by no means incompatible. There is all the difference between deciding that A equals B merely on the evidence of one's senses—and tentatively proposing it after some study, for lack of contrary evidence, and with a mind left wide open. It is like the difference between the "fact" and mode of survival (p. 107), as with colour and vision and indeed matter itself.

Such considerations may make little difference to everyday life but they do affect the outlook of the individual. If one thinks in terms of reflection, one can more easily appreciate and evaluate how colours change with the light by which we see them. This, by the way, like the similar difference between "dry" and "wet" colours, is of course a most important factor for the archaeologist in the field.

Conversely, if we believe only the evidence of our unaided senses we impose an unnecessary limitation; we refuse, roughly speaking, really to consider that anything can be other than it seems. This can be a handicap, particularly to the excavator who can clearly transcend the immediate limits of his five senses as soon as he recognizes and accepts them.

Once he has done so he can safely allow his sixth sense full rein. My earlier reference to this (p. 70) was perfectly serious. However unfashionable it may seem, there is a sixth sense as surely as there is a fourth dimension. Probably a semi-material explanation in terms of a (long-term) conditioned reflex is not enough. Equally important, the vital medium of the actual touching-off process may be creative: imagination (pp. 41, 100).

There were two features about my student life that impressed themselves forcibly on my consciousness. One was in the nature of an atmosphere which pervaded the place and (nearly) all its activities: an earnest concern for the concepts of limit and error.

From the first we were urged to be quite clear, before we started our experiment, about what precisely it could tell us, and how precisely we could make it do so. The foundations of science were concerned, we were told, not only with accurate measurement but equally with an accurate knowledge of how accurate our measurements actually were.

This preoccupation, I remember, struck me as slightly pedantic and disdainful. Yet limit and error have stalked through the whole of my thinking life ever since like two guardians of good sense. On these two concepts the whole of this chapter is based, and ultimately the philosophy which gave rise to the book: the whole of the microscopical attitude to archaeology—or to anything for that matter.

How much can we know? I have stressed this because I believe it is one of the major pivots on which understanding between archaeologists and scientists may turn in the desired direction (p. 97). If there is one thing that scientists accept as a body and without question it is this interplay between limit and error (p. 68). This very statement would puzzle them, as much as any non-scientists, though for the opposite reason; and that is the whole point: neither side is really aware of this pivot. With a little more attention from both sides it would cease to be the seized-up part which it now often is in the machinery of communication.

The other thing that particularly affected me was an event. Occasion and speaker are long since forgotten but I can still remember the quality of the evening lecture. A lively, learned gentleman took us mischievously and completely away from all that we were being taught. Along strictly scientific lines he proceeded to demonstrate that scientific method as such and by itself was at best utterly sterile, and at worst complete nonsense. Of course we loved it. The argument went something like this.

Scientific method is concerned with the cycle—observation, measurement, analysis, conclusion, hypothesis, experiment, observation . . . and so on. It does not much matter at which point we enter the cycle, but we must obviously follow the logical progression. It all looks nice and simple and something is bound to come out of it. The trouble is that the whole business can just go on for ever churning out results which are completely useless. Something vital is missing—what is it?

Obviously, if you take all of them into account, there are so many possibilities that, even working in an extremely limited field, one might go on for years systematically testing one after the other and finding, as far as one gets, all of them wrong. Selection therefore becomes a matter of vital importance. How is one to choose? What is to determine the manner of selection?

We began to prick up our ears. Luck was quite a help; if you were lucky enough to hit on the right approach straightaway you saved yourself an awful lot of time and work. Excellent. This meant that you could get on faster. Admirable; but what is the rest of the magic formula? It seemed impossible now that it should be anything at all ordinary. We waited expectantly, and were richly rewarded.

Well, gentlemen—with a sly glance at the Professor in the

Chair—it is quite obvious that if one is to get on and produce any worth-while results at all one must be a good guesser. There was complete silence—could we have heard aright? Yes, we had. You must have the touch, the knack, the sixth sense, the intuition—call it what you will; and if you haven't you must learn or get it somehow, otherwise all the equipment and time in the world will be of no avail.

This from an elder scientist to budding scientists, in a shrine consecrated to the Scientific Method! We howled with delight. There followed example upon example, each better than the last, of how all the important discoveries, if they were not due to chance, had started with a good guess. The lecture rollicked to its close and we stamped our approval. When the Professor rose he faced an overtly rebellious situation. He cleverly saved the day, but Scientific Method had been put firmly in her place, and I have a shrewd suspicion that he got more than he had bargained for.

This kind of lecture, given to laymen and particularly to archaeologists, would be refreshing in every way. It would help to dissolve the notion of the scientist as some sort of personalized game of questions and answers. Conversely, similar talks the other way round would assist in disposing of archaeology as a mental picture of a complicated system of fossilized thought.

Here is the place to continue that quotation from Aldous Huxley (p. 70):

> And on their part, of course, the specialists (if any of them aspire to be genuine men of science and complete human beings) should turn, out of their respective pigeon-holes, to the artist, the sibyl, the visionary, the mystic—all those, in a word, who have had experience of the Other World and who know, in their different ways, what to do with that experience.

Imagination unfettered but not unchecked (p. 41). This might perhaps be taken as the basis for the attitude which I have been trying to describe.

As a human, the specialist will be restricted, just like the archaeologist. Force of habit will incline him more to distrust the evidence of his senses, particularly the sixth, but otherwise he will not differ greatly.

As a member of his profession, he will indeed have different ideas about many things, and the limits within which his activities move will differ correspondingly. They will also vary with his speciality, being here dependent on state of knowledge, perfection of method and equipment, condition of material supplied by the excavator, and others to be described below. It is unfortunate that many excavators tend to bracket all specialist services together, though perhaps natural enough if one regards the specialist merely as a general purveyor of useful answers to awkward questions.

The ultimate limit of the specialist's help is defined by his understanding of the purpose and method of archaeology. He is often unfamiliar enough with the physical background of an excavation to be at best extremely cautious, and at worst frankly suspicious. He is rarely concerned with more than one aspect—and at most two or three—of specialist examination for archaeology and therefore cannot always be expected to appreciate the whole into which his own contribution is designed to fit.

If one considers his work in terms of the kind of limit mentioned earlier (p. 72), the scope for error here is clearly much wider and the degree of precision often dependent on so many assumptions that the result can only be a more or less reliable approximation.

The archaeologist, in turn, has accepted all this because he has had to in order to function at all, and it hardly occurs to him to think about it. But the scientist does not feel safe between such wide limits. For him too many factors are unknown or uncertain to permit the definite answers to which he is accustomed. He is worried by bald statements in archaeological reports that may strike him at first sight as inadvisable or even preposterous. He is anxious lest some of his own work might be used as a peg on which to hang too long a string of circumstantial inference.

Most of us tend to venture with some seriousness across the boundary between our own speciality and others, and usually we do little harm. But there is in this a special kind of danger, insidious and therefore important, because it is difficult to assess and confine, and also because ill-informed opinion and downright fallacies may be perpetuated.

Paradoxically, it is often the specialist who is guilty. After some contact with field work he may develop his own imaginative reconstruction. Because he has a reputation his scientific colleagues will listen to him, and he will gradually acquire another one. But, because he is out of his field and no longer bound by its standards, he may not admit when he is out of his depth and could deceive not only himself but others also. Newton wrote a book on astrology, too.

There is a more involved and dangerous aspect. A scientific specialist may imperceptibly re-transfer some of his newly-found freedom into his own field. He may pick on a particular feature in the metallographic section of ancient artefacts and interpret it in a certain way. He may be right, and then all is well. But he may be wrong and then all is lost because nobody can prove him so. The feature may in part be due to a long-term effect, unknown and not repeatable. There is then no way of checking up on the interpretation. A point can be reached, in examining archaeological material, when even something as clear-cut as metallography may become a "matter of opinion".

It can happen as easily the other way round. An excavator may have worked on a number of sites showing evidence of metal-extracting activity. After properly taking specialist advice the first few times, he may decide to manage on his own.

Even an experienced modern smelting technician would hesitate to judge a lump of slag simply from its appearance. The best copper slag would contain mostly iron oxide and silica—fused fuel ash and glass and even vitrified pottery bear a family resemblance to slag. We should not trust our memory unaided any more than our senses. It is manifestly the mark of a true specialist that he is always the last, most diffident and least definite interpreter of a situation in his own field.

Those of us who are concerned with archaeological material are perhaps particularly prone to rush in where others fear to tread because it is comparatively difficult to prove us wrong. Just as the specialist may be a danger, the archaeologist with a reputation, speculating about technology to other archaeologists, can be an absolute menace. Yet there is a growing conviction, as Sir Mortimer Wheeler put it, that "we armchair archaeologists" have attached too much importance to the non-technical development of the things that ancient man made for his use. Technological affinities are probably always more reliable than typological ones. It is most important to ensure that due consideration, and even pre-eminence, is given to this matter. And this from a leading archaeologist to a group including some of his most distinguished colleagues, in a shrine consecrated to the Archaeological Method!

Luckily the archaeological menace is easier to deal with than the scientific "danger". For instance, while it is rarely possible for the excavator to produce evidence to settle an intricate technical point, it is usually quite easy to put an archaeological hypothesis about ancient metallurgy to the practical test.[C14, W20]

Much has been done also to check up on ideas about ancient activities that were not strictly technological—one has only to recall the copy built of an Iron Age hut whose remains were found at Little Woodbury, and the experiments in transportation from South Wales to Stonehenge.[A17] But such highlights, magnified in the press, are almost a mirage. What is more truly reflected is the general appreciation and awareness of this forensic science for archaeology. It is becoming more difficult now to get away with anything, both for the ancient who dunnit and for the excavator who thinks he knows how. Here, literally, is reconstruction. It is perhaps the most convincing way in which archaeology might stake and maintain its claim to be considered a science. But an immense amount remains to be done before we are justified in feeling half as confident about some of the simplest things in ancient life as we often appear to be.

These limits imposed directly by the human factors are very important. But there are of course many other limits of entirely different kinds—though they, also, are basically due to human factors. There are, for instance, not enough specialists active. Sometimes there is a lack of equipment. Always there is too little time.

It is therefore essential to choose material for investigation according to the potential general value of the result (p. 72). Thus it may seem far more useful for the radioactive carbon content of samples from a site A to be determined—because the presumed date falls within a period from which there have been few samples—rather than for a comparable series from a site B and of a period that is better served in this respect. Yet B may archaeologically be more important than A, and may have produced more and better material all round.

Another critical part of the field aspect is the sampling technique. A soil sample, for instance, must be representative of the layer from which it has been taken. But it is not always easy to decide precisely how the sample might be most representative. Sampling may be by cork-borer or spade according to the reasons behind the excavator's questions. Usually control samples from all round the feature will be needed for comparison.

There is sometimes an "internal reliability factor" which must be borne in mind. The excavator may not be aware of it, and the specialist may not know that. Even under ideal conditions, certain kinds of evidence may remain inevitably incomplete. Thus pollen is not formed by every plant, or dispersed by the wind when it is; and then, of course, it is not always found where it might have been buried, or preserved uniformly when found.

Then again, contamination of freshly exposed sections by present-day pollen may be very rapid and can make a sample useless or, even worse, entirely misleading. Altogether, the very fineness of structure that the microscopical attitude reveals to us introduces fresh hazards (p. 57), and clearly the value of samples falls very steeply as rigour of sampling is relaxed.

These three considerations—choice, sampling and reliability—in their turn impose fresh limits. The excavator may hesitate, wondering whether any samples he might think worth taking would get looked at, in a reasonable time. The specialist may accept a set of specimens eagerly, hoping they may help in his own research, only to find that some insignificant circumstance throws doubt on their validity, or that there is no control and therefore no real solution.

One could take all the samples that might possibly be useful. It is better to be safe, for there is rarely any question of going back. The other course has almost everything to commend it, especially in developing long-term collaboration: the specialist must go to the trench. All the important and exciting work of this kind has always been based on the specialist's continuous first-hand knowledge of the excavation's progress. There is no better way—ideally no other—but there are not enough specialist-hours and travelling reduces the precious few still further.

Finally, limits are imposed by the method of analysis. These appear to be the most frustrating. But taking a wider view one is amazed by the range of what has become possible even during the past two decades. In most cases accuracy is already far greater than would be required for most archaeological samples. Notable exceptions include Carbon-14. Also, accuracy proved in a specific connection often needs confirming when a modification is used on archaeological material.

Basically, there is a reciprocal relationship between state of knowledge and state of technique. The actual methods will thus always be affected by the nature, state and size of the archaeological sample, and, to a similar extent, the assessment of results by what is known to be possible at the time. It is because the effects vary in direction and degree that the specialities differ so much. Reliable, numerical and useful results will come streaming out in one case—only a slow, doubtful trickle in another. Or a whole pound of sample may produce only "4,000 ± 200 years", yet some minor constituent in a few milligrams will be determined to within one or two parts per million. While in many cases, in fact, the very state of the sample is of particular interest, the amount is usually far too small.

I have stressed the multiplicity of factors throughout, but especially here, because an appreciation of it seems indispensable for a proper understanding of scientific method, and methods of analysis in particular. In the beginning I drew a distinction between the fundamental interests of science and archaeology. The archaeologist, concerned with any human situation, is ever instinctively on the look-out for the single dominant factor; but scientists would probably agree that in general there is no such thing.

Now my excavator friends are not interested in how a machine works, or an iron pan is formed in the soil. They want to know how the results from the machine can help them, and what the position of the pan may be made to tell them. But in order properly to realize the limits of scientific aids one must appreciate at least something of their nature and complexity.

When one considers the large number of complex operations involved in something like radiocarbon dating, each carrying several sources of error like so many possible centres of infection, one wonders that any healthy results have come out of it at all. And as one comes to grasp something of the different forms in which iron pans can exist, and of the various ways in which they may be formed, it becomes clear why they can indicate several things and why we can rarely be sure which it is in any given instance. The unity as well as the identity of man-made and natural features alike is suspect. "Bits", only, may fail or deceive. Things may be just not wrong enough to be spotted at once, and then whole weeks or even months may be completely wasted.

Yet some bits are less likely to cause trouble. Provided we remember the complexity we need not be dismayed by it. But nothing will be gained by thinking that any present limitations in technique are due to *one* difficulty. Neither will it help to assert that an iron pan—because it will usually form where there is archaeological reason to believe the surface had been trampled—invariably means a trampled surface.

When specialist methods are studied as a group, the differences between them immediately become apparent: differences in approach, range, technique, state of knowledge, usefulness to archaeology and, conditioned and reflected by them all, differences in limit as they concern us here.

First, the mechanical limits due to equipment where such is used, and especially where it is complicated. Refinement of apparatus, and sensitivity to interference from outside, unfortunately cannot help going hand in hand. Vibration, dust, fluctuations in temperature and humidity may assume an importance out of all proportion to their normal and tolerated nuisance value, and their suppression or control can become vital. This makes the equipment more expensive, difficult to house and run, and therefore less accessible to the archaeologist.

The machine itself may usually be compared to an experimenter: it does something to the specimen, observes the result and records it. Again, roughly speaking, each of these stages may be affected in three different ways: chemically, physically and electrically. These three are really different aspects of the same thing, and it is important to bear this in mind, but the traditional distinction is useful here.

In the normal type of X-ray generator used for radiography, the excitation process of the analysis is limited by factors such as the heat produced at the source, the amount and kind of X-rays that will pass through the tube window, and by electrical insulation. There is a practical limit to the thickness of iron, and others for other metals, through which X-rays will usefully penetrate within a reasonable time. At the recording end of the analysis is a photographic film. The limit here is dependent on the grain, i.e. the degree of fineness to which particles of silver salt can be dispersed in gelatine, and on the extent to which the chemical reaction caused by the X-rays can be sensitized.

The next example is far more complicated. In radiocarbon determinations, the sample is first chemically purified; the significant residue is then isolated, gasified and finally collected in a counter that must be rigorously freed from contamination. This preparative stage takes the place of the excitation. It is followed by the detection of the (very small amount of) beta radiation due to Carbon-14 in the sample by absorbing this radiation in a suitable medium which is thereby ionized. The quanta of resultant discharge are finally counted.

The whole assembly will be dependent on the efficiency of the chemical transformation from soiled charcoal or bone into pure (organic) carbon dioxide or methane or acetylene; on the physical efficiency of the very high vacua required throughout, and of the response of the medium to radiation; and finally on the possible vagaries of the electronic counting equipment—though, of course, these are all accepted by the workers to the extent of having become "irrelevant".

In many cases no complicated apparatus is required, but most specialist examinations involve a microscope at some stage or other. The most useful level for any given purpose will depend entirely on the size of the characteristics. An image that is too much magnified may be more unhelpful than what the eye can see direct. It is the reverse aspect of the photographic limit of grain size: the sovereign's eye on a Saxon coin—possibly vital evidence of personality,[D11A] obscured or worn—will be no use, however clarified, when it fills the microscopical field. We do not see the wood for being locked in a particular cell of one of the trees.

The limit of resolution of the optical microscope is thus generally not important here. But we may *want* to look at the cell or its walls, or even to study the helical build-up of one layer of such a wall. We can already see the larger molecules forming these helices, under the electron microscope. But thereabouts is the present practical limit, and it does affect some aspects even of this work.

Another distinction cuts right across the previous one—it is made between methods where a definite answer is possible and others where it can only be relative. Roughly, an ordinary chemical analysis can say no or yes, and how much; a fibre can be firmly identified in that sense, and traced back to its origin. But the fluorine or nitrogen content of a bone only indicates its age in relation to that of other bones found with it. And the origin of a stone, or the exact nature of a bone, can only be determined by matching with similar known material. This may depend entirely on what is available in museums and can even lead to disagreement between specialists. As a result any given size and state of sample may be more than good enough for one kind of analysis, and hopelessly inadequate for another.

Chemical analysis has had a long start. It is usually capable of great accuracy even with a minute sample whose state does not really affect the issue since the analysis itself merely seeks to detect certain units. How these may have been derived from something that is archaeologically significant is another aspect of the problem altogether.

The determination of fibres and their origin is a far more recent activity. But then it works at another level, and we have enough detailed knowledge for our present needs. The state of the sample is here of decisive importance. If certain significant features of structure have been preserved, then identification is possible and firm—if they are missing it is not.

The fluorine and nitrogen contents of bone are determined by chemical analysis. Again the interpretation of the figures is another matter. Very little material can usually be spared but no more is needed. The method as a whole is comparatively young.

Petrology is much older but does not compare with chemistry in experience, tradition, or "structural simplicity" of material. Where time is a factor in accumulating knowledge, therefore, it cannot pin things down so easily. The same applies in some measure to systematic osteology where, in addition, the preservation of certain details, especially the articular processes at the ends of a bone, is essential as in the case of a fibre—only in a different way and at a level dealing in much larger units.

Rocks are commonly defined by the minerals they contain. The limit here is thus reached when we only have a few mineral grains, loose, and with no certainty that they ever belonged to one piece of rock. Even such evidence may be significant, but there we pass into soil analysis.[P3] Similarly although small, isolated units of certain bone or fibre structure may differ significantly from others, such discriminations will eventually become lost in a purely chemical or physical unity, at the next level down, with a corresponding shift in limits.

Then there is the *natural* complexity (p. 228), probably the greatest single factor making for a distinction between absolute and relative techniques. Minerals are not necessarily chemical compounds. Bones and fibres have been part of animate systems and thus subject to possible minute individual variations. Beyond a certain level, precise laws become unpractical. It is easy to mistake the multiple for a single cause, and to set limits in the wrong places.

How do these general precepts, and the limits between which any arguments based on numerical results must move, work out in practice? First, certain types of analysis can operate only by internal comparison. They differ from other "matching" methods by requiring their comparative material *in situ*. While the identification of rocks and bones is linked to museum specimens, fluorine dating of bones is based on the relative amounts present in different bones found together. The same principle operates in most kinds of soil analysis for archaeology and also partly in pollen analysis. But whereas the last deals with marked changes over wide areas the other two are often concerned with relatively minor differences individual to each site, or even to limited areas on any site.

Thus, however much techniques may improve and data accumulate, such methods of intrinsically relative analysis, and particularly dating,[K5] will always be at a disadvantage in principle until it becomes possible to discard the relative approach. However, the "lucky strike" factor operates here as elsewhere.

The exceedingly accurate estimation of traces of fluorine in a minute quantity of drillings from a precious bone—or of manganese in a soil sample—may be a great achievement. But its direct value may seem negligible, giving the age of one bone as a multiple of that of another—or indicating that a stain in the soil is more likely than not to be due to human activity at some unspecifiable date. Yet the first glance at a thin section cut from a rock specimen—or at some bone fragment—may pinpoint the quarry where the stone for a neolithic axe came from—or reveal the age and diagnose some abnormality of a person who died five thousand years ago.

A similar situation is seen from slightly further away, the more precisionist attitude becoming that of specialists as a group. At their most extreme the points of view may seem diametrically opposed. The archaeologist will say about some particular feature, "I *know*, even if there are no detectable remains"; the specialist, "I *don't* know *until* I can find them". The one will start by assuming that some obscure object is an artefact, the other that it could be natural. Even as they face each other over a common experience they cannot help approaching it from different sides.

And yet the specialist may argue the air stale on the available evidence—the excavator will walk out into the open and dig up some more that settles the matter conclusively. However intuitive his approach, here is the evidence, as in the discovery of the Alpine lake dwellings "the life of the Stone Age was resuscitated".[C6]

It remains to add a third dimension to this examination of the kinds of limit which the various methods of analysis themselves bring to the work. If the methods are considered, not according to the equipment they require, or the type of answer they can give, but by dividing the work broadly into routine and research, then some new factors come into play.

There are usually both routine and research applications of any one particular method to archaeology. The conception of research is common to all scholarly disciplines in the widest sense, but I think non-scientists find some difficulty in truly appreciating all that is involved in a severely experimental branch of an exact science. Added to the vagaries of apparatus is the formidable problem of correctly designing the experiment.[F5,Q1] There must be no doubt that the results are a true measure of the quantities involved, and a true reflection of the qualities that are significant.

Clearly all this has a devastating effect on any attempt to compare the work, and particularly the time, that may be required by different specialized investigations. The spectrographic analysis of a sample taken from our bronze dagger (p. 55) can take two hours or two months. If we want to know the approximate tin, lead, arsenic and antimony contents—a routine job for the particular laboratory—then ours is merely another sample. But if we are asking whether any of the more unusual elements such as thulium, niobium and tantalum are present at trace level, then it may need standard material and plates, checking and cross-checking various combinations whose components may distort each other's registration, and finally running off a whole set of exposures before deciding that one could be reasonably certain—of what? Maybe only that all the things we are looking for are absent. Such negative evidence is often useful, and sometimes vital, but at the end of a long time of waiting or working, as the case may be, it can be somewhat discouraging.

It is perhaps an hour's work to clear and mount some fibre remains and decide they are bast fibres, probably flax. But the archaeologist may want to know, in view of traditional uses and recent suggestions, whether it is in fact flax or nettle. To my knowledge it has not been possible to make this distinction for material found in the customary poor state; one would have to approach the problem from both ends, collecting all the material available from archaeological sites, and successively degrading fresh fibres to see how the characteristic features disappeared. It might all take some months' full-time work, or more.[K3A]

The fluorine dating method provides a useful example. Over a period, various improvements in analytical technique were developed in the Government Chemist's Laboratories.[H18] It is now a routine job carried out in a standard manner with nitrogen and other analyses and on several samples together, all in a matter of hours. But the research continues at the British Museum (Natural History) in another direction: the systematic collection of data on the conditions under which any given bone was buried. This will give us a better idea of the degree to which various factors influence the fluorine and nitrogen contents, but it may be years before we can date bones absolutely from a formula which also takes these conditions into account.

Here we come up against our "relative limit" in a new and serious way. For the purpose of a definitive account of some particular development in the human cranium, or the pelvis of ox, comparative material simply may not exist; one has to be ready for it as it comes out of the ground. This may be a life's work, or even a task for several generations. Yet a start has to be made.

Basically it is from this evolutionary standpoint only that such materials are of value to the anatomist or osteologist, who alone should undertake their examination. Relics of Iron Age arthritis or trepanning, and the degree of wear on teeth of Roman ox, may be important intrinsically; but unless the specialist is interested in what happens on burial to bone structure as such, he gets less out of isolated routine identifications than colleagues in other disciplines.

Much the same is true of other fields where archaeology asks primarily for identification of material, as in most other zoological investigations and the majority of botanical and mineralogical ones. The condition of timber is probably always of routine interest to the specialist, and so is the composition of Roman concrete floors. But limited resources have forced many institutions to consider only what might help them in their own researches.[T1]

Still, the connection is sometimes unexpected to all concerned. A botanist studying a certain sedge may become interested in mounds that are archaeologically "pre-1066".[C18] How convenient, in turn, for the intending excavator to have sedge plants (in south-west England) which will declare unequivocally that the slope on which they are growing was there in Norman times—though not, unfortunately, that it was man-made.

A sound case could be made out for the importance of routine work. A very great deal has been added to our biological knowledge of antiquity as a result of routine analysis. And yet virtually nothing is known about the kinds of clay from which the ancient made his pottery, of paramount importance to him and to us alike. That is because the provision of routine data on the mineralogical make-up would at this stage be practically useless.[S8] Research is the primary need here. Though it is an exceptionally difficult task, new techniques may bring rapid returns.[E6,R14]

Where research projects are actually being worked on, as in pollen analysis, everything that fits in with them is welcome, but all other material cannot, for the moment, be touched. In other cases there may be a sort of pernicious oscillation about the aim of the specialist study. The human anatomist interested in statistical variation may have to wait for a large and reliably dated, homogeneous cemetery. But when this appears there may not be enough staff to cope with the sheer volume of the work in a time reasonable from the excavator's point of view. Luckily, as in many other cases, the material would normally not deteriorate and could be left over for intensive study at a later date, the results of a proximate examination being published with the excavator's report.

In petrographic examination, perhaps more than in any other field, the routine identification of unknown specimens is usually a waste of the specialist's time. Except in tracing erratics, his primary concern is to study material whose origin is known, to describe, classify and relate it to material from other known sources.

There is here no evolutionary factor. The archaeologist wants to know if the rock could have occurred naturally, whether it could have been carried there by ice and or some other natural agency—or whether it must have been brought by man and, if so, where it could have come from.

All this goes right against the petrographer's vein. Lucky matches apart, the composition of rocks is such a complicated business, compared to "simple" structures like the end-grain of woods or the bones of animals, that it is not even worth starting on a detailed description of isolated specimens as a routine unless some likely sources can be postulated.

It might be argued that, even here, routine work would justify itself over a long period. But clearly the limited resources are far better spent on something like the researches on Stonehenge,[T3] or the Tievebulliagh axe factory,[S1] or even the long-term programme of routine "slicing" of stone axes which is making such good progress.[S12, S27]

The last is a timely reminder that most research work, after all, involves an enormous amount of routine observation. All the same, especially where skilful and tedious manual preparation is involved, as in the examination of fibres, or (with some mechanical aid) in making thin sections of rocks—or again where the work consists in detailed measurements made by hand, as on human bones—it is preferable that the routine work should be done for some fairly specific purpose. One of the most comprehensively automatic instruments designed for material supplied by the archaeologist and art historian—the ideal apparatus to use for a wide variety of routine operations—Hall's X-ray fluorescence spectrometer (p. 237), is deliberately set aside for research work.

And yet, there is a very real danger in over-stressing the distinction between routine and research. In the study of electrolysis, for example, the research worker now speaks a different dialect from the observers of routine phenomena in industry. Between a large amount of detailed and accurate information about fundamental concepts, and millions of tons of industrial chemicals, there is an enormous gap. Fundamental concepts find the plating shop floor slippery—industrial phenomena are received in academic quarters with scepticism or even presented a duck's back off which they obediently roll, back into the lake of common routine data on which the research worker floats, serene and immune.

Classed with the botanists of today, there are plant physiologists concerned exclusively with the living cell in the plant. Their tremendous potentiality lies in being able to profit from comparisons with other unit cells throughout the biological world. The possible danger is that the plant itself may altogether escape them. *Is* it a danger? At their level the (after all artificial) boundaries between animal and vegetable (p. 250) may quite naturally and most desirably fall away. Yet we can become so absorbed in how something works that we may entirely forget what it is.

The research worker needs to be isolated to follow his imagination freely; it makes him often interested and helpful. All the same, much of this work tends to suffer from a pre-eminence of research. The increasing isolation makes for greater difficulty in finding the right specialist. Above all, the exclusiveness of research transforms the simple term into a magic password.

Quite naturally this must remain so as long as the archaeologist continues in his present rather weak bargaining, if not actually begging, position. His material is rarely considered on its own merits, or for its possible archaeological significance. But as these may be controversial, the important questions become: Who is to decide what is important? And what is to happen to important material that does not fit into any current research programme?

Archaeological evidence is not quite like any other. It has its sedimentary stratigraphy, including the biological material, and in fact depends almost exclusively on the type-fossil.[C7] The concept is here extended to any material characteristic of a stage of development, but primarily artefacts. This is legitimate precisely because one important way in which archaeological differs from geological evidence is in being the result of human activity. Despite the superficial resemblance, the other great difference lies in the degree of change that can occur on exposure. Whatever is unearthed, once it is removed from the environment with which it has been in equilibrium, it often deteriorates very quickly—unless conserved—sometimes perishing altogether. In this it differs also from corresponding unburied material that is in existence now.

Organic deposits furnish obvious examples (p. 142), but badly rusted iron objects also seem to deteriorate more rapidly on exposure to air. Many bronzes begin to break up very quickly, especially under humid conditions, and even pottery and some kinds of stone may spring out of shape or crack, or have their surface flaked off by crystallizing salts. Perhaps the most serious losses involve minute traces of perishable remains on otherwise robust materials—such as possible food residues in pots, or textile remnants on bronze objects—which may be washed or scraped off before their presence is suspected.

Two principal points emerge. Each piece of evidence, every archaeological moment—being the result of human effort—clearly has a unique quality in the same sense as every human action. This means that every individual indication of this human effort is potentially unique and correspondingly important.

It follows directly that every such trace of material evidence should be searched for and salvaged, examined and recorded in the condition in which it is found. This is a serious responsibility—and a tall order. Often this very condition may be of primary interest to the specialist—either for archaeological reasons, or because he himself is studying the relevant causes and changes. Material not fresh from the ground is hardly ever suitable for such specialist research.

Yet the excavator in the field is too harassed to bear this in mind all the time; he must concentrate on the more orthodox things that can be conventionally demonstrated. The museum worker has his own problems and, inevitably, exhibition value will influence his attitude when examining a find. The specialist, who alone can finally evaluate the material as such, is usually unaware of its existence unless it is brought to his notice. There are the usual rule-proving exceptions; but in general, while there is a vast specialist potential, the danger of missing or losing material is still disproportionately great. Whose responsibility is it to be?

The research element appears as far and away the most decisive single factor in the whole complicated business of scientific work for archaeology. When it is properly taken into account, many superficial puzzles are resolved, and the way lies clear to consider the various methods against the "limiting" background. This clarifies their present position, individually, and also their relative usefulness.

In the case of Carbon-14 analysis, for instance, not so long ago the equipment was the most limiting factor. The results are already extremely useful, as they are absolute and independent of any other evidence, with certain small reservations; yet it is far from plain sailing for the excavator. Though a routine operation by now, the method must continue to be cross-checked[W16] and used on material with research priority for some time, and in general remains a rather frozen asset in Britain.

The fluorine and nitrogen dating methods are in a completely different position: the analysis is a matter of chemical routine; yet the results are relative and their value limited. In pollen analysis, the most complicated unit involved is the human eye, apart from the microscope. But the work is exceedingly tedious and therefore likely to be research-bound for a long time, even though the results are widely applicable and of great general and almost, if not quite, absolute value.

The latter term has a double meaning here. In the dating sense, the main expansion of certain trees can be related to definite stages of human development for given areas. But the connection between pollen and dates rests ultimately on the stratigraphy established by the quaternary geologist; it cannot, like radiocarbon analysis, stand entirely on its own feet. The other sense is that of the comparative criterion I have used: pollen analysis is still limited, not so much with trees but certainly with herbaceous plants and particularly weeds, by the lack of exact knowledge of pollen morphology through the vast extent of the plant kingdom.

The identification of bone, stone and fibre can be similarly limited: not seriously for the last, except in fine distinctions, but more so with bone and often quite decisively for stone. Of the three, only bone really comes near to having some value also in the dating sense (other than by Carbon-14), although the potentiality exists for fibre (p. 122) and, obliquely, in the remanent magnetism of heated ferruginous rocks. Fibre and stone require mounting and microscopes—bone only calipers: it emerges, therefore, as a far more useful material than it might at first appear to be. Much depends on the state of the sample. Bone has the advantage of a better chance of preservation than fibre, and this outweighs its more "comparative" status and the need for much bigger units.

Stone would seem to lag behind. Yet the value of a quick, close match is potentially far greater than for bone or fibre evidence. On balance, however, bone remains the most useful of the three. Against such a generalized background (fig. 2) each individual case should still be considered on its own merits, as other factors can easily upset the general pattern.

Out of this immense quantity of diverse considerations arises the

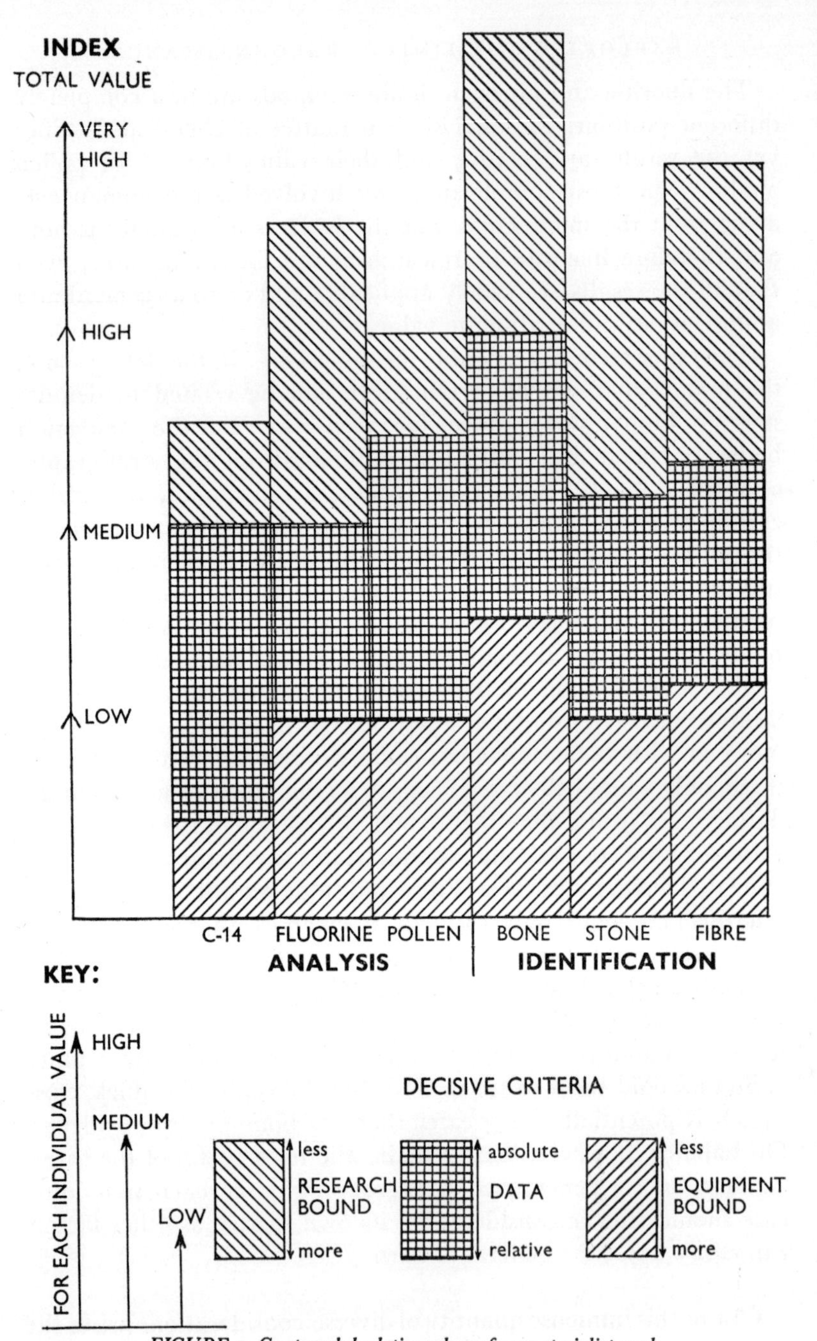

FIGURE 2. Compounded relative values of some specialist work.

need for middlemen: scientifically trained non-specialists with an ear to the archaeological ground. Specialists have no time to study each other, or their relation to the whole, but when a layman tries to find out what is happening he often cannot understand what he is told. Like another "practising scientist in an entirely different field, I believe that I can understand [the various languages] and I have tried to write down what seems to me to be happening and why I think it is urgent and important".[P13]

The interpreters, working close to archaeologists and speaking the same general language as specialists—and interested in problems of communication—can discuss the aims and limitations of the one with the other. They are the chief pivot minders (p. 76), postmen or ambassadors, catalysts or buffers, conductors or insulators, lubricants or shock-absorbers. They must be prepared to suffer all the occupational hazards associated with these concepts; to be grumbled at, recalled in disgrace, exhausted and poisoned or precipitated, sent up in smoke or ground to a fine powder.

They might perhaps be better able than some, as an occupational benefit, in the words of the *Bhagavad-Gita* to "act sacramentally and be free from all attachment to results"—even as they remember that "freedom from activity is never achieved by abstaining from action". Unfortunately, when it comes to the use which is made of the results, they tend to get the blame equally for the specialist's scruples and the excavator's indiscretions.

In a way a specialist study in itself, the interpreters' research function is to probe the bounds of possibility. Because they alone can properly balance scientific against archaeological considerations, *they* must decide, ultimately, on what is clearly the most definite and difficult of all the limits—the limit of purpose: How far is it worth while pushing an investigation that is perfectly possible, in any given instance and at present? And theirs is the final responsibility for the maximum extraction of any material evidence and for the fate of currently "untouchable" reference material (p. 91).

In another sense, though, their own first commandment is: "Don't touch!" As in the field, so in the lab., look at it first from all possible angles. No matter how certain you are about material and condition, do not even turn it over before ensuring that it will come to no harm. The odd piece of shale, found moist and stored under water, may squash into mud at a touch. Do not remove anything at all until it has been recorded, and even then not unless it is absolutely essential. Try all the non-destructive methods first, and even if they do not immediately help leave the thing on one side and think again a few times—always provided you keep it as it was found.

Having got so far, one might begin to wonder whether the object of the whole activity had not become slightly obscured. Might ancient *wo*man (for once!) not justifiably join her modern sister in the complaint of Cole Porter's song:

> He simply loved my larynx
> And went wild about my pharynx,
> But he never said he loved *me*!

Also, on a different plane, how does any work ever get done at all? Before these important points are answered by demonstration, two possible impressions require comment.

The various techniques might appear to be worked very much in isolation, and this is partly true of the physical facts of the work itself (p. 55). But it should not apply in the organization of the work to a particular end, where several techniques may be used to solve one problem.

Again it might seem that all I have said is realized in the course of the work. On the contrary, it is the result only of reflection. Activity merely develops the conviction that, besides research, *something* must be done *ad hoc* at every opportunity, literally to be going on with.

There is in the end also a limit of space. Normally, it should be quite clear from any excavation report what the specialist finds as a result of trained observation, what he thinks about it from his experience, and what the excavator makes of specialist evidence in relation to the rest. So closely are they interwoven for lack of space in certain reports that the results may become completely valueless.

For example, when we read that some timbered structure rested on sleeper beams of fir, this might suggest that a botanical examination had been made of wood fragments found *in situ*. If we then discover that only slots were found, with a filling that differed from the surroundings, and the sides showed impressions of "grain" which somebody had said looked like fir—then the situation is radically altered. Now fir might generally be regarded as having been introduced to this area only very much later than the date of the structure concerned. Hence the wood was either imported in sufficient quantity to make its use in sleepers economic, or there was some now unknown source of it near by—if the statement is reliable! At best, checking may involve much tedious inquiry—at worst, the excavator may be dead, the information behind the statement irrecoverable, and the statement itself therefore quite useless.

In another case a sleeper trench appeared under one corner of a concrete floor. More commendably, the report said that, judging from impressions of "grain", and residues of wood in the concrete, the beam which had lain in that trench had probably been made of birch. But birch may not now grow in that area. That again might mean a change in ecological status, or efficient transportation. It is therefore important to note that the botanist had actually said the wood was a diffuse-porous hardwood, *possibly* birch. Other diffuse-porous hardwoods may be growing there today and make so sharp an interpretation impossible.

Then again, a report on the charcoal fragments from an excavation may not only name the woods (as oak, hazel, etc.) but also give the species in each case. Normally it is not thought possible to determine charcoals down to species, and such a report would be controversial, to say the least. It may appear that the botanist determined, say, "oak" definitely, and made it *Quercus robur* L. simply because that was now native to the region. But then some would maintain that it was *Quercus petraea* Liebl. which was originally native, and that *Q. robur* had not appeared till much later. It will be difficult to discover because such differentiation is no longer clear when one is left with the timber only, but in the meantime little will be gained by assuming what we are trying to prove.

The distinction may not seem worth the fuss, archaeologically speaking—anyway, is not "oak" good enough? The several possible shades of "no" are symptomatic of exactly the shifting attitudes I am considering. There are even practical advantages in precision—for instance, in economic interpretation, and not least for the future when work may be concerned with a different aspect of the same pieces of material evidence.

Even as a challenge to the present, "there is lying unexploited, and in some cases neglected, a very large body of *direct* evidence of the former presence of the various species making up [our] flora, at sites and at times which can be adequately dated by reference to the chronological framework of Quaternary history"—nothing like *History of the British Flora*[G8] could in fact have been produced without just such meticulous attention to detailed record. The book also clearly shows how much archaeology owes to botany, both for back-projecting the natural environment, and for producing much-needed dates from bogs as out of hats.

Similarly for the other specialisms. Excavators absorbed in their responsibility for the final interpretation may tend to forget their duty of asking all the specialists to vet it—all of it. This has the added advantage of limiting errors of that other kind, due to one specialist's excursions into the fields of others.

All this does not mean, of course, that specialist reports should be confined to facts. We are returned to the mystery of imagination (pp. 41, 76). The known facts must be our starting points: the best "specialist-type expert facts" that effort can provide. But they are only the beginning; we must be determined, like Socrates, ". . . not merely . . . to record the opinions of other people without any risk to ourselves, but to participate in the risk . . .". The tale of the Bosham bottle well illustrates all these points.

In April 1954, two stone coffins were opened in the nave of Bosham Church, near Chichester in Hampshire. In the smaller of the two there was found a bottle corked and sealed with sealing wax which carried the impression of an armorial stamp, and containing some dark brown fluid. The bottle was handed over to the Government Chemist's Laboratory from whose reports the following salient extracts have been made:

> . . . The bottle was closed with a bark cork which, although appearing to be a good fit, did not in fact provide a gas-tight closure to the bottle. . . .

> The liquid had the objectionable smell usually associated with decaying organic matter of protein origin. It was primarily aqueous and afforded no evidence of the presence of alcohol. . . .
>
> The ratio of the nitrogen to the total solids suggests that the solids consist of protein and/or the decomposition products of protein. . . .
>
> In view of its possible importance, the chloride figure was determined and found to be only four parts per million as chloride ion in the original liquid. . . .
>
> The liquid has a high bacterial population of a mixed character including motile forms. . . .
>
> Interpretation of results:
>
> The low ash content and the very low chloride content preclude any possibility that the contents of the bottle consisted substantially of wine or embalming fluid or any material derived from the human or other animal body.
>
> The exact identity of the original contents of the bottle remains a matter for conjecture. Some source of energy in the form of oxidisable material must have been present to support bacterial life. In addition it is likely that some source of fixed nitrogen was available although the possibility of bacterial fixation of atmospheric nitrogen cannot be entirely ruled out. These sources of energy and nitrogen would have to be materials which had practically no ash content; i.e. probably materials refined by distillation or crystallisation.

Subsequently, after some discussion, the analysts found it possible to extend their interpretation:

> . . . Nitrogenous animal fibre structures of the type of wool, hair or silk would fulfil the requirements imposed by the analytical results. . . .
>
> The findings are consistent with the decay of any of these materials in an aqueous medium but you will appreciate that the findings do not amount to proof that any such material was present.

So far the modern facts and their immediate interpretation; now for the more subjective reactions, especially to some earlier facts.

In 1865 a coffin was opened at Bosham Church. From the dimensions then recorded, and the uncommon size (only 4 ft. 3 in. long inside), there is little doubt that it was the same coffin. In the Vicar's account of the discovery, made at the spot traditionally regarded as the burial place of King Canute's daughter, we read:

> . . . The mason in raising the lid, which was firmly fixed to the

coffin by concrete, broke it in two places; but when it was raised the remains of the child were distinctly visible, and Mr. Varley at once made a most correct and careful drawing of the coffin and its contents....

Unfortunately the drawing only shows the coffin containing a vaguely skeleton-like object. But amongst the correspondence produced by an account of the find of 1954, there was a letter in which occurred this rather curious passage:

... (The Vicar) told me many times that the small stone coffin contained the body of a little Saxon girl, aged about eight. The body was wonderfully preserved and had Saxon features and flaxen hair, but it crumbled into dust after exposure to the air....

Now the coffin was four to five inches thick, and the lid seven inches thick, both being made of relatively impervious material. If we accept that they were firmly cemented together when found in 1865, the state of the contents might have been as then described, even after 850 years. Yet the bottle is clearly of nineteenth-century date, and the seal was placed on it about the same period, by or on behalf of a lady entitled to arms.

If it were suggested, therefore, that some hair had survived to 1865 as hair which was recognizable and could be picked up and put in a bottle; that a lady of position, associated with the discovery, had the bottle filled with some spirit to preserve the hair, carefully corked, sealed and stamped, and finally buried—then such a suggestion would not be inconsistent with the evidence now before us.

There appears to be a slight discrepancy. *Spirit* is stipulated, yet we have "decay in an *aqueous* medium", and "no evidence of the presence of alcohol". However, after some time cork and seal "did not in fact provide a gas-tight closure to the bottle". Alcohol vapour could have escaped, air carrying bacteria would have taken its place. When the alcohol content had sunk so low as to lose all power of protection, the bacteria could have established themselves very quickly. They would remove the rest of the alcohol by feeding on it as well as on the hair—with a result similar to what was actually found.

Other difficulties are elusive and less easily removed. Perhaps most important is the Vicar's insistence that nothing was disturbed, and everything was reburied as found—and not a word about any bottle, never mind the hair. But anyone who has studied records a bare generation old will know how tantalizingly misleading certain details can be. Again, if the bottle had held a hank of someone else's hair—or for that matter some fur or feather, silk or horn—the results could have been the same. There is no reason why it should have done but that cannot affect the material evidence. On the other hand, the lady's motive in trying to save some of the only palpably human remains would be understandable, and on this the whole business will have to rest for the present. There is a hope that the arms on the seal may eventually provide further clues, but so far the heraldic ramifications have made the task extremely tedious.

It remains to illustrate the practical limits of such meticulous attention by equally detailed reference to some simple examples. In each case the work was straightforward and the results definite. They represent the ultimate pieces of the jigsaw. The business of assembling them with their respective neighbours is quite another matter. But about the pieces themselves there is little ambiguity. This is the kind of work all specialists are quite pleased to do. Although—or perhaps because—the results are in themselves limited they are within their limits conclusive.

Often, part of the material that is of special interest must be separated from some other to which it is attached—indeed, it must first be recognized. On the surfaces of a corroded iron sword, a chance find near Harrold in Bedfordshire, we noticed certain areas where bundles of thread-like incrustations produced random wavy patterns (pl. 7).

Portions of rust showing a woody grain were certainly recognizable. In some places the wavy bundles protruded from beneath these woody rust flakes and thus lay between them and the surface proper of the sword. It was inevitable that someone should have asked, in time, if the bundles might perhaps represent the remains of a "fur" lining to a wooden scabbard.

Fragments of bundles were sent to the laboratories of the Hat and Allied Feltmakers' Research Association. There, J. A. C.

Watt was able actually to release some fibres, intact, for mounting and microscopical examination in the usual way (pl. 7).

There was no doubt, from their scaly surface and size, that the fibres were of animal origin. They were there still, after some 1,300 years, as protein, as the actual animal's "hair" itself. Judging by the dimensions, they could have come from cow, sheep, goat or deer.

More often than one might think, even an apparently simple and single job can become rather more complicated. The urn shown in pl. 8 came to us from an earthwork called Devil's Ring, on Brightwell Heath, in Suffolk.[G5] It was clean and in fair condition; at first sight all it needed was emptying and, perhaps, strengthening a little.

But these very circumstances intrigued us. It was the first time that I, at any rate, had had an intact Early Bronze Age urn brought to me straight from the earth, indeed with some of it still in, full to the top.

Perhaps not only the material but also the distribution was significant? Resisting the normal temptation, we did not tip the urn upside down but decided first to see what was inside without actually having a look.

For probably the first time, an urn in these circumstances was X-rayed, and with surprising results (pl. 9). That X-rays should go through two thicknesses of pottery and some seven inches of sand, and still show up burnt bones so clearly, was perhaps more than one might have dared hope.

Even allowing for enlargement of the shadows thrown by the bones that were some inches from the film, their greatest length was considerable and probably the maximum that would fit comfortably into the urn. There were certain dark areas evidently free from bone, and also a brighter egg-shaped inclusion which appeared to be different from the rest of the material. It seemed as if most of the bone fragments, including the large ones, were concentrated near the bottom of the urn but clear of its base.

With a special tool made for the purpose the contents were then micro-excavated, inch by inch and (for the first three inches) quadrant by quadrant. Despite great care, not many of the friable bone fragments compared in length with what was seen on the X-ray. The dark areas in the X-ray turned out to be due to charcoal, and the bright egg was a smooth white vein quartz pebble.

The filling of each quadrant, and every inch, was separated by hand into three fractions: bone, charcoal and sand. Each fraction of bone was weighed; the other two kinds of fraction were placed in orders of decreasing contamination (for the sand) and increasing bulk (for the charcoal) from a visual examination.

Clearly the largest concentration of bone occurred at -5 and -6 in. The pebble was also at -5 in. Most of the charcoal was at a higher level, with one fragment at the top, and none at all at the bottom. There was some bone, if only a very little, present in the top inch, too.

Whatever one may feel about the interpretation that is given later (p. 109), the filling of the urn was obviously a deliberate affair; for instance, the sand was an integral part of it and was not taken from the immediate vicinity of the cremation pyre because, unlike some of the sand from the filling of the pit in which the pot was found (upright), it had not been reddened by fire.

My third example shows another kind of difficulty met over an apparently simple question. From the Saxon town of Thetford,[K2] in Norfolk, came a fragment of pottery (col. pl. II). It was a rather nondescript piece—evidently part of the slightly sagging base of a pot about a foot in diameter—but had one quite remarkable feature. Its inner surface was uniformly and completely coloured a light purplish-pink—rich and clear.

We thought it might be some fruit juice stain. Under the microscope the colour itself appeared as a thin layer just below the pottery surface. After some deliberation I flaked off a tiny fragment and held some of it over a gentle flame: the colour charred easily, and on stronger heating burnt away completely, leaving the clean, bright, faintly cream pottery.

I put the rest of the flake into acid, which turned it a faint but definite yellow; when washed and dropped into alkali the flake regained its former colour, though with a slightly redder hue. The colouring matter was evidently organic in origin and behaved like a natural indicator of the type familiar in litmus.

Fruit juice now seemed likely and I consulted the Horticultural Research Station at Long Ashton, near Bristol. But it appeared that no known fruit juice would be expected to behave exactly like our specimen. This was later confirmed at the Food Investigation Laboratory in Cambridge.

But during the discussions there it so happened that another visitor, from his knowledge of vegetable dyestuffs, at once suggested that the colour was probably due to madder. Since madder lake is used as a pigment, the Paint Research Station agreed to look into the matter. Owing to its characteristic colour, a recognized way of identifying madder is to record the precise manner in which it absorbs light. Such an absorption spectrum is conveniently obtained by dissolving the material in, say, alcohol and allowing a beam of light to pass through the solution in a glass cell. The *amount* of light that passes through, as the *wavelength* (i.e. colour) is gradually changed, is then recorded.

Despite various difficulties (p. 111) the work was successfully carried out by C. P. Cole in a modified way (fig. 3). It is impossible to be certain without chemical analysis, which in this case would probably destroy all the material, but madder has been confirmed as much the most likely material.

The facts take us thus far; I have in each case deliberately stopped short at the demonstrable observations (p. 98). They must now be re-examined, both as regards intricacies of method and argument, and also in relation to what they may be taken to mean.

Starting to look for fur lining on all swords, we had difficulties with the very next lot, from Holborough in Kent.[E8] In the initial samples, fragments of wood from the scabbard, and other vegetable debris including root hairs, kept on obscuring the issue. In the end, patient search was rewarded and even led a little further. The material was almost certainly wool. Closer inspection by D. Haigh suggested that the whole pelt of the animal had been used.

In a related case the conclusions pointed in a different direction. On the site of the medieval Chertsey Abbey,[G6] near London, a "brass" ring which had corroded comparatively little carried an isolated bump that stood out clearly (pl. 10). Under the hand lens one could see something that clearly needed the help of a specialist in textile remains. In due course the report came back, Miss E. Crowfoot describing the weave of this "positive" textile fragment in some detail. A small amount was then sent away for fibre identification as before.

Imagine our consternation when the analyst could find no fibre of any description. There were a few lumps of fibrous material that looked as if they might be modern root fibres (p. 187), also some fibrous "fossils", but all attempts to prepare these for proper microscopic examination ended in their complete collapse into an amorphous powder.

What had happened? Sampling had not been at fault this time for even the entire ring provided no further evidence. The whole business clearly raised a number of problems. Most of the scientific detail is discussed in the next chapter (p. 122). On a general level, the problems are symptomatic: when the experts disagree, what is then the truth to be? Was there any textile or not? If yes, why was the fibre so elusive? If no, what produced the appearance of weave? Was material or organization the more significant criterion (p. 75)? Whatever the "right" answers, how could the other side best be told? Luckily, everyone was quite ready to be proved wrong; this virtue was here well rewarded for in the end it became possible for everyone to be right.

Evidently textile had been present when the ring was buried. In places, corrosion products from the ring hardened round the outer surfaces of the textile fibres more rapidly than these could be eaten away by microbiological attack. But the bulk of the fibre did presumably disappear in this manner and its place was gradually taken by mineral matter. Thus the outer semblance of the weave had been fixed by "petrifaction" while the material of the fibre had been completely replaced by another.

Clearly one's appraisal of the nature of a material can change without affecting the basic truth of its organization. The material itself should never be the only criterion; yet it must, of course, be invoked always. At the same time one ought to approach every observation prepared for fresh kinds of evidence (p. 75) and without imposing previous experience on it too inflexibly.

On another level, perhaps the most striking aspect of the fur remains was the direct link with the sagas, which refer to various similar practices.[D3] The swords were so sharp, for a start, that they were difficult to keep in anything as safely and efficiently as was necessary for their own good as well as for their owners'. At the other end of the time scale, a similar sword made recently by Anstee[A12] soon started to rust-bloom in its scabbard, even though this was made from the best available thoroughly-seasoned pitch pine.

One may conclude, then, that the Harrold sword was buried in its wooden scabbard which had a fleece lining. The pelt had probably been dressed with oil or fat to make it serviceable—and also, quite incidentally, more resistant to decay on burial (p. 134).

Characteristically, this seems little enough to say—indeed hardly more than the original remark made in conjecture. Yet there is, of course, all the difference which comes from a close objective study of the actual material. Taken with the work on the Chertsey ring, this example is perhaps the most telling in the context of the present chapter. It makes one sharply aware of the limits—or, rather more generously: it shows how much is in fact possible, and that one tends to take it for granted until suddenly confronted by such material as appeared on the Chertsey ring.

In X-raying the Devil's Ring urn we were probably rather lucky. Had there been more iron in the pottery or the sand—had the soil been chalky or stony, or the pot much larger—it might not have been possible to see so much so clearly. As it was, only two exposures preceded the one that is shown.

Two similar urns came in later from other sites. They were larger and squashed into the bargain. The X-rays showed, rather dimly, the presence of bones and to some extent also their size and nature. But neither clear deduction nor micro-excavation was possible because the filling was in one urn composed of hard concretions, and in the other matted together with roots: a further way in which these can be troublesome (pp. 123, 187).

Yet it was just for this last urn, from High Wood near Wareham in Dorset, that X-raying turned out to be quite useful. The calcined bone could not be recovered by the anatomist except in fragments so small as to be indeterminable. Had the bone been deliberately broken up into tiny pieces after cremation? This custom is well known and of some importance to the excavator. Sizeable pieces were visible in the X-ray, and the pieces *as found* had clearly not been comminuted.

And even the Devil's Ring X-rays were most useful. They did, after all, plainly show the distribution of the material in the urn, something that one could in no other way have come to know with such certainty, if at all. In another context it might be more valuable to show, perhaps, an otherwise unsuspected stratification in a coin hoard. Yet even here, the X-rays suggest that (despite all our care) what came out was not quite what was in the urn when it was found; and in any difference of opinion one would, of course, support the X-ray evidence against that from micro-excavation.

What can be made of it all? I think it allows us to suggest the following. After the cremation, some of the larger bone fragments were carefully picked out and laid in the urn, in such a way as to become tightly wedged at an angle and clear of the base. Sand—unburnt, and thus not from the area where the bones had come to lie after the fire—was gently heaped or even sprinkled on the bones in the urn until they were almost covered. The pebble was deliberately placed. Then, more briskly, charcoal was scooped up—with some small bone fragments, but again free from adjacent sand—and put in the urn, perhaps a couple of handfuls intentionally placed to one side of centre. More small bone fragments were piled on, and then more unburnt sand until the urn was full to the brim. It seems to agree well with the deliberation reflected in the other evidence from this burial—but that is another part of the story.

Finally, the dyepot fragment from Thetford also presents a number of different aspects of interest. There is, as yet, no relevant literature to speak of—though publication has increased enormously over the past decade.[G3, I1] One cannot look anywhere under "pottery, purplish-pink colouring of inside surface" for references to all the things it might be, all the work that had been done, and for suggestions about "what to do next". As for a wider, systematic search of the literature—as in many rapidly developing fields it is usually quicker to start again from scratch. It has been calculated that in A.D. 2,000 there will be no fewer than 1,000,000 scientific periodicals.

All the circumstances combine to induce hesitancy. The specimen is clearly valuable in several ways. It comes from an important town in Saxon England. Although part of a huge collection of some tons of fragmentary pottery, it is the only one of its kind. More than that—no information can be found about anything similar from anywhere in Britain, of any period.

Again, unidentified organic material has survived burial for perhaps a thousand years under known conditions. The occasion being, in its way, unique and the amount of material exceedingly small—a very thin film well protected from direct analysis by a skin of pottery—twice is not enough: one must think at least ten times before acting. In this context some specialist could benefit far more than the archaeologist, and would in turn be able better to serve the excavator next time. The important thing is to have enough material left for this particular specialist.

The development of acuity in this as in any other sense brings improvement in time. There is increased facility in apprehending patterns of evidence and action—passing into experience and reinforcing acuity by confidence—growth of this and other experience, of the circle of contacts, of the knowledge of possibilities and limits. Yet even with experience and if properly pursued in the best single-minded Scotland Yard manner, in the limit such problems involve a definite risk that the last test may at the same time prove nothing and use up the remains of the evidence.

Of course, this example has been artificially elevated—it is only one of countless similar yet individual little questions. And ultimately, it was not a vital piece of evidence in the context. However faithful one is to the "Don't touch" principle (p. 97), the time comes when one has to. Having decided that the colour was probably functional rather than decorative, I started on my minute preliminary tests. The opportunity came for an easy approach to Long Ashton. The specialist offered to examine the fragment but neither of us felt very hopeful; so on the occasion of a visit to the Food Investigation Laboratory, in Cambridge, I took the sherd with me—and by chance found someone who suggested the right answer.

I then read that madder had in fact been analysed thoroughly in a few antiquities, but only as a pigment.[C1] In the absence of light, i.e. during burial, the "lake" appears to be very stable indeed; and even in the ordinary way the colour is surprisingly persistent. The Paint Research Station, who were at the time advising on the renovation of the roof over Big Ben, were prepared also to confirm the Thetford madder pot.

Even then the difficulties were not over. The residue on the pot base would not be the madder extract itself. In order to get madder colour to take, a mordant such as alum must be used in the dye solution or the cloth. But the pot substance itself contains alumina and would attract some of the dye so tenaciously as to require acid to get it off. This is unfortunate when one wants to use a minimum for analysis and retain the most of what little is found for show.

Also, acid makes the colour of the solution unstable, and there is only a narrow margin of acidity and time in which madder is in solution with its colour unimpaired. C. P. Cole therefore decided to measure the absorption spectrum in a back-handed fashion: by reflection instead of transmission. This method requires no solution and in fact no material is removed or destroyed. But it needs a very smooth and flat (as well as clean) surface on the specimen to make the reflection true and efficient. The colouring matter is not isolated from its background of pot, and the result—apart from being more difficult to get—cannot be directly matched with the standard (solution) curves. So a further curve has to be prepared of the background—the uncoloured pot—by itself. Luckily, for transparent dyes, these things are additive. Thus it is possible to take the background away from the total reflection and be left with the curve for madder (fig. 3).

After some inquiries about methods of use, it became possible to suggest the following general picture to the excavator. The vessel of which his find was a small fragment had clearly been associated with some part of the operations involved in dyeing, most probably cloth, with madder. It had been heated on a fire, but not overcooked or boiled dry; nor had the piece passed through a fire after being broken. Furthermore, none of the sherd's edges had been cracks while the vessel was in use, and breakage occurred when the madder stain here was quite dry. One is left, then, with the impression of the familiar household accident, or perhaps abandonment and/or crushing by the collapse of a structure. The vessel could, of course, have been used for preparing the dye, and/or for the dyeing operation itself.

Having beaten the present bounds, I shall now try to trace the beginnings of possible patterns within them.

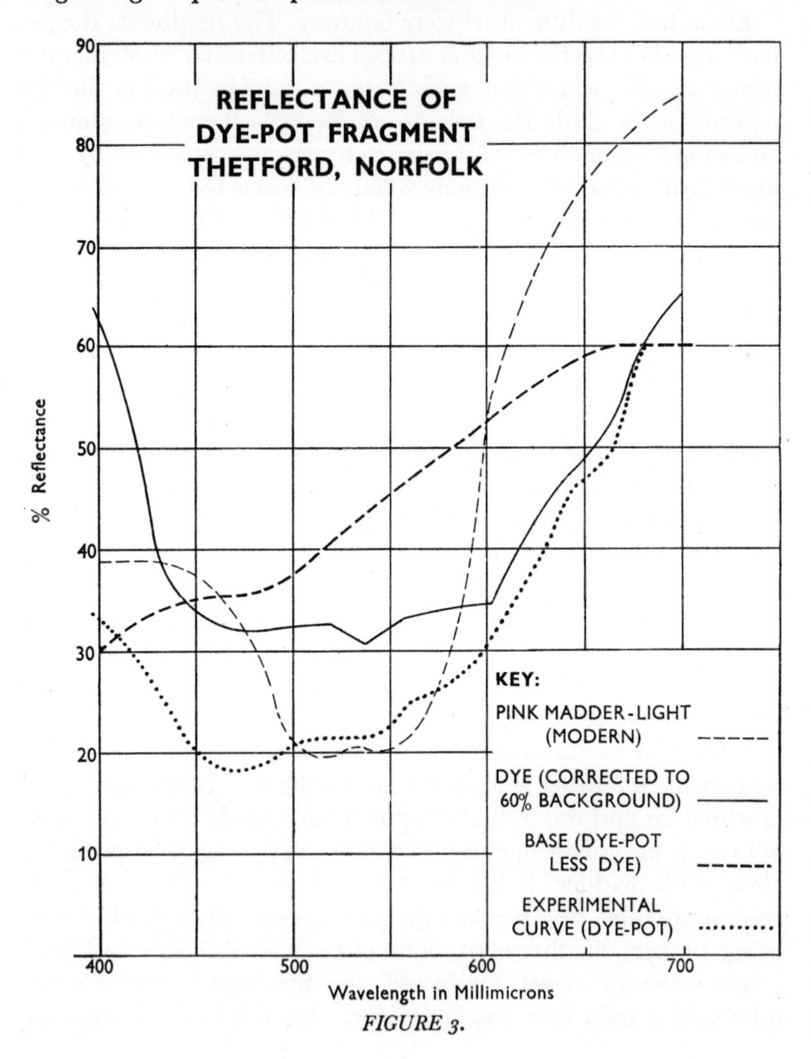

FIGURE 3.

CHAPTER FIVE

Finding Connections—Liaison

As the interpreter progresses his experience begins to fall into place. Becoming a specialist in liaison, he starts finding all sorts of connections everywhere. First between behaviour of materials and conditions of burial. Then between lines of research—and, for that matter, routine operations—in different fields; between effects of a given treatment on a variety of materials, and of a variety of methods on a given material. Later, connections and comparisons between manners of approach, to similar problems, by specialists in widely separated disciplines—or even within the same disciplines. Finally, such finer links and distinctions as those between the same material in different states, and even between different states in the same personality.

The interpreter cannot help this universally comparative outlook. It is one of these hen-or-egg conundrums; to turn my second sentence inside out: starting to find connections everywhere, the interpreter becomes a sort of specialist in liaison. This is equally true.

In the process, continuous nourishment and stimulation of his scientific curiosity leads him straight into the most exciting intellectual adventures. Often he is squeezed out into no-man's-land between specialisms. Sometimes there is the exhilaration of being among the first to catch a glimmer of a new relationship. Many surprises attend the pursuit of the ramifications of this experience; equally, some of the odd ramifications will turn up in unexpected quarters and disguises.

The business has its disadvantages. It becomes difficult to look at anything simply and in isolation. Every answer turns sour on the tongue—there is a feeling of something missing, the danger of a misleading emphasis. Add to that a kaleidoscopic progression of the grey matter reshuffled, sometimes hourly, into vivid new patterns of unfamiliar attitudes to well-known materials and situations. The physical strain is like listening to a long and fluent conversation in a foreign language which one understands just enough to be caught and held.

Then there are the external tensions. I am dealing with the development of the connective sense now, rather than the purely detective one. But as the connective sense is, after all, only the detective sense applied at one remove—to the detection of relationships between pieces of evidence—I shall have to jump back and forth between the two, as also electronwise between the various levels that are involved.

In theory, the passage of a "small find" through the laboratory takes place in a continual state of tension. The controlling force is the necessity of completely conserving all that has remained of the original. Opposed to this is the desire to learn as much as possible from the find, about the materials and methods used in making it, the changes it has undergone. Opposed also, curiously enough, is the need to clean the thing, to return it as far as possible along the road it has travelled down the ages.

Questions immediately arise. How can one be sure of what is original, and what has been added later by man or time? Which aspect of the original is to be conserved or exposed—colour, texture, shape—if justice cannot be done to them all? It is simple enough to formulate an ideal principle: "to remove what does not belong, to reveal all possible detail without taking any away, and not to polish, work, or add to any archaeological specimen; where making-up is essential, as in the case of pottery and on some other rare occasions, this must be done in such a way as to give a clear picture of the whole to the layman, and of the original to the expert".

Mutatis mutandis, it applies equally to field work at any given stage: "to remove what does not belong, to reveal all possible detail without taking any away . . ."—it is the excavator's dream, as well as the basic frequency to which is attuned the ear of the specialist listening for evidence in the trench.

Yet in practice decisions can be very difficult. Paradoxically, the most important aspects of a find may be linked precisely with what does not belong. Iron objects can rarely be cleaned without losing too much detail. The surface of a bronze, in this sense, often carries as much information as the object below, if not more. The fundamental question here always concerns material organization of the total find.

Often there will be an optimum order in which work should be done; sometimes it may be crucial to carry out certain investigations first, because subsequent stages may destroy that particular aspect of the evidence. With an early iron saw, for example, a point of primary importance may be to find out whether there had been any "steeling" or other hardening of the teeth. The saw may be in a bad way and amenable to treatment only by methods involving some heat. The particular feature of interest in the metallographic structure may be very sensitive to heat. In such a case, treatment for exhibition purposes would inevitably destroy any evidence of "steeling".

Large quantities of material led to a search for methods of rapidly discriminating between more and less important evidence. "Rescue" (p. 30) directly influenced my approach. Just as the whole job was concerned with carefully peeling off and recording the accumulated history of a threatened field layer by layer—before, for example, a housing estate was built—so on a microscopical plane it seemed important to interpret what could be seen before it was destroyed.

The initial impetus came from the conservation angle. It was necessary to know what a certain appearance meant in order to know how best to clean. For in practice our "opposing forces" are weakened by being dependent on one another. More often than not, a small find is best conserved by being cleaned, and cleaned the better the more is known of its creation and history.

Yet from the microscopic environment it is a logical step to the macroscopic conditions in the field. This led to a more general consideration of circumstances on the site, and in particular of their obvious interrelation. In this almost abstract view the individual find begins to disappear, much as prehistoric man is lost in the group whose activities alone are accessible to us. Indeed the whole process had about it an inevitability like that of museums or even of archaeology itself.

Scientific curiosity, in the broadest sense, works along many different levels, but perhaps it will do to consider just three. The levels are linked and adjustable and often run parallel. Yet they are as undeniably separate as microscope objectives with different magnifications.

Take our question No. 1: "What is it?" (p. 67). What is, for the sake of argument, this iridescent, opaque little fragment of uncertain shape which looks as if its gilt—or is it silver?—coating had been badly put on and was beginning to peel off? *Glass*, did you say? But surely this is not what we know as glass—what *is* glass?

The answer on the first level would hardly go beyond immediate physical properties; yet even here there is a divergence between the physical and chemical aspects. In one sense, glass is a state: a supercooled liquid; and for the physicist the definition can stay as open as that. But on this basis anything from slag to vitreous silica can be a glass, and here the chemical definition may be helpful, narrowing down ordinary glass to a "compound of silica and metal oxides". In ancient glass as well as today, the chief metal is nearly always sodium and/or potassium, with some calcium and aluminium, or, more rarely, lead. The former are metals by chemical definition rather than popular conception, and neither lead nor aluminium is of course present in glass as anything remotely resembling its normal everyday self (but cf. p. 168).

This approach leads down to the second level. If given in terms of a chemical analysis, for instance, the answer does at least make for reproducibility. Other things being equal, the material is going to be exactly comparable, in both senses: it will be precisely the same as another piece with the same analysis; and a variation of composition, in these terms, will make possible a direct comparison of properties as functions of the composition. On such grounds the natural coloured glass such as obsidian is a true glass, whereas the colourless silica glass, plentiful in the Libyan desert, is not.

For many purposes this answer will be perfectly adequate, making possible the control of quality, a discussion of the "softness" of certain soda glasses compared with certain lead glasses, and of the connection between depth and hue of colour, and amount and form of copper or cobalt present.

But one has to go down even nearer to the evidence in search of a really satisfactory explanation of fundamental "glassiness", and of the reason why a quantity of copper oxide will turn a certain glass ruby red, while an extra grain will make it a pale watery green. At this level one needs such concepts as valency and electrically charged (groups of) atoms known as ions, and proper manipulation of the vast empty spaces separating these ions even in such a "close-textured" material as glass.

On the way towards the next types of question one inevitably gets involved in manufacture. We cannot explain What it means, let alone, What was the nature and skill of the human activity, until we know How it was made, or to be precise, How it could have been made.

Going down as before, one man would answer in terms of phases, sand, soda and lime, the next use instead reactions, silica, sodium carbonate and calcium oxide. The third would dive into the molten mass for his reply, try to transfix the moment when surfaces become disturbed and, atom by atom, rearrangement begins.

With artefacts any answers might seem biased towards our first level, describing simply what materials were used, and with what skill, to make a brooch such as that shown in pl. 10 almost 1,400 years ago—rather than the exact nature of the alloy layer between the silver and the gold, or the reaction when the black decoration was applied.

The study of artefacts will thus rarely pass our second level, roughly that of ordinary analysis. And yet pl. 10 shows what happens when one does consider the alloy layer.[S3] In another case, a Greek precursor of Sheffield plate was demonstrated.[T5] Minute traces of "odd" elements in both gold and silver—perhaps only a few parts per million—can help us begin to group Greek coins, on a material basis alone, into natives and foreigners.[E5] This may in due course show lines of communication in much the same way as car lights at night are traced on a time exposure. As for that black decoration, X-ray diffraction can already "date" such materials as earlier or later than about the eleventh century.[M5]

But even on this level it is important to look in certain principal directions. However ravaging metallic corrosion may be, its effect is mild compared to the total disorganization of (non-mineralized) biological structure under normal conditions of burial. The metal and mineral disposition is comparatively clear. The organic residues must be sought—directly or indirectly. The archaeologist sees an object as he thinks it must have been before burial; but paradoxically, our first concern here—like the layman's—is with the surface as found, for that is where evidence of any organic material will be.

When some bronze jeweller's scales from a Jutish cemetery in Dover [E9] first came to hand the areas around the rings felt curiously soft—a good example of the sense of touch coming into its own, as it does quite often. The microscope then showed what is seen in pl. 7, both on the pan and also on the beam. The Shirley Institute's report opened up a new dimension of possibilities. Traces of fibre could clearly remain in the circumstances—and should thus be sought even on such a humble object. And a great deal could be made of the remains (see pl. 7 and also p. 162):

> ... From the appearance and the dimensions of the fibres, the purplish blue coloration obtained with Shirlastain, and from the cross markings, we are of the opinion that they are bast fibres, most probably flax, but we cannot make any further tests owing to the size and state of the sample ...

Thread was evidently used, then, in suspending Jutish scales in England, and small amounts of thread material have survived burial in chalk for over 1,300 years. The first aspect, however limited, is the thing that is important to the archaeologist; it is what, after all, to him the whole business is for (pp. 45–49).

But the other aspect shows the scientist that copper corrosion products can be removed with complexing agents from ancient buried fibre, to reveal how well it has weathered, comparatively speaking. To the interpreter it is important to know the reasons for what can be seen, at the closest level which the significance of the particular object seems to warrant (p. 97).

No chain was found and it seems reasonable to suppose that only thread was employed for suspension. But then no length of thread was found either—only traces on beam and pan. Had the rest completely decayed or was it lost? If lost, was it thrown away in antiquity or missed during excavation? But if not lost, why had it decayed—or rather, why had any traces been preserved at all?

There can, of course, be no definite answer in such an isolated instance where too many factors are unknown or uncertain (p. 79). But sooner or later it begins to fit sufficiently well into the jigsaw to clarify the puzzle.

And even an isolated fact, although it may keep its ultimate secret, can often be made to yield up a suggestion, perhaps provide an impetus to research in a field with which it has no obvious connection (pp. 50–51). Assuming that thread had in fact been there and decayed away, were copper compounds responsible for preserving traces on pan and beam?

Now this already fits in somewhere. After all, copper salts are widely used today in a variety of similar ways—for rotproofing wood, and in the garden; indeed, in this very capacity, for the protection of fabrics exposed to aerated moisture and therefore to rapid microbiological attack—in tents and similar canvas articles.

Perhaps the actual mechanism had been more akin to the action of anti-fouling paints used to protect ships' bottoms: due to a very slow leaching-out of the almost insoluble copper carbonate—which is normally also abundant in the type of corrosion product seen on the scales. The slow mineralization [V5] may here have surrounded the traces of thread soon enough—more effectively than at Chertsey and for twice as long (p. 107)—with a barrier protective against chemical attack, and sufficiently toxic to living organisms. This investigation, and ultimately the feel of the rings, first put me in direct touch with the significance of the surface.

In general, any chemist would naturally start by classifying problems on the simplest elemental basis. Hence metals are obvious favourites. Complications arise almost at once—when there are two different materials in one object. Bronze-plated iron articles are a particular nightmare. Bronze normally encourages the rusting of iron and is itself protected in the process. In such cases, therefore, a grotesque caricature of the iron component is often found, tenacious but brittle, with the bronze misshapen in consequence but relatively sound and temptingly clean.

Other headaches are caused by enamelled bronze fittings, or decorative ironwork firmly rusted to a wooden door, or an odd fragment of a wooden box, say, which has just about survived with some shreds of decorated leather still fixed to its surface with brass studs.

Yet such problems are comparatively straightforward because the evidence is present clearly and in bulk. The fibre on the scales showed up the effects of one material on another, too, but above all else it lifted clear of the normal level the importance of inferential evidence on the material plane; of seizing on minute traces of materials other than that of the object itself.

One goes on to look for evidence in a reflected or even refracted form—where the shape has remained but the material has altered or been replaced (p. 107), or even where no shape remains but only traces of some material that somehow does not seem to belong (p. 114)—and ultimately to a routine examination of every surface.

The analogy (p. 115) between field and laboratory salvage is quite literal. Each object is a microcosm; its discovery, also, entails the destruction of the surrounding evidence. As a result of centuries of mutual interaction the ambient soil and the object's surface when found carry between them one of these unique units that all together make up the Archaeological Record.[C7]

The study of the micro-surface is, in other words, only an extension of the archaeologist's usual attitude to the surface at the occupation level—an extension down the vertical approach (p. 56) but without change of angle. As we descend, the importance of the surface becomes more vivid. For a surface—any surface or interface above the atomic level—is the plane on which two different materials meet. It is there, fundamentally speaking, that everything happens and only there that anything can ever really happen.

This is equally true of the bottom of the waterlogged pit into which an iron key falls, or of the key itself; of the membranes which enclose the bacteria that swim around it, or the grain boundaries between the crystals which make up the body of its metal. At the normal level, it is the surface that is the immediate expression of the material, gives it texture, shape and contrast—indeed, as far as we are concerned, confers on the material its individual existence.

Clearly, though it may sound like a paradox, such an attitude is anything but superficial. After the work on the scales, fibres appeared everywhere. Thread stitching had survived in three places on some fragments of Roman bronze scale armour (*Lorica squamata*), found at Corbridge in Northumberland. At the Shirley Institute it was found to be "... yarn or twine of anti-clockwise twist, and made of bast fibre, probably flax".[A11] But it raised a fresh problem.

Why had thread survived in only three out of over a hundred possible places? To run through the standard argument: the fragments may have been from discarded armour and already without most of their thread before burial—with the backing material ripped off deliberately, or after mouldering away in an obscure corner. Corrosion during burial had perhaps been uneven: very slow decay of the bronze would be less protective for the thread. Most of the thread might have been eaten before the poison got to work. More thread may have been lost on removal from the ground; also, many of the pieces were single and incomplete scales not in very good condition. Still a slight puzzlement remains.

Many other fibre samples, on the other hand, turned out to be "epidermal cells of the grasses or straw", or "probably a minute piece of stalk. . . . As some fibres such as flax, hemp and jute are simply elongated plant forms it is difficult here to distinguish between fragments of these and fragments of stalk and other plant parts that may have been introduced accidentally. Also, of course, in many textile fibres there are fragments of stalk attached to the fibre proper, for example the 'spit' in flax that is present in the final fabric". Some clearly fibrous fragments were found altered almost beyond recognition. Mostly their behaviour indicated a vegetable origin, and the cross-markings a bast fibre. Even under high magnification their green colour was noteworthy; yet they readily broke up into minute spindle-shaped cells (resembling wool in this respect, just to confuse the issue) and thus seemed to be largely petrified.

For a systematic study one would need to know, apart from the significant properties of the fibres, everything about the conditions of burial—soil, metal and corrosion products, and any other materials also present, as well as some index of the soil's "cellulose-degrading activity"—and, of course, the date. Yet if all this information were collected every time the results would quickly yield multiple benefits (p. 45), although special techniques are needed to overcome present limits due to the state of the sample.

Fibre remains between two pieces of Roman bronze strapping found by S. S. Frere at Canterbury were a little more obliging: fragments of yarn, probably remains of fabric, on which the twist appeared to be both in S-direction and Z-direction, giving a herring-bone effect. Flax or hemp was indicated by the Shirley Institute's report, but the average diameter of the ultimate fibres was rather less than would have been expected for either.

Once the difficulties of distinguishing flax from hemp and nettle (p. 89) are resolved, stalk and roots ruled out (also p. 187) and shrinkage distortions allowed for—could the mean diameter of the ultimates be statistically significant?

The present standard range is quite wide for both flax (5μ–38μ) and hemp (10μ–51μ). Yet our samples have all had average diameters of 16μ–17μ—that is, a value *twice* as far from the maximum as from the minimum for modern flax, and five times as far for hemp. It is tempting to suggest (cf. pl. 23) that mean diameters were smaller in Roman times than they are today (also p. 188).

Could one use this criterion in reverse, to suggest a date? If so, fine distinctions would at present be impossible as one would need to know the age of a specimen before it could be identified. It seems worth while therefore to collect average diameters of ultimates as well—and also the cellulose contents. This returns us to partial petrifaction, as seen on the Chertsey ring (p. 106).

Such pseudomorphism is, of course, well known in fossils of geological age where replacement can take place literally molecule for molecule. From the experience with the fur (p. 104) it is easy to be misled into assuming that preservation would be complete, in a material sense, here also.

Normally, organic materials become unrecognizable or disappear from view; alternatively and exceptionally they remain much the same in both organization and material. Intermediate states clearly exist (e.g. Bishops Waltham[A13] (p. 181), Winklebury[M1]) but the situation as a whole is difficult to assess. A given time factor cannot be simply transposed from one site to another (p. 61). Also we often assume, from purely circumstantial evidence, that some organic material must have once been buried at a certain spot. But such inferences are "knowledge" that is different in kind from what we can actually see, much changed perhaps, but sufficiently preserved for standard examination. The difference between stains (in postholes) and waterlogged wooden piles is a case in point (pp. 61, 74).

In general it is theoretically impossible to establish any useful range within which intermediate states between presence and absence might be recognized. All the same, progress here depends on the study of just these aspects of material preservation which seem least rewarding and are normally ignored[G2] (pl. 11). Apart from particular benefits, such experience sharpens awareness—much as specialists will see far more on an "illegible" coin than an X-ray has shown them, but only *after* they have seen the X-ray!

The various specialists are interested in the pseudomorphism we met on the Chertsey ring. They are concerned at the frequent interference of roots, in this way and in others (pp. 106, 108). Though here merely puzzling at first, it can be vitally confusing. On a second ring from Chertsey, some yarns were actually found "embedded in root". The archaeologist is unmoved: he would like clear-cut distinctions and brief answers to pointed questions. There had been fabric touching the Chertsey ring when it was buried—good enough. Yet the distinction between fur as protein on iron swords, and fabric pseudomorphed on brass rings, is plainly of direct importance even to him.

The fibre on the first ring can no longer be identified; on the second it can, if only just: "All the evidence suggested they were protein fibres." There was even "a faint trace of scaliness" in the embedding matter here and there. Once again, D. Haigh reported that "no certain evidence was found, but it is likely that the material was a wool fabric". Yet on the swords, the fur fibre itself remains (p. 104).

Here we have, in effect, sheep's hair on its skin—preserved (even under normally less favourable conditions); and yet sheep's hair taken off its skin, spun and woven—not preserved (though luckily still indicated by its fossil). Why?

Could it be due to changes resulting from the removal and conversion of the hair? Most of the wax would need to be scoured out before spinning was possible; yet this very wax may have protected the intact fleece lining of the scabbard during the crucial period immediately after burial, before the rust forming on the sword had enveloped the fibres (see also wood, p. 128).

On such a fleece lining, furthermore, the fur must clearly remain on the skin and the skin itself supple. Normally that is not an easy combination of requirements. To make leather the tanner carefully removes all fur. Ordinary (vegetable) tannage would anyway spoil the fleece; yet left untanned the skin would harden, shrink and crack.

However, if the fresh, though part-dried, skins are dressed with oil or fat, the fleece can remain unaffected and the skin supple. This would confer the additional advantage of a water-barrier and automatic greaser on the scabbard lining.

It is difficult in practice to make a rational approach to this problem of intermediate stages and specialized types of preservation. One good opportunity was afforded at the Jewel Tower (p. 61, pl. 5); another again at the Chertsey Abbey site (p. 106).

Pl. 12 shows a brass buckle and belt end roughly in the relative positions in which they were found. Clearly there are pieces of the leather belt, altered but recognizable even to the unaided eye, under and among the corroded metal. As the belt got further away it gradually passed into a dark stain and disappeared. Poisonous copper compounds had evidently diffused outwards to inhibit leather-destroying organisms, but the concentration at a certain distance was clearly below the toxic limit.

Tests along such stains will show whether both copper content and organic matter in fact decrease uniformly away from the metal. A knowledge of the date, nature of soil and metal, and of the soil's "leather-destroying capacity" in each case might make it possible in time to talk in terms of rates of copper diffusion per century. This could provide a further independent material check on dating that is, in the absence of stratigraphical evidence, so far still based solely on typology.

Similarly, the excavation of a Bronze Age barrow at Arreton

Down, Isle of Wight,[A5] revealed a bronze dagger. Under it were fragments of very dark brown material, coherent and separate from the soil. In the soil, extending "upwards" from the broad top of the dagger, i.e. at the top in pl. 12, where it is just visible, there was a stain which (under certain conditions) seemed to stand out in the shape here outlined for clarity.

Dark material and stain were submitted to the Government Chemist for analysis together, on the pedestal of chalky soil which came to the Laboratory, since they were suspected of being organic residue. The material was in fact found very rich in nitrogen—containing more than ten times the amount present in the surrounding soil—and subsequently its microscopical structure was shown by Miss B. M. Haines to be comparable to that observed in ancient leathers.

The stain proved most intractable, on the other hand. Neither its nitrogen nor its phosphorus content differed from the values found in the unstained soil. In view of previous experience at Bishops Waltham (p. 181)[A13] further investigations were asked for, but proved fruitless.

The activity of copper in preserving wood is well known and widely used though not, perhaps, as completely understood. The two following examples—while it is of course the fact of preservation which made their examination possible at all—are given rather to show how this work prospers when it is of direct interest to the specialist.

A chance find by Mrs. R. C. L. Ashbee (then Miss Disher) at Great Chesterford in Essex brought to light an assembly of small bronze fittings—handle, bands and side plates—which had once held a wooden bucket. Attached to one of the side plates was a small, flat fragment of wood.

J. F. Levy found the structure sufficiently well preserved to be able to say without doubt that the wood was yew. There had been some attack by wood-rotting fungi, whose hyphae were plainly distinguishable. What was remarkable was the way the fungus appeared to have kept away from both large surfaces which were comparatively sound. Now these had been in intimate contact with the (corroding) side plate, clipped jawlike round this part of the wood. The copper absorbed into the surfaces, though not noticeable, seems to have been sufficient to deter the fungus.

The other specimen (col. pl. II) is a three inches thick uniform section cut (in modern times) from what had reputedly been a pit prop in a Roman part of a copper mine in Cyprus. It was found by R. Emmerson to be part of a young cedar (*Cedrus* sp.) about four inches in diameter. Some bark still remains. Even more remarkable than its state of preservation, literally perfect, is the abundant presence of copper not only as the usual greenish coloration but also as specks of bright metal. An X-radiograph has confirmed (pl. 24) that the metallic copper is concentrated in the outer rings and present uniformly throughout the depth of the specimen.

There are a number of ideas about the mechanism. The thing is a challenge: partly to understand how it has come about, partly to try and do it again. Clearly it fitted straight into a fundamental university research programme sponsored by a commercial concern interested in the preservation of timber by copper salts.[B7, P11]

How did the metallic particles get there, and in what form is the non-metallic copper present? Electronmicrographic pictures should give a good idea, but this work will take a little time.

Preliminary investigations have already been made, however, of the overall distribution of copper as element, and also of the proportion of different forms of copper present in a bulk sample. The results are fascinating. There is nearly 20% of copper, calculated on the dry wood substance. Of this fifth, a fifth again is metallic copper, an incredibly high figure. There is little variation in copper content from bark to pith—an ideal effect unattainable in modern practice.

Finally, a large amount of the non-metallic component is "unpaired"—i.e. in excess of any of the normal partners found (such as sulphate), which would have accompanied the copper during absorption into the wood, as salts from solution in water. It would seem as if polyphenols might be active in this context, too (see Chapter Six).

There is no question of anything like this resulting from a deliberate treatment by the Romans. The apparent uniformity of copper content may be due to an overlap of two effects: the high concentration of metallic copper in the outer rings, and a rising gradient of non-metallic copper from the outside to the centre—the latter again quite contrary to normal experience.

In the only comparable case traced so far,[F8] the sole emphasis was on the curiosity of the metallic copper. This was analysed in great detail but few other data are given. The same relatively high concentration in the outer rings was found, although the metallic specks were smaller and the overall copper content was only about a hundredth of ours.

But this specimen had been freshly felled when the phenomena were observed and recorded. So archaeological connections may in the end prove to be partly or even entirely irrelevant. All the same they have already led to a reconsideration of the whole question of getting copper into timber. The pitprop may have started a fascinating cycle of work and ideas which will ultimately be back where it began: with a Cyprus mining company growing trees on their own copper-rich soil for use as durable pitprops underground. And it might be, of course, that they would only be doing something the Romans were already up to some 2,000 years ago.

Eventually an occasion arises when a whole range of objects of the same age is found buried together under the same conditions, with interesting material phenomena, as it were, presented for comparison. Anglo-Saxon pagan cemeteries, in which people were buried with full military or domestic honours (according to sex), furnish good examples as a rule. Unfortunately such sites usually lie near the surface in chalky or gravelly soil and preservation is uniformly poor. Still, some interesting observations are possible even here.

A selection from Finglesham,[C4] in Kent, went back from the Laboratory with at least one item of specific interest on every object revealed and characterized by specialist examination. In two of the half-dozen cases, as many as four separate investigations were carried out.

An iron ferrule fragment carried textile remains. What was first described as an iron weaving batten showed a pattern-welded core (p. 165) in the X-radiograph—a most surprising revelation. An iron sword had also been pattern-welded, but differently, and buried in a "fur-lined" wooden scabbard. A conglomerate of iron and bronze was plainly resolved by X-rays (pl. 13), and there were remains of textile and some wood-like structure. Finally two separate kinds of non-ferrous metal decoration appeared in the X-radiograph of an iron spearhead fragment, which also held textile remains and some of the ashen spear.

Among several interesting aspects is another of those sets of phenomena straddling the borderline of preservation (p. 122). Where wood is buried with iron, in such circumstances, it seems more of the wood remains nearer to *wood* (as a recognizable state) wherever there is locally more of it than iron, especially when the iron encloses it to a large extent, as in shafts and sockets. By contrast, thinner pieces of wood in contact with greater masses of iron (as in sheaths) and wooden parts not enclosed by iron (as in handles) tend to lose their identity: less remains, and that is more mineralized. This may reflect a definite and relatively slow rate of penetration by iron compounds.

There was on the conglomerate a pad of some thickness and length which resembled such "wood". The bronze tube was thought to be a needle case that might have been plugged with leather or wood. There was nothing suggesting leather, but one had hopes of this pad of "wood". Anything firmly in the mouth of the tube when buried would have left some trace (p. 119)—yet there was none. Removal from the sphere of copper into that of iron would change the mode and lessen the chance of survival for any such plug.

Botanically, the only fibrous material seen by C. R. Metcalfe, apart from roots, was too badly disorganized to show any significant structure. Yet there are suggestions, at one end of the pad, of the cut-off sections of fibre bundles of some sort. Is it some incidental grass (p. 121)? Is it a rudimentary or makeshift plug made of a tightly compressed little bunch of vegetable fibres? Either suggestion would accord with the idea that conditions here might preserve the structure of wood, but not that of the less tightly organized fibre bundles of the lower plants.

In agreement with this, examination of the textile on the same conglomerate again failed—despite a clear weave including a border of diamond twill—to isolate any identifiable fibre. Rust had fossilized the bundles, which disappeared with it. Yet they were plainly seen at the Shirley Institute to be bundles, indicating that the yarns were of vegetable origin, most probably made from a bast fibre.

On the other hand, even in the small sample removed from the scabbard there were a number of actual fibres, some sufficiently well preserved to show their discontinuous medullation and well-defined scale structure. They were almost certainly wool.

Other forms of deposit on metal may be equally informative. Numerous black spots on the copper roof of Lancaster House in London had attracted attention. A few holes had appeared and some connection between the two was suspected. Under the hand lens the spots seemed to be almost entirely soot, and this was later confirmed chemically. Often they sat on little mounds in the metal, and when undercut the soft copper rolled up neatly with the spot inside it.

When unrolled in the Laboratory the spot was found cracked off the metal, which was quite clean. There were some tiny surface pits but these could have been there on the newly laid roof. Other spots were similar and thus clearly harmless and nothing to do with the holes. Indeed they had possibly even protected the copper, certainly preventing the formation of the patina which is otherwise among the best developed in London.[V4] They are most probably the remains of tarry specks of soot which had first settled on the fresh, near-metallic copper surface.

Later some fragments of medieval bronze cauldrons were dug up at Hangleton, in Hove, Sussex.[H17] The basic materials, copper (alloy in this case) and soot, were common to both roof and cauldron, but period, conditions of exposure, use and nature were completely different. There was also another important difference. On the cauldron fragments, the soot invariably lay on the fairly thick skin of green corrosion products.

This was puzzling at first. Soot could not have been deposited from the fire on to the green surface, and contamination in the cold was equally ruled out. Clearly then, the soot had become separated from the metal on which it had been deposited. It is difficult at first to visualize the metallic surface receding towards the interior during corrosion, yet a moment's thought about perforation will persuade, however much the growth of a skin may obscure the issue.[R19a] On the cauldron, corrosive influences had evidently penetrated the soot, indeed been intensified by it, and had gently lifted it off the metal in forming their patina.

The nature of the soot itself might indicate its origin—not so much on the outside of a vessel as on the inside where it is of course also found. Infra-red spectra suggest the presence of a complex mixture consistent with a fatty origin. The work is in its early stages; but in the rubber industry, for instance, where the quality of the carbon black filler in tyres is of great importance, special methods are used to determine whether a "black" has been produced by burning gas or oil. The "shape factor" of archaeological soot may in time be made to suggest what kind of dinner got overcooked.

A related effect is found today[C3] on the internal surface of improperly annealed copper cold water pipes where a carbon film—though adherent and uniform, and in itself protective—is in service highly corrosive to metal under any tiny fault. It is covered up by a scale of calcium carbonate, stained green with copper oxychlorides. The conditions are rather specialized; yet archaeological soot layers embedded in corrosion products cannot be ruled out.

This fluidity of the surface is an important general consideration. The original metallic surface was not where metal ceases now, nor at the present interface between corrosion products and soot. It was somewhere in between.

Delicately chased decoration visible on a patinated but seemingly sound bronze object may therefore be well away from the present metallic surface, and thus uncleanable. Similarly, the normal fate of an iron object during prolonged burial is well known, yet one still tends to be misled by its appearance. When it is recognizably bloated out of all proportion, because it must have started as a knife or a key, there is little doubt, though even then it is easy to exaggerate its original dimensions (pl. 13).

But when its shape is obscure one cannot allow for distortion and is frequently surprised that a cleaned object emerges much slighter than expected. X-rays are again a good guide, but experience is needed for accurate interpretation (pl. 14). An object almost invariably grows more corrosion products outwards than inwards, but this is often masked by unevenness, producing pits and delaminations.

It is clearly impossible to clean back to the original metallic surface. Also, because cleaning must follow the corrosion process, one cannot even simply take off the skin: instead, scaling occurs because of the way in which the object was made, to expose a kind of "lunar" landscape that was carved out subterraneously.

There is a vital distinction, here, between (completely non-destructive) *revelation* of significant evidence, and its (attempted) *exposure* by some form of "cleaning". The former, usually by X-rays or similar means, in almost all cases provides the required information—and more simply and quickly—without removing any evidence that might later come to be considered valuable. The latter must clearly be destructive of some aspect, in any case; more dangerous, it can never escape being subjective. If cleaning is chemical it follows the corrosion process which has produced what is found, and must be arrested at a stage judged to be most in accord with preconceived ideas about the original. If cleaning is mechanical it becomes a kind of secondary sculpture. Luckily the weaker objects are most easily "revealed"; the less detail they show on an X-radiograph the sounder they must be, the smaller is the risk entailed in "exposure".

Better understanding here would make excavators realize what they might reasonably expect, and what they never should. Interpretations of original dimensions would become increasingly cautious, and hence more useful.

Another kind of evidence was carried in the corrosion products on a medieval silver pin, found in the top stratum of a storage pit filled with rubbish not far from, but well above the present tidal level of, the Water at Southampton. The pin was *white* when found, but by the time the legend had been written on its envelope it had turned mauve.[W4] Now this—though the fundamental reaction underlying normal photography—had been something of a puzzle in relation to buried objects, reputedly always found mauve, and the composition of the surface layer was clearly of interest. Some sixteenth-century coins from the Atlantic bottom off Bermuda were also kindly lent for examination by Miss I. Gedye as possibly helpful comparative material.

It was found at the National Chemical Laboratory that most of the coins were heavily concreted with a black corrosion product, which X-ray crystallographic examination showed to contain silver sulphide (Ag_2S—*Acanthite*). Silver chloride was also shown to be present in substantial quantity by chemical means.

> It is believed that the initially formed chloride, produced by the action of sea water, had been converted partially to sulphide by the action of hydrogen sulphide present in anaerobic mud at the sea-bottom, or sulphide may have been formed directly if the coins were well buried in mud.
>
> The pin presented an interesting appearance in section. A central metallic portion, dull grey in colour, was surrounded by a narrow annulus of black. This in turn was surrounded by a pale violet annulus and an outermost region of black. It did not prove possible to separate these zones physically.

X-ray diffraction patterns showed mixed sulphides of silver, antimony and lead. Chloride was again found in quantity by chemical examination.

The thin outermost layer was almost certainly part of the pale violet annulus and thus due to that "photographic" change after excavation. What is the significance of the complex sulphides? Known to be black, they must have been concentrated in the inner annulus. The coins were plainly carrying the simple sulphide but no complex ones were evident; on the pin, the situation was reversed. Obviously the pin contained some antimony and lead. Their deliberate addition would imply awareness of the effects, among them an increase in hardness—and such back-handed analysis is valuable in using only what does not belong (p. 114).

But the results indicate, quite incidentally, even more remarkable aspects of evidence. The environment must have contained decomposing sulphur compounds. Countless electrolytic cells would be set up by the differences between the various metallic components; a skin of complex sulphides would grow on the original surface of the pin, permeable enough for further reaction of the metal with either sulphide or chloride.

Yet the appearance suggests such a predominance of chloride

in the outer annulus—even if there is no proof that it is absent from the inner one—that a fairly abrupt change in conditions is indicated. This may represent the natural end of the rubbish pit's useful life—or a significant drop in the water table. In either case some relation of annulus thickness with time might gradually be discovered and utilized. At any rate the saline element clearly assumed and retained control.

Such clues are normally undreamt of, yet they might far surpass the object itself in importance. Once the systematic study of surfaces had become general routine, it could quickly yield valuable information, unobtainable in any other manner.

The surface of certain metallic objects may indicate the effects of fire also in other ways. It has long been known that one efficient way of preserving things for all time was to get them burnt! For organic materials the absence of oxygen is critical, and it would be better to say "charred". Anything from tiny seeds and wheat grains to massive logs of timber can remain so perfect morphologically that dimensional analyses and comparisons are confidently made.

In a rather different way it can apply also to metals, particularly when there *is* a good supply of air. A characteristic colour effect is often found on buried iron. Where it is striking the entire surface will be covered with an intensely bright skin or dusting of (jeweller's) "rouge"—in fact the identical material. More restrained tones and other, steely-blue or grey, colours are also clear. As they become less intense their patchiness still tends to make them noticeable by contrast with the rest of the surface which is rusty. Colour indications are accompanied by a relatively good state of preservation which in itself attracts attention.

Judging from field associations and modern phenomena (p. 134) it is difficult to imagine how such outlines and colours could have survived unless fairly soaked in appreciable heat. This can be turned to good account. The contrast seems particularly clear in an assemblage of nails found together[S4] (col. pl. II).

However, in the absence of any striking colour or preservation it is not safe to exclude firing. Plate 24 shows an X-radiograph of the same group. The original outlines of the corroded nails are clearly visible, especially where they appear drawn very sharply in livid white. Such livid lines (pl. 13, p. 130) are usually an indication of another metal, denser to X-rays, at the original surface of the iron now rusted over; yet here they are subtly different and evidently due to a sounder oxide skin.

Had the protection afforded by this skin not been enough? We know that fire would produce just such a skin,[G1] and also that on exposure the layers immediately below it tend to suffer first. We may imagine corrosion processes breaking through in places, but afterwards in general by-passing the skin on their path of least resistance; literally sucking out all the good metal (in this sense inferior to the skin) and in the process converting it into clouds of rust solidifying around the skin. The latter may appear on a piece of wrought iron fresh from the forge, or on cleaning the metallic surface of an object that was covered with rust when found. But in practice a normal wrought iron object is unlikely to leave the forge with such a perfect, smooth and uniformly coloured mill scale; and it is the mill scale, forged into the surface, which is almost certainly responsible for the patches that appear on cleaning.

An exception which proves the point handsomely in a back-handed fashion is described for certain Etruscan and Spanish swords.[C13] Here a special effort appears to have been made (and clearly necessary) to produce just such a skin. It was done for the sake of appearance but, again, incidentally had a protective effect (p. 108). The degree of perfection of the skin seems to be decisive—also, the steely-blue colour of the main thickness is probably more significant than the superficial red.

The deliberate use of fire is of course an important cultural indicator, particularly for very early man.[O1] But even the common evidence from later periods can be interpreted in greater depth. Consider, for example, the details of manufacture[R12] and two important characteristics of charcoal—owing to its porosity in effect surface all through.

First, charring will draw to all of this surface the mineral salts which ultimately become "pot ash". On burial the major, water-soluble fraction will thus be leachable from the whole body of each fragment at once. This is important in considering the deliberate scrub or forest burning which clearance for early agriculture must have involved. It is also, theoretically, a possible basis for a crude form of relative dating.

Similarly in smelting, all the salts from the charcoal are accessible to the liquid metal. In the researches mentioned on p. 238, all the trace elements are assumed to have come from the metal-bearing mineral. Yet theoretically some that are present in charcoal could pass into the metal to a comparable extent. Experiments may show that this would be most unlikely, but they remain necessary and so far undone.

Again, as the temperature rises, wood ash can easily coalesce and form misleading, because not metallurgical, slags. An extraordinary variety and amount of material can be produced from different plants on ashing (table 1). Not only will the ash of a wheat grain melt to produce a glass bead, but all kinds of curious and unexpected substances come to light. Calcium has been shown up in ancient glass to an extent that is altogether remarkable. The ancients were clearly unaware of this—indeed they advised against adding much lime as we would today. Equally clearly, vegetable ash contributed almost all of this calcium. Again, the extensive use of (potassium-rich) beechwood for glass-making in the Middle Ages is reflected in the uniformly higher potassium than sodium content of medieval window glass.[C1A, T12]

The interpreter has now arrived at the internal surface. The techniques applied to its study, of all I have described, are some of the most commonly used and completely understood in the industrial and scientific field today.

Metallographic examination, for example, here involves preferably cutting and mounting, and then polishing and microscopical inspection of a very small but suitably selected portion of the metallic object. This may sound simple but is, in fact, a long chain of skilled operations. All the same, in return possibly for the tiny fragment of rarely vital material, and a larger, but not excessive, quantity of specialist labour, such examination can tell us nearly everything about the object's present state and much of its history that we might wish to know. The technique has been used most successfully in showing up the properties and methods of manufacture of various kinds of artefact made of gold,[T5] silver,[T6] copper,[C14, E2, T4] iron [C12, P1, R11, S14] and their alloys, even antimony[C2]— and back as far as some 6,000 years to Ur.

TABLE 1

Composition of Keli or Ash from the Syrian Desert Plant " Chinane "

(*From Turner* [T12])

Parts per 1000

Part Soluble in Water:	600	Part Insoluble in Water:	400
Sodium carbonate	450	Calcium carbonate	340
Sodium hydroxide	25	Calcium phosphate	40
Potassium chloride	45	Magnesium carbonate	10
Potassium sulphide	30	Carbon	10
Silicates, phosphates, and other inorganic matter and water	50		

Composition of Kelp from the Orkneys

(*From N. Graeger, Die Glasfabrikation, 1868*)

100 parts contain 6·8 of water, 63·4 soluble material, 29·7 insoluble

Soluble Material		*Insoluble Material*	
Potassium sulphate	4·5	Calcium carbonate	6·4
Sodium sulphate	3·6	Calcium phosphate	10·5
Calcium sulphate	0·3	Calcium sulphate	1·1
Magnesium sulphate	0·9	Magnesium carbonate	6·8
Sodium sulphite	0·8	Sand	1·6
Sodium hyposulphite	0·5	Alumina	0·1
Sodium carbonate	5·3	Organic matter	2·87
Sodium chloride	26·5		
Potassium chloride	19·3		
Calcium chloride	0·2		
Magnesium iodide	0·3		
Sodium sulphide	1·6		
Sodium phosphate	0·5		

(*This table is reproduced as originally published. The minor arithmetical inconsistencies do not effect the argument.*)

It can also be useful in giving an idea of the type of alloy, although (except for iron) it is not very precise, and will clearly demonstrate small amounts of material different from the bulk, as in pl. 15. This proved conclusively that the cast iron tiles roofing Big Ben, on the clock-tower of the Houses of Parliament, had been hot-dip galvanized in the eighteen-sixties.

At the same time metallography, too, can help in the search for evidence of firing. A Bronze Age bronze awl was brought in with this problem.[G4] The object was found with cremated bones. It shows no obvious signs of fire. In connection with the ritual, it is important to know whether the awl had passed through the pyre with the body or had been added later when the burnt bones were buried. Is it possible to tell?

It was difficult to find precise information. According to weather conditions and location of the object in the pyre, it might be subjected to temperatures of "up to 1,000°C", enough to melt the normal kinds of bronze used, if only just. But the awl might never have been in so hot a part of the pyre. On the other hand, I was told of a bunch of modern steel keys found as a fused conglomerate after a fire in a wooden country house.

Now a metal will faithfully record, on every affected crystal surface, any distortion of the whole system (i.e. a wrought object) or of sharply defined areas such as the edge of an axe. This distortion may be associated with heat, or work carried out in the cold. Again there are barren gaps between certain temperatures; often the effect is a time-temperature product, and may thus be due in a given case to much heat for a short time, or less for longer. But in the main, where truly fossilized, the metallographic record is extremely valuable.

If it could be done without too much damage, this was obviously the best way of tackling the problem of the three awls—for two similar ones from Snail Down, kindly lent by N. E. W. Thomas, had by this time joined the first—especially as a dagger "twisted by fire" from Devizes Museum was also available. The four are shown in pl. 14 with their structures.

In some ways the metallographic landscape is like an aerial photograph. What shows up, as always, is contrast: boundaries between similar crystal fields, especially when inclined and catching the light differently; junctions between dissimilar materials, indicating a change in texture; predominant directions of working. The significant features here are parallel double dykes called "twins", and the "stringers" of material known as "slag". The size of the crystal grains is also of diagnostic value. Twins indicate cold work revealed by annealing, and distorted twins show further cold work. Slag is drawn out in the direction of, and in proportion to, such cold work. The larger the grain size, the longer and/or hotter has been the final anneal.

There could be no definite information if the whole system had been on the point of melting. But in practice any melting on a pyre would probably be either uneven or complete, and hence obvious. On the other hand, the absence of firing as the last event is equally unambiguous.

From their structures the last thing that had happened to the three awls was clearly cold work. There was evidence of some previous annealing heats but the objects had not been through the pyre; they showed still, with remarkable clarity, the microscopic imprints of the awlwright. The dagger was a rather doubtful case. At first it seemed to have suffered some cold work at the end of its active history, before burial. At the same time it did look, superficially, indeed "twisted by fire".

Various explanations were possible. Had it been on the pyre, but at some stage dropped from a height with its point on to a stone, the microscopical picture would have been understandable; the dagger could have been at the same time soft enough, crumpled up, and thereby cold worked. Alternatively, it might have been (ritually) bent in the cold, after a symbolic (annealing) heat, and passed through the pyre, if it did, only at "annealing range".

These details show how intricate the interpretation can be. As it was, looking again at the polished section in relation to the object as a whole, the metallographer felt some considerable degree of heat was after all more likely as the last event before burial. The evidence of cold work was possibly part of the making that showed through. The heat had probably been brief and local —for no incipient melting was seen in the central area that alone could be examined without serious damage to the object.[E3]

Although very valuable, this is clearly not enough. More such work is needed, but also a systematic approach from the other end (cf. p. 89). The Fire Research Station have recently started a particular series of experimental fires in which by courtesy of the Director we were allowed to take part for that purpose. In a specially built house, the ground floor is in effect a furnace providing the temperature whose consequences are then observed on the first floor. Luckily for us this involves the use of wooden cribs, each very like a pyre, and a continuous record of the temperatute is kept at various strategic points.

Two such firings have shown that the furnace atmosphere is reducing—though not as completely as one might have thought—and that temperatures of up to 1,100°C are reached easily and quickly at the ceiling. Oxidizing conditions of course exist at the single window as soon as it blows. The next step is to expose various materials together at some of our strategic oxidizing and reducing points.

Evidence of fire may appear clearly and unexpectedly from X-radiographs also in a different manner. What prompted me to take one of the lumps shown in Plate 15 (*lower left*)? It is always more economical and far safer to do so when in doubt.

In passing, perhaps the most incredible revelations come from just such mixed conglomerates. This is of course the application of X-rays most widely known. But here it is like X-raying a bit of haystack and getting a mass of needles (pl. 15, *upper*).

In our lumps (pl. 15) there are clearly fragments of spoon, bone and possibly wood. The X-ray also reveals a monogram—and some sharp discs of what in the circumstances must be lead. After a brief search these blobs of lead were found—as the X-ray suggested, perfectly spherical. Such lead "shot" is made by dropping molten lead from a height into water. The imagination at once soars to the roof of Salisbury Hall, near Walthamstow in London,[H5] the medieval manor house which stood on the site of this particular excavation. If a fire had melted the lead on this roof and the metal had run and dripped into the water of the moat, then splashes of it could have come to rest on the debris there and would look just like what we found.

Much conjecture could be built on this—but first other possibilities must be considered. It might simply *be* lead shot. The variation in size seems too great. Luckily there is a simple check. To solidify in spherical droplets, lead must contain a critical few per cent of arsenic and/or antimony. In one of our blobs T. A. Read found less than one per cent, so it could not have been formed at all in falling through air, for whatever reason. The most likely explanation involves lead molten among charcoal.

While far less specific and exciting, it remains evidence of fire.

From a survey of the whole field the wider view also imprints itself on one's experience of conservation. In the search for a universal cleanser (cf. p. 83) one soon finds that the standard method for cleaning sound ironwork, although usable, is unsatisfactory for copper alloys. At the same time, it will not do to suspend iron objects in the cleaning fluid with copper wire. In both cases copper is dissolved, and redeposited on the cleaned surface.

This is directly related to what goes on underground on buried antiquities. For instance, brass often shows a copper-coloured skin even after proper cleaning. Without scraping one cannot tell the original colour unless the copper is patchy; this is common, but even then the surface is not a reliable guide anywhere, because the copper in the skin has clearly been removed from other areas where the hue would thus be depleted.

Similar factors apply in the case of lead in copper (p. 73), and of copper in silver objects (col. pl. I). The same fundamental processes occur with iron when corroded copper alloy is cleaned in the standard electrolytic bath using an iron anode, although the visible effects are different. (All this assumes the absence of any peculiar modifying effects: p. 201.) Generally, what happens above ground is essentially similar, too, and provides valuable comparisons.

Before the interpreter knows where he is, his automatic comparator is taking ever bigger jumps. A method that had been used in the laboratory for the treatment of *iron* objects was clearly related to the standard way of making *copper* from some of its compounds. It was accordingly tried out on friable bronzes and has proved very useful (p. 261), for various reasons losing favour almost completely for its original purpose. Later I found a record of its use for "reducing bronzes" back in 1856.[C5]

In connection with experiments using sodium fluoride—a material employed in the fight against *dry rot*—while looking for a suitable method of detecting fluoride, I came across a reference to a stable and colourless iron fluoride complex.[S19] The significance of this will be clear to anyone who has had to deal with *iron stains* in any connection whatever.

Morpholine is a powerful organic solvent with a rather unusual combination of properties. Reading about its usefulness as a selective solvent in the conservation of *paintings* I found an account of it as a tarnish inhibitor for *silver*. Though on reflection quite plausible, this was a surprise not only to me but also to some colleagues directly concerned with the latter aspect, who promptly proceeded to use it.

In the standard electrolytic method[F4, P9] for the cleaning of sound bronzes (p. 201), iron is deposited on the cleaned object in the process. In studying this highly undesirable phenomenon, I found the form of the iron deposit somewhat unexpected and useful for various entirely irrelevant purposes. In my effort to understand the workings of this *bronze*-cleaning bath I have probably learnt more than from any other source about the corrosion of *iron*.

As contacts with specialists ripen, developments in one field, taken with those in another, bear unexpectedly bigger and better fruit in one's own. In return, the interpreter travelling from field to field inevitably helps in the cross-fertilization of ideas—again to his own benefit as much as others'.

In the process—at least for the interpreter—the solution of science in archaeology, and of both in the general scheme of things, gradually begins to clarify—and then to crystallize in a form that might become universally acceptable.

CHAPTER SIX

Polyphenols Ubiquitous—Cohesion

IN 1950 EXCAVATIONS in the Hungate district of York produced a quantity of pre-Conquest and medieval material from waterlogged silt and clay in a remarkable state of preservation.[R15] There were several leather soles—some of Roman sandals with iron hobnails—some uppers and scraps of waste. Much wood and other vegetable matter were present in the shape of hurdles, posts, brushwood matting, as well as fragments of bowls and a flute, a piece of rope and layers of compressed leaves. A selection of this material and of the metallic finds is shown in pl. 16–17.

It was the condition of the metal, and of ironwork in particular, that was most striking. Copper alloy came out golden with an occasional thin and gaily coloured patchy film of tarnish, silver only slightly darker. Lead objects had a somewhat thicker skin that was deceptively coloured and quite unlike the appearance of leaden objects buried under "normal" conditions (col. pl. II). This difference was marked for every material but nowhere more than with the iron.

There was no rust at all on most of the iron objects or in the soil around them. Patches of intensely blue colour (col. pl. II), varying from deep royal blue when wet to bright powder blue when dry, occurred frequently, and indeed indiscriminately, on all the materials. Some of the iron objects carried a smooth, hard, glossy black skin, others a rough, matt cement-grey and somewhat irregular covering similar to the soil. But in all the typical cases the outline was incredibly well preserved, and in many the metallic surface was clearly only just below this outer skin. Plate 21 shows two comparable objects typical of normal and waterlogged burial, respectively; in the latter the metal actually shows through the skin in places.

This was my first experience of such conditions and naturally of great interest. I was concerned primarily, then, to know the nature of these unusual skins and colours, so as better to be able to clean and preserve the objects. "Vivianite" was mentioned in connection with the blue colour, and I found references to this form of iron phosphate in scientific notes attached to some archaeological reports on finds from similar conditions.[F7] Having proved chemically that phosphate was present, I took the opportunity of a visit to Teddington to discuss the matter with the Corrosion Group of the National Chemical Laboratory, in the Department of Scientific and Industrial Research.

It appeared that conditions on the site at Hungate were in many respects similar to what were generally thought of as media very aggressive to present-day buried iron pipes, and good preservation at Hungate was thus naturally of great industrial as well as scientific interest. Other specimens from Hungate were examined, soil samples were taken at the site, still partly open, and tests were carried out at Teddington. When the results were published in 1953 [F3] it seemed as if something new had been added to the study of this particular aspect of corrosion.

Under aggressive conditions of the kind typified by waterlogged clays containing sulphates, the normal electrolytic corrosion of buried iron would not be able to proceed. But a certain kind of bacterium, the so-called "sulphate reducer" (*Desulfovibrio desulfuricans*), almost universally present and extremely hardy, can and usually does make things go, after all, by depolarizing the corrosion cell of hydrogen. At the same time the sulphate is reduced to sulphide. The process very rapidly attacks the iron and can perforate a pipe in some ten years or less, while the bacteria (in presence of a little organic carbon) can flourish as long as there is an infinitesimal amount of iron and some sulphate accessible.

This had clearly not happened at Hungate. The bacteria, though present, were inactive. It seemed that preservation there was somehow connected with the large amounts of organic material. Phosphate would obviously have been available and would have helped in the circumstances but, although known to be protective in solution under certain conditions, it was not here thought to be enough.

A remarkable feature was the presence, as judged from results of textbook tests, of what is loosely known as "tannin". Extracts from leather scraps, and from the soil, seemed able to stop the bacteria from multiplying. Low concentrations of ordinary tannic acid were then tried and found to have a similar effect. Tannin was suggested, for the first time and with some confidence, as a remarkable addition to the range of possible underground corrosion inhibitors.

There was no suitable opportunity for a thorough study of all the organic material. But when similar conditions were uncovered in a Roman well near Chew Stoke in Somerset (pl. 20), later in the same year, we were ready for them. Specialists went to the site, and even some "laboratory" work was done there in cleaning and preserving some of the objects. Specimens and samples were sent straightway to other specialists who worked on them in their respective laboratories. The scope of the work has been described elsewhere (p. 189). Altogether there were some five thousand pieces of evidence from the well alone, and some three thousand from the rest of the site complex. It is not surprising that work is still being done on some of the material and will probably continue to some extent even after the report has been published.[R7]

What struck us first, once again, was the superb condition of the metalwork (pl. 20), although there were as before much leather, bone and wood (pl. 21), and again vegetable remains had persisted in almost incredible detail, including delicate mosses and cherry stones with some flesh still on. It was possible to deal with all the most important aspects simultaneously and as expected, only more so, their interdependence at once became apparent.

We knew fairly well, of course, what to look for in the first place, but as usual each piece of work brought its surprises. There were two finds of outstanding interest and these were investigated in detail. One was the copper jug shown in col. pl. II, with one iron handle (remaining of two?). The base, neck and handle had been soldered to the body. The copper looked bright, golden and smooth. All the excavators had to do was to wash the silt off before they took the picture. The iron was typically blue, black and grey, the solder had a thin, dark tarnish, and no change in shape seemed to have taken place. The other find, in some ways even more remarkable and valuable, was a fragment of a wooden writing

PLATE 1. *Upper:* Kenchester, Herefordshire. Aerial photograph with cropmarks of streets and ground-plans of buildings in Roman settlement. *Lower left:* Rothamsted Experimental Farm, Harpenden, Herts. Exhaustion land experiment—the dark diagonal line is due to barley still growing better along a strip dressed with phosphate fertilizer a century ago, and not again since (p. 28). *Lower right:* Litton Cheney, Dorset. Solution holes in chalk surface masquerading as postholes under prehistoric barrow (p. 75).

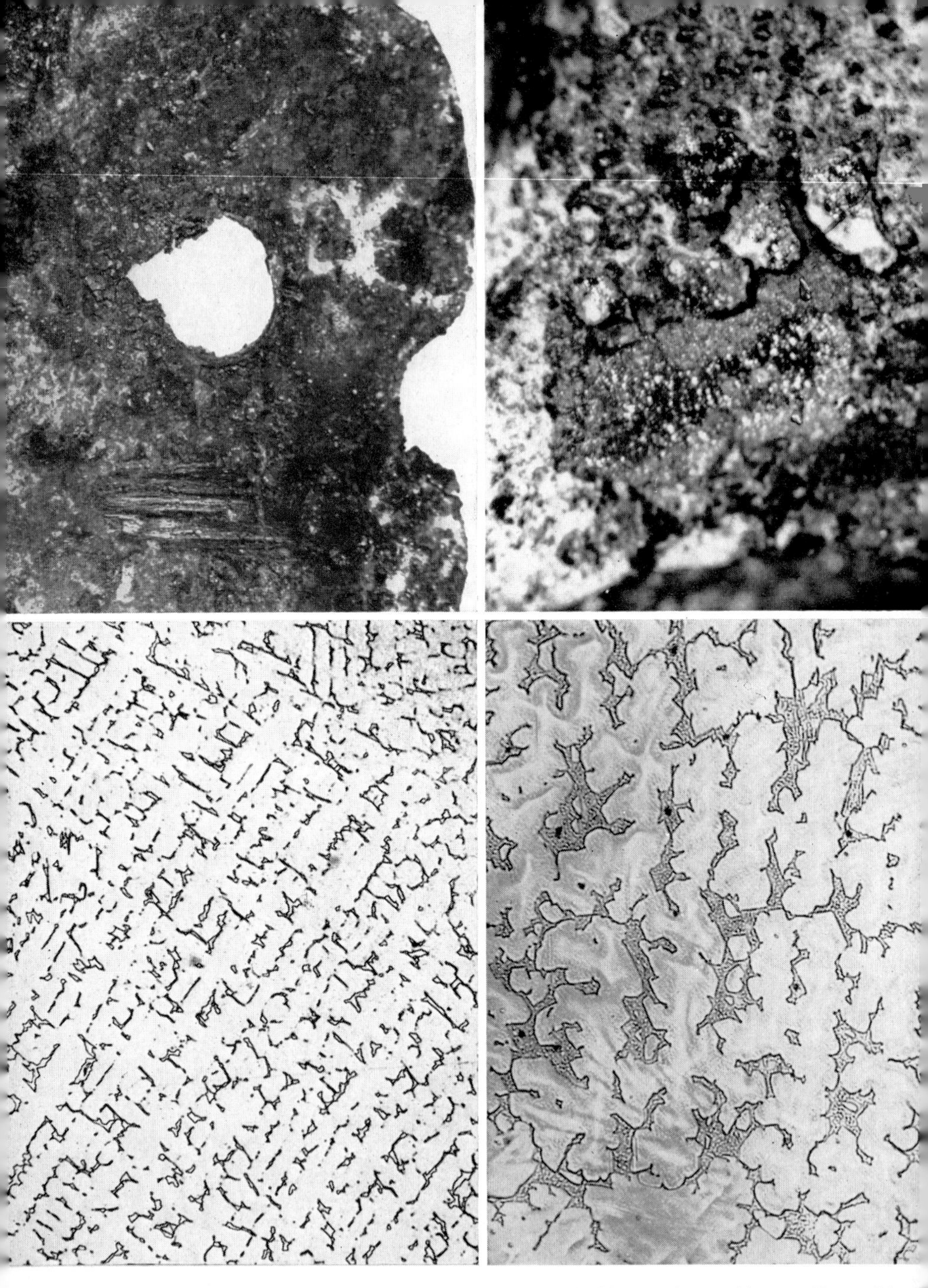

PLATE 2. *The Vertical Approach, I* (p. 58). *Upper left:* Detail of bronze dagger (Arreton Down, Isle of Wight, Bronze Age barrow) showing rivet hole and fibrous grain, possibly due to remains of wooden handle (×10). *Upper right:* Scale of surface corrosion products, mainly basic copper salts (light) with sand, etc., partly broken off (below centre) to show underlying red cuprite crystals (dark specular) (×30). *Lower:* Microstructure of cast 10% tin bronze, showing alpha bronze dendrites (dark) in a matrix of alpha-plus-delta eutectoid (*left*—×120; *right*—×360).

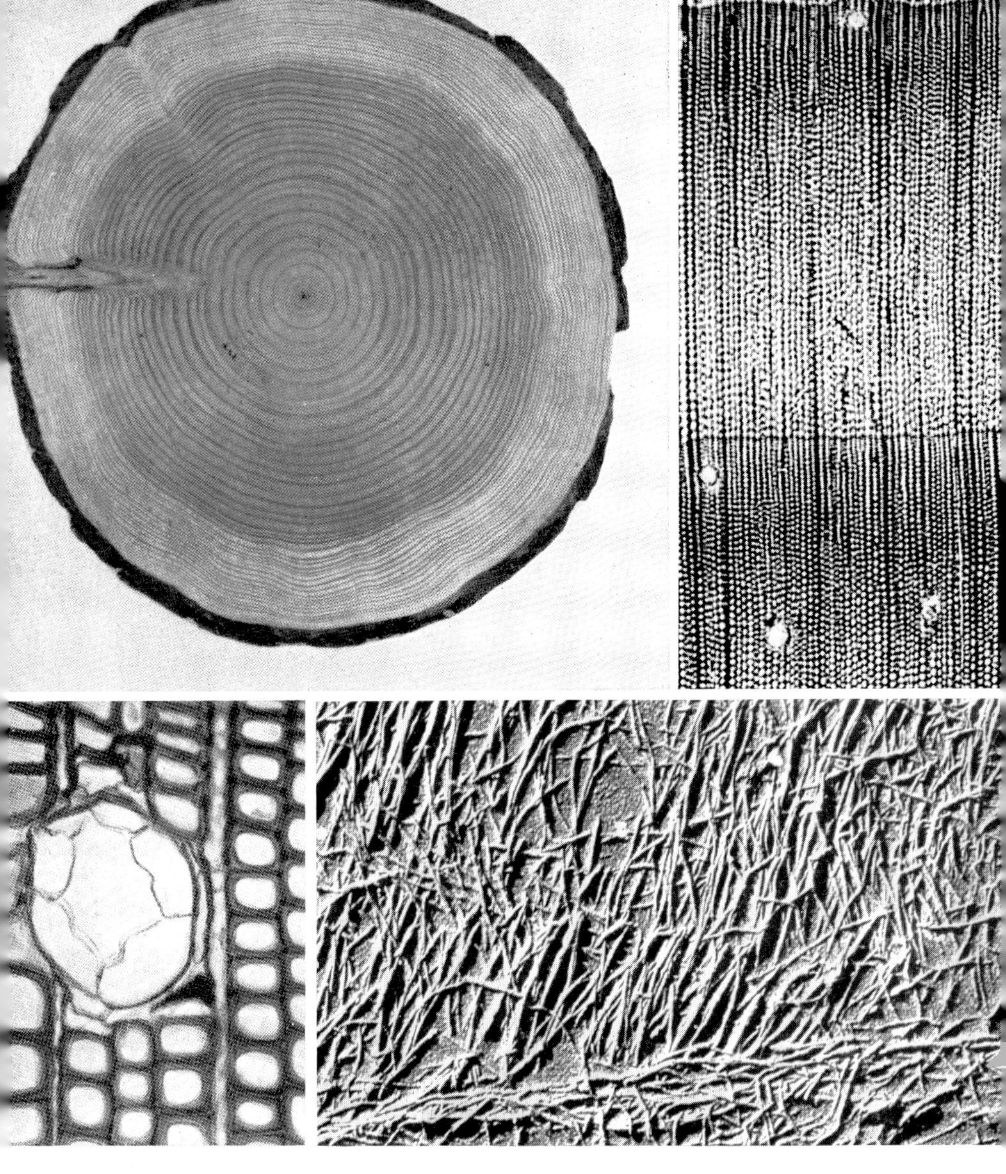

PLATE 3. *The Vertical Approach, II* (p. 59). Structure of pinewood in cross section. *Upper left:* Tree showing growth rings ($\times \frac{1}{3}$). *Upper right:* Growth rings showing vertical resin canals (larger voids) ($\times 25$). *Lower left:* Resin canal containing thin-walled epithelial cells ($\times 250$). *Lower right:* Microfibrils in the outermost layer (S1) of the secondary wall of a tracheid (cf. fig. 1)—($\times 42{,}000$).

PLATE 4. *Size and Scale* (p. 60). *Upper:* Limestone "grikes" near Malham, Yorks., showing characteristic weathering patterns. *Lower:* Stonehenge, top of stone no. 152. Although in this picture the size of the features is comparable, the disparity in scale is indicated by the dale (*top background*) and foot-rule (*bottom*).

PLATE 5. *Wooden Piles and Stakes.* Jewel Tower, Westminster (pp. 61, 124). *Upper left:* Piles preserved in clay (removed). *Lower left:* Stains of piles in gravel. *Upper right:* Intermediate condition. Note partial preservation *below* general level of clay where junction has been displaced by driving of pile. *Lower right:* Farncombe Down, Berks. (p. 74). Hole in chalk part-filled with humic residue of stake, showing cavity (A) formed by decay and here *not* filled by collapse of (fairly compact) overlying gravelly clay.

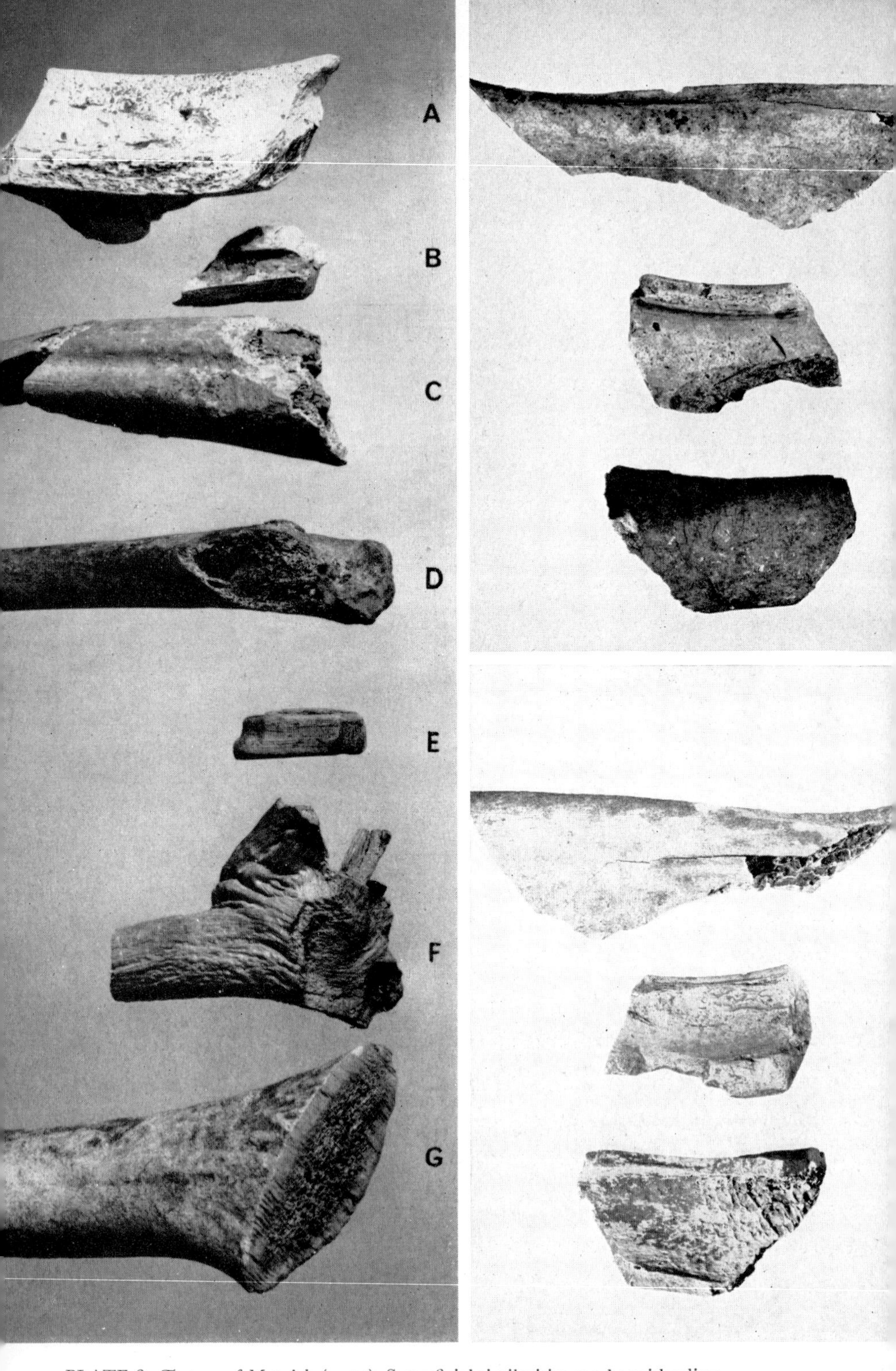

PLATE 6. *Textures of Materials* (p. 74). Superficial similarities can be misleading
A: pottery; B–D: bone; E, F: wood; G: antler; H, K: bone; J: pottery— *Upper:* "obverse"; *Lower:* "reverse".

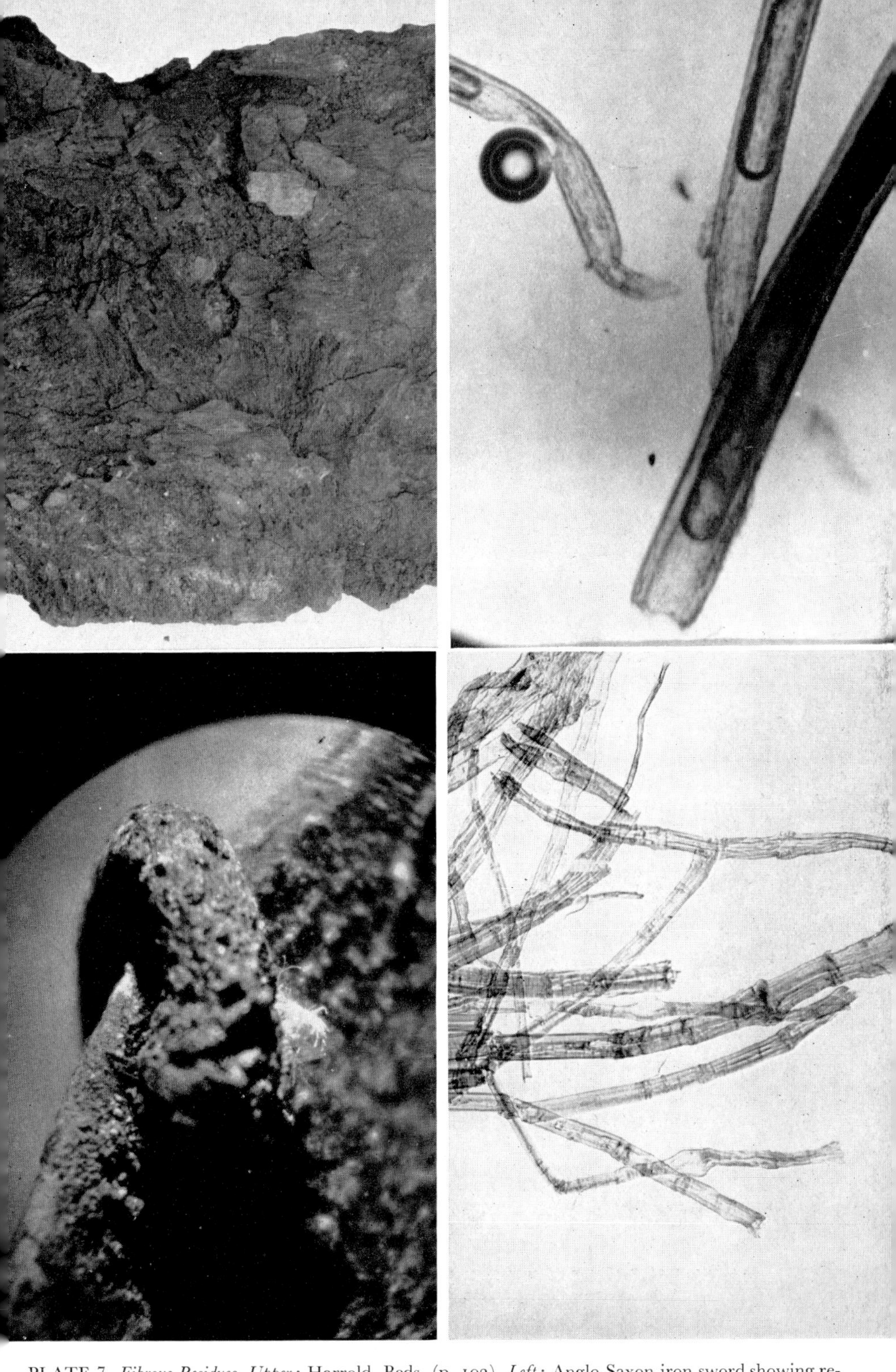

PLATE 7. *Fibrous Residues. Upper:* Harrold, Beds. (p. 103). *Left:* Anglo-Saxon iron sword showing remains of wooden scabbard (parallel striations across top right) partly overlying residues of its "fur" lining (wavy lines, mainly down—centre, lower right and bottom edge, × 2). *Right:* Some of the animal "fur" fibres (× 150). *Lower:* Dover, Buckland (p. 118). *Left:* Jutish jeweller's scale pan showing remains of thread on ring (× 15). *Right:* Some (vegetable) bast (probably flax) fibres of the thread (× 130).

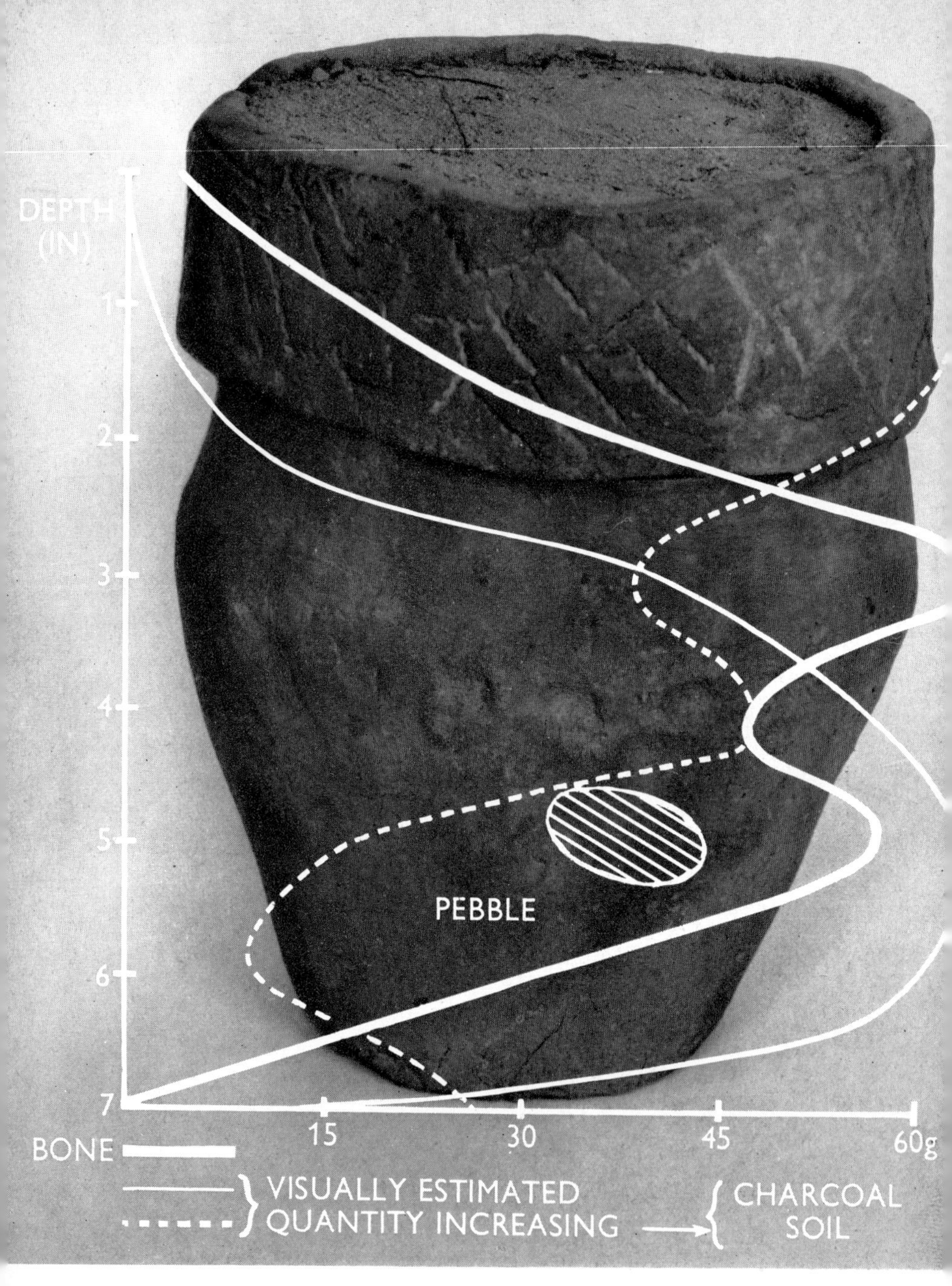

PLATE 8. *Devil's Ring, Brightwell Heath, Suffolk* (p. 104). Bronze Age urn as received, with superimposed graphic representation of contents found by micro-excavation (see X-radiograph in Pl. 9, facing).

PLATE 9. *X-radiograph of urn* shown in Pl. 8, facing. Note white egg shape due to pebble, dark area on right full of charcoal (transparent to X-rays in this exposure), and various sizes and shapes of calcined bone seen as "sections of pipes". Bright band across top is due to combined effect of maximum thickness of sand and extra thickness of pot collar in the path of X-rays.

PLATE 10. *Chertsey Abbey, Surrey* (pp. 106, 122). *Upper left:* Annular brass brooch with "textile remains", e.g. "bump", right; also on pin ($\times 1\frac{1}{2}$). *Upper right:* Mineralized textile fragment of the "bump" showing traces of "weave" ($\times 8$). *Lower left:* Pseudo-fibrous indeterminate fossils from the "bump" ($\times 100$). *Lower right:* Lower portion of the Ramecourt Fibula (p. 117)—silver, mercury-gilded, with (below) characteristic "rosette" in positive microchemical reaction for mercury.

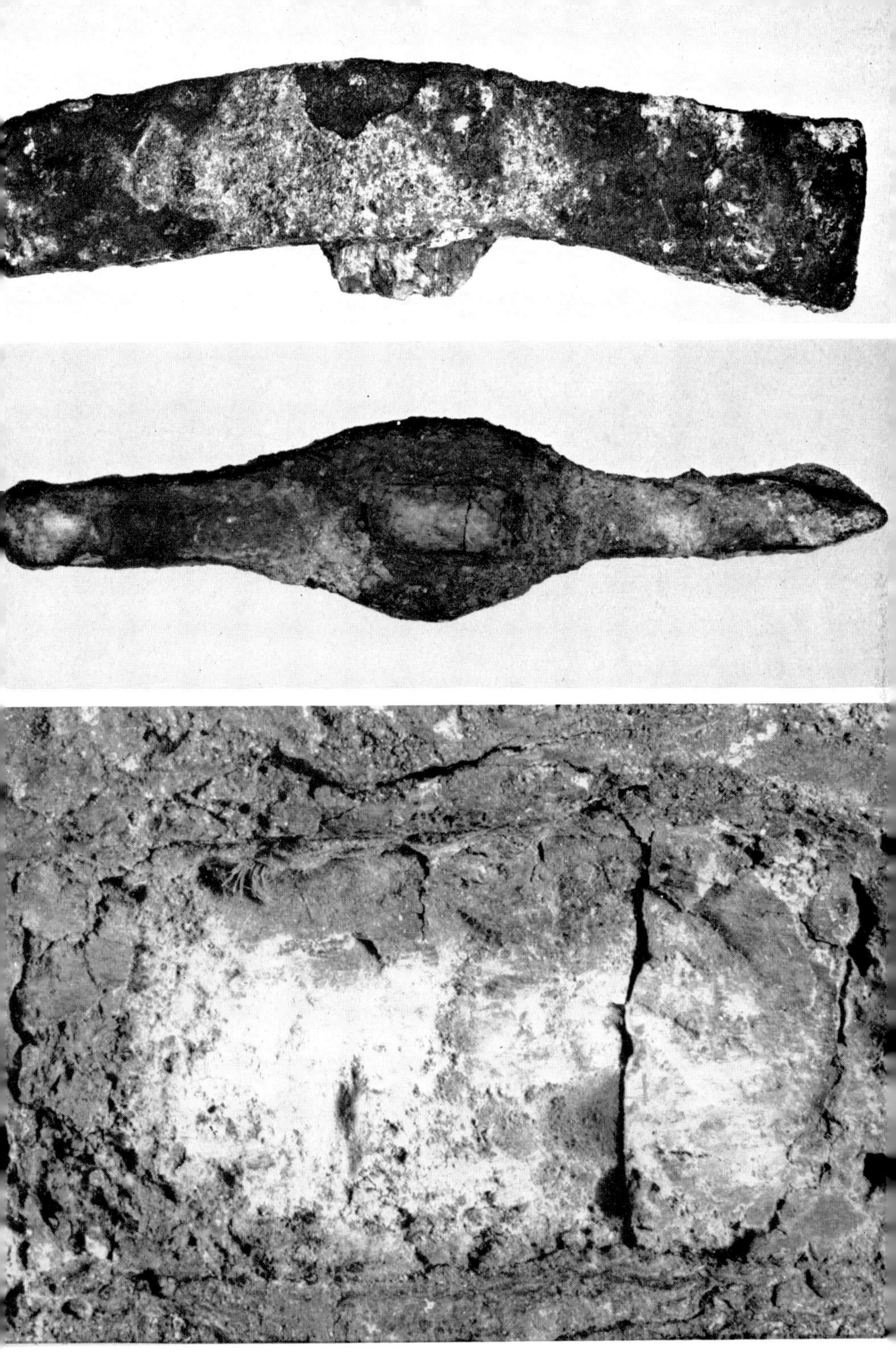

PLATE 11. *White Castle, Mon.* (p. 123). Iron pick with fossilized remains of handle. *Upper:* Side view; *Centre:* View from top (both $\times \frac{3}{4}$). *Lower:* Detail of socket in central view ($\times 5$). Material retains enough characteristic structure for identification as ash (*Fraxinus* sp.), even though its mineral ash content is 65%, probably mostly iron compounds. Note also fibrous sleeve or collar, especially top left.

PLATE 12. *Stains due to Organic Materials* (p. 124)—(× 1½). *Left:* Chertsey Abbey, Surrey. Medieval brass buckle and belt end as found, with remains of leather inside and under them. Dark outlines indicate extent of stain seen in the ground. *Right:* Arreton Down, Isle of Wight. Bronze Age bronze dagger, as found but displaced slightly to right to show underlying dark material (probably leather) at bottom and centre left. White broken lines indicate extent of stain (due to handle) seen by excavator.

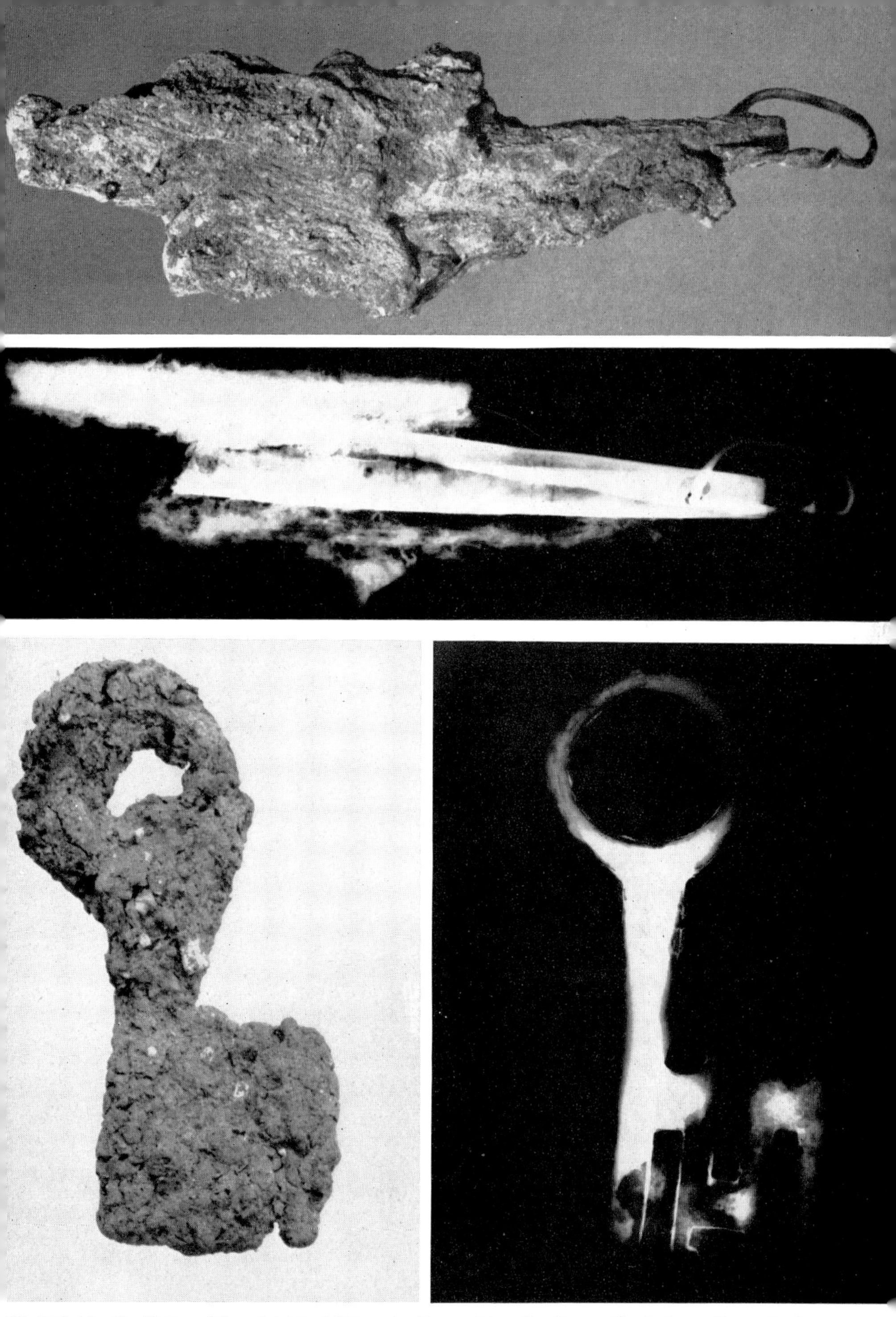

PLATE 13. *Elucidation of Corroded Metal Objects by X-rays, I* (× 1½). *Upper:* Finglesham, Kent. Anglo-Saxon conglomerate of bronze tube (*centre*) and iron rods. Note also fossilized textile fragment in striated portion (*top left*) (p. 128). *Lower:* Canterbury, medieval iron key. Original surfaces are indicated in X-radiograph by livid white lines due to non-ferrous metal plating (p. 130).

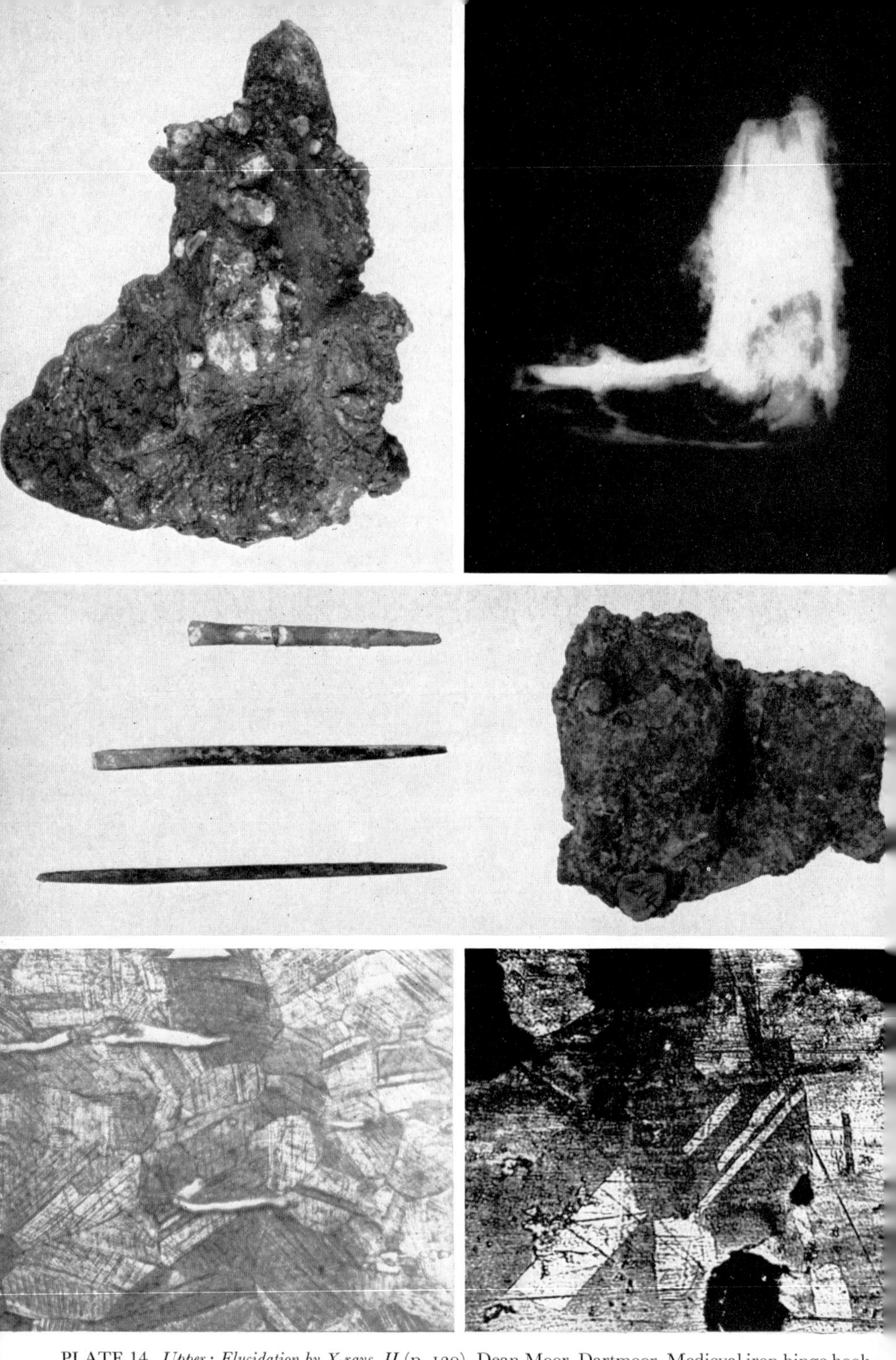

PLATE 14. *Upper: Elucidation by X-rays, II* (p. 130). Dean Moor, Dartmoor. Medieval iron hinge hook. *Centre:* Bronze Age bronze awl from Marshfield (upper), two from Snail Down, and "twisted dagger fragment" (right) from Devizes Museum (all $\times 1\frac{1}{2}$), with, *beneath*, metallographic structures of (lowest) awl (*left*, $\times 680$) and "dagger" (*right*, $\times 155$) (p. 137).

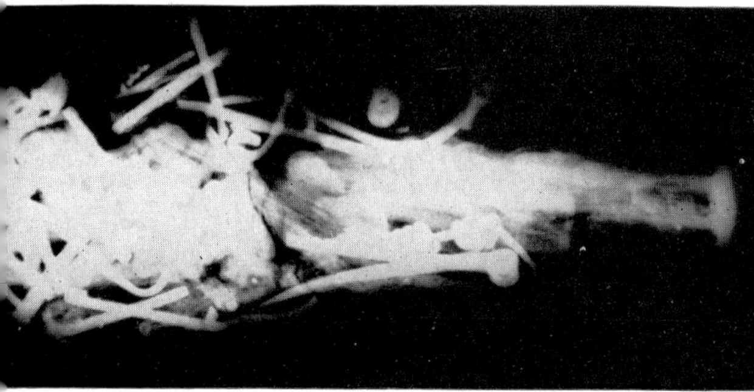

PLATE 15. *Elucidation by X-rays, III* (p. 139). *Left:* Wroxeter, Shropshire. Conglomerate of Roman bronze fibula springs and pins, iron nail, etc.

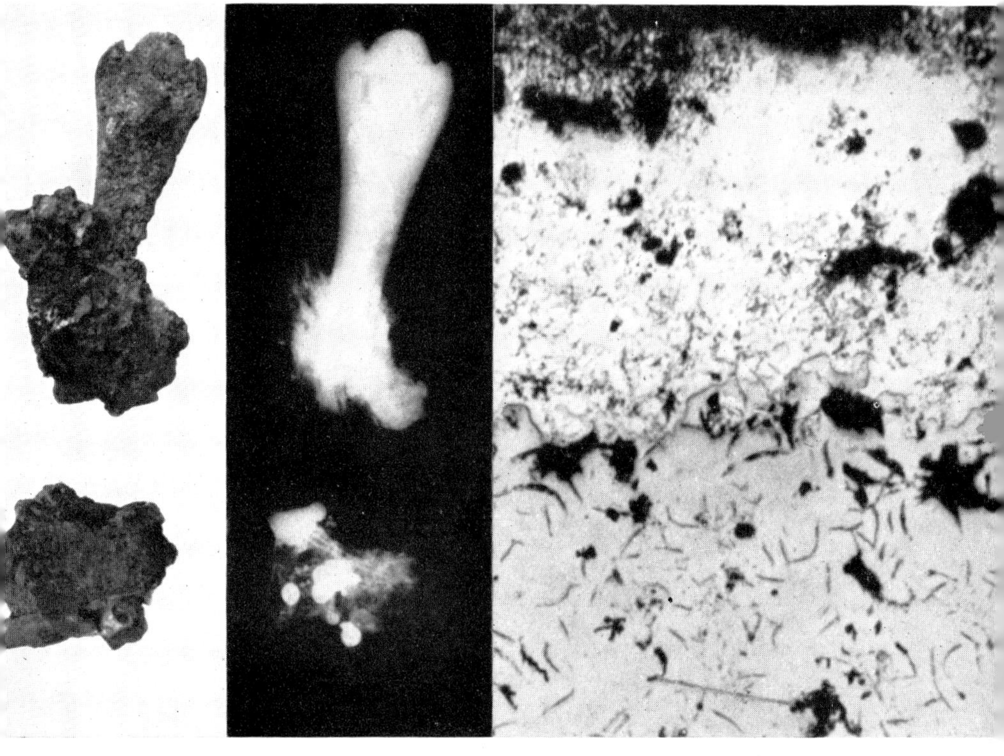

Above left and *centre:* Salisbury Hall, Walthamstow, London. Brass spoon fragment with bone and other debris. Note monogram (above) and bright blobs of lead (below). *Above right:* Cast-iron tile from roof over Big Ben. Metallographic section across (protected) top of surface showing zinc coating (white) nearly 0·03 in. thick still firmly attached to cast iron (grey) a hundred years after hot-dip galvanizing (p. 136) (×70).

PLATE 16. *Hungate, York* (p. 142). Well-preserved objects from waterlogged Anglo-Danish levels. Underside of bowl fragments turned out of (?) maple wood repaired with iron rivets in antiquity, and iron knives, one with bone handle, as received. (See also Pls. 17 and 21, and Colour Pl. II.)

PLATE 17. *Hungate, York* (p. 142). Well-preserved Roman hob-nailed sandal sole ($\times \frac{3}{4}$), Anglo-Danish rope fragment and (twin) leather snippets, clearly cobbler's waste. (See also Pls. 16 and 21, and Colour Pl. II.)

ACID

Podzol formers			Brown Soil Formers	
Heather	extremely strong		Birch	Some but ? amount
Pine	" "		Holly	nil
Bracken	" "		Grasses	extremely few or extremely small amounts
Beech	" "	Oak strong (galls)	Hazel	strong
			Ash	nil
			Aspen	weak

PLATE 18. *Relationship between Vegetation, Extractives and Soil Profile* (p. 152). Table of plants on acid soils divided by G. W. Dimbleby (Department of Forestry, University of Oxford) into podzol formers and brown soil formers, and annotated by E. C. Bate-Smith (Low Temperature Research Station, University of Cambridge) with their tannin reactions. Podzol formers, and oak which can act as one in suitable circumstances, give a strong reaction, the rest contain no tannins or only negligible or extremely small amounts, except for hazel which so far occupies an anomalous position.

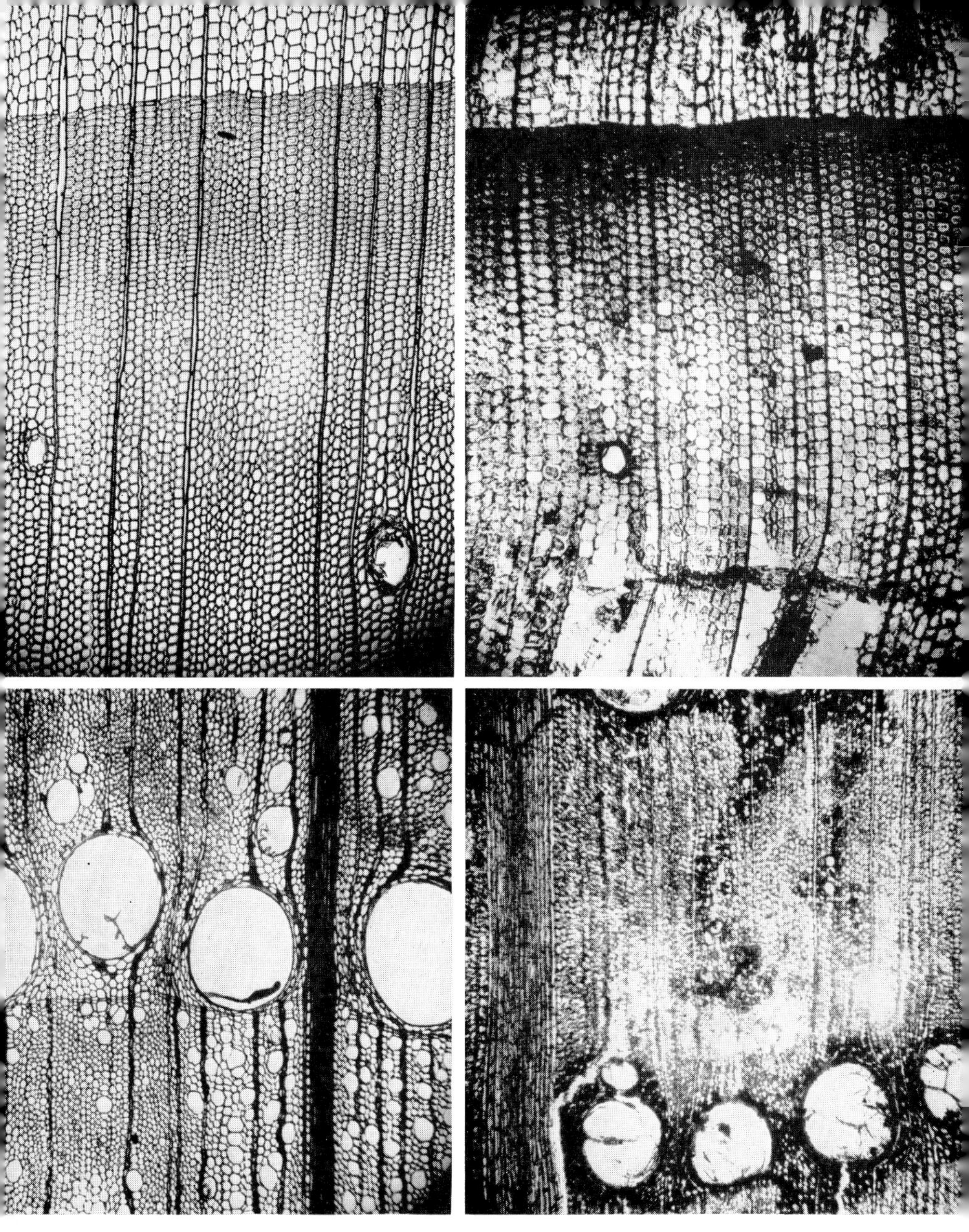

PLATE 19. *Cross Sections of Wood.* Differences in appearance due to structure (down) and age (across). *Upper*, larch (*Larix* sp.); *lower*, oak (*Quercus* sp.). *Left*, modern; *right*, from Roman well at Chew Valley Lake (p. 146; see also Pls. 20, 21 and 24, and Colour Pl. II). Note darkening, clogging and distortion of cells characteristic of age. Lateral direction of tree growth is towards top of page (× 50).

PLATE 20. *Chew Valley Lake, Somerset* (p. 144). *Left:* Aerial view of site during later stages when initial flooding of reservoir area had made it an island.

Above: Iron bucket eyes and handle fragment from Roman well filling, found completely corroded (*top*) in upper levels but well-preserved where waterlogged lower down (*centre*—as found; *lower two*—cleaned, clearly showing many marks of manufacture). (See also Pls. 19, 21 and 24, and Colour Pl. II.)

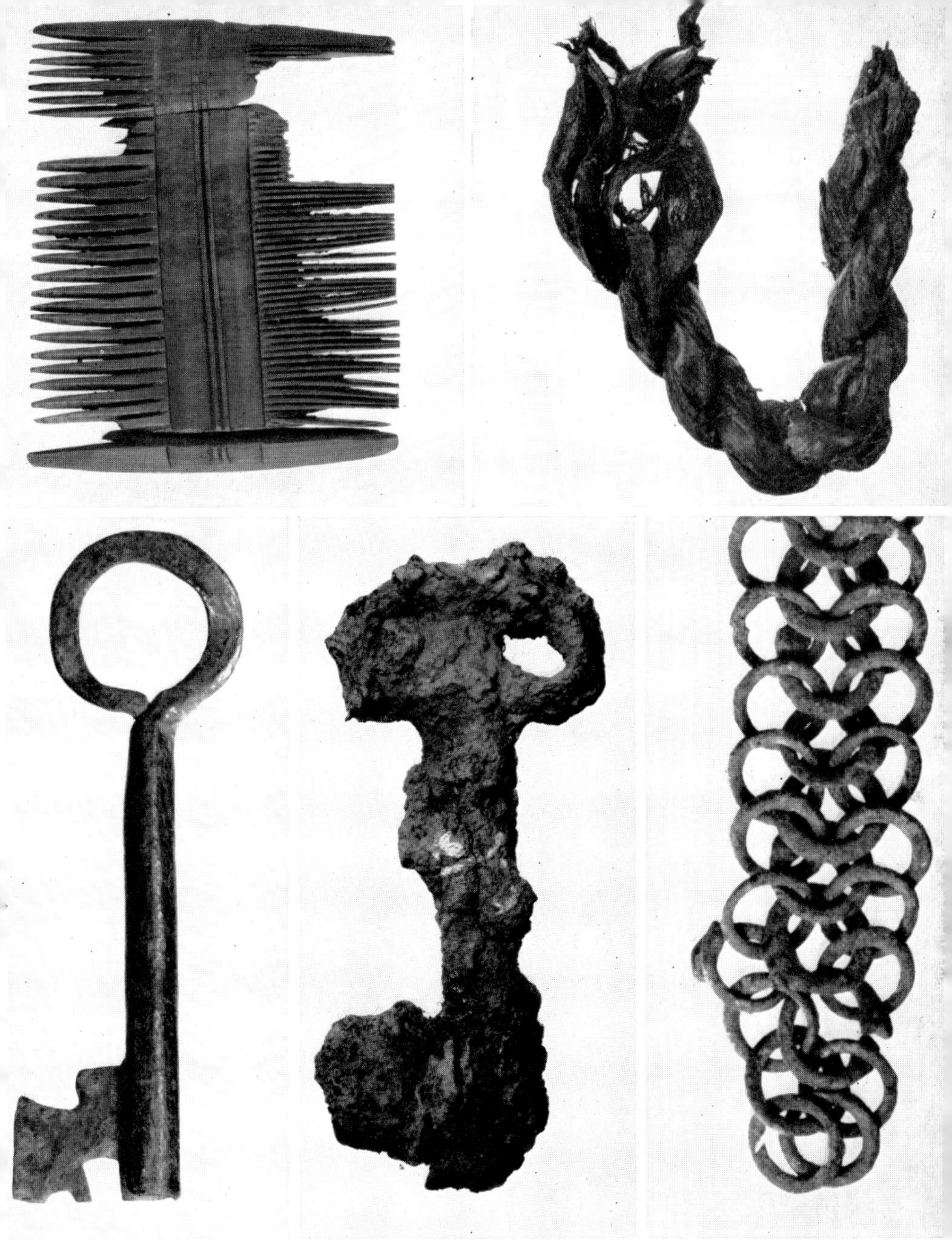

PLATE 21. (All items as received.) *Upper: Chew Valley Lake, Somerset* (p. 144). Comb made of boxwood ($\times \frac{3}{4}$) and fragment of rope made of (cellulosic) bast fibre found in Roman well filling, preserved by waterlogging. (See also Pls. 19, 20 and 24 and Colour Pl. II.) *Lower left* and *centre:* Comparable medieval iron keys found under waterlogged (*left*, Hungate) and normal aggressive conditions. (See also Pls. 16 and 17, and Colour Pl. II.) *Lower right: Richborough Castle, Kent.* Fragment of Roman "brass" (chain) mail ($\times 3$). Outer lines, closed rings; central line, riveted links (p. 162 and fig. 5).

PLATE 22. *Modern Pattern-welding by J. W. Anstee* (p. 165). Three wrought iron rods are flattened into strips, twisted and hammered with two filler rods into a bar. Cutting edges are welded on (*centre* view shows lower portion of "sword" turned through 90 degrees about long axis, with respect to *left* hand view). The finished portion of the blade is taper-ground, polished and etched (detail *right*, about natural size). Note change of pattern, as thickness of blade decreases towards tip (cf. Pl. 23 upper left).

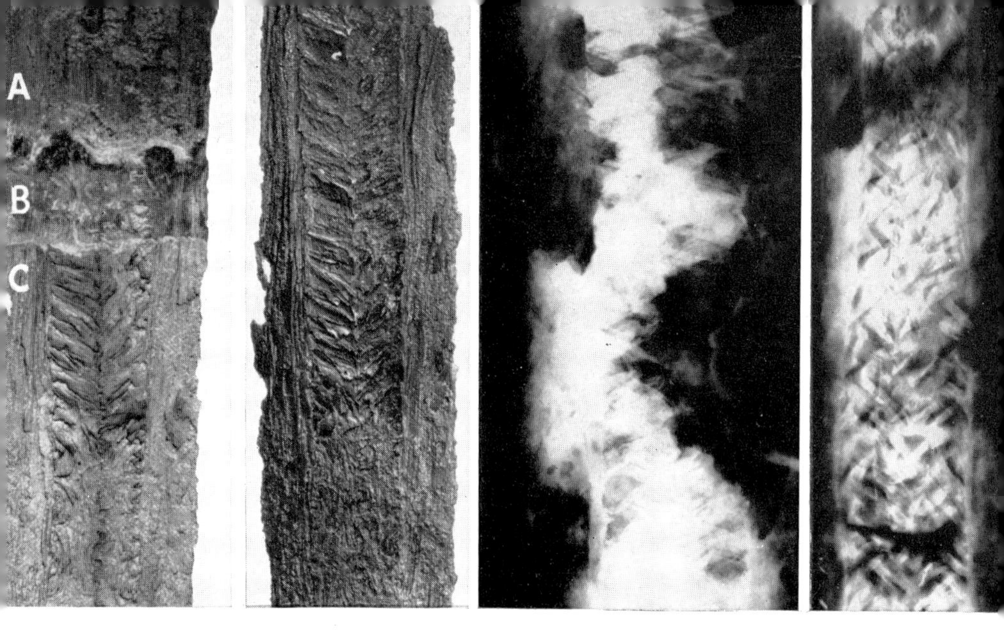

PLATE 23. *Upper: Ancient Pattern-welding* (cf. Pl. 22, p. 165). *Left* hand pair: Two views of Palace of Westminster Sword—partly-cleaned, and cleaned. (A) mineralized oak scabbard remains; (B) rust scale carrying convolute pattern (cf. Pl. 22, *right* lower) which changes on removal of corroded layer to herringbone pattern (C) at a lower plane (cf. Pl. 22, *right* upper). Convolute patterns are still metallic near bottom owing to uneven corrosion. There are *four* composite rods (cf. Anstee's *one* in Pl. 22) in the core: two visible side by side (opposite twist), backed by two similarly on other side. *Right* hand pair: X-radiographs of swords from Southend, Essex (*left*, two comp. rods each side) and Brentford, London (three rods each side). *Below:* Bishops Waltham, Hants. (pp. 181, 187). *Left:* Silhouette of "skeleton" in "coffin". *Right:* Teleutospores of (*upper*) a rust fungus found on coffin bottom and (*lower*) *Puccinia graminis*, a modern counterpart (both × 1700).

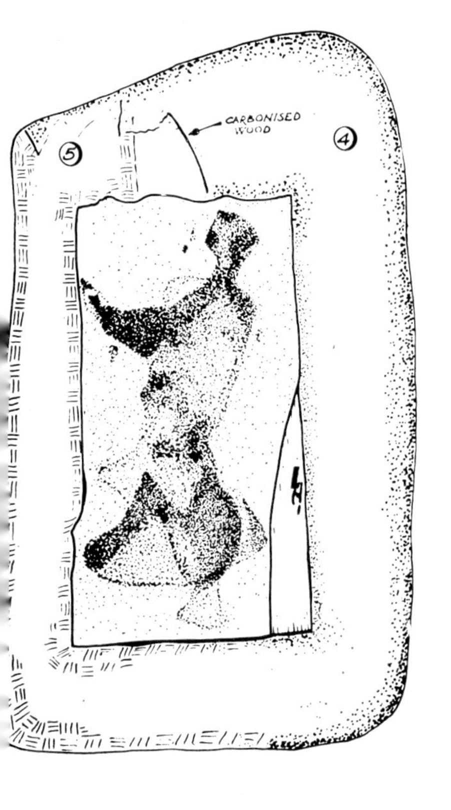

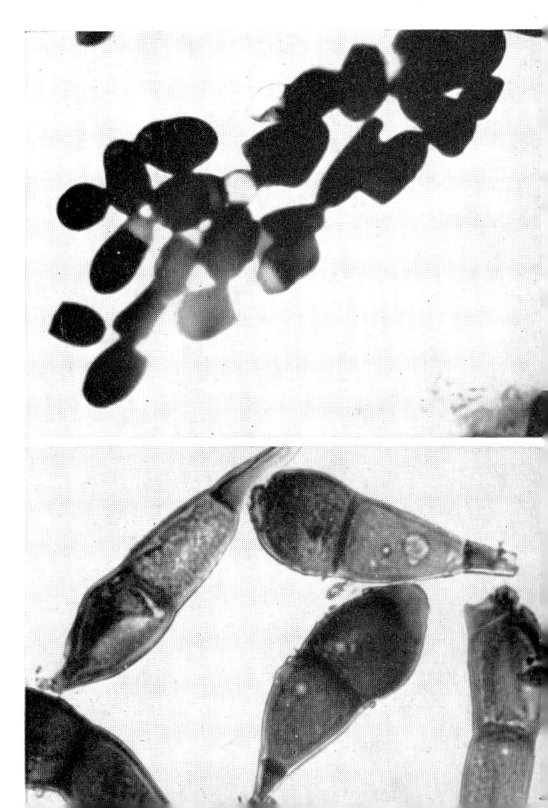

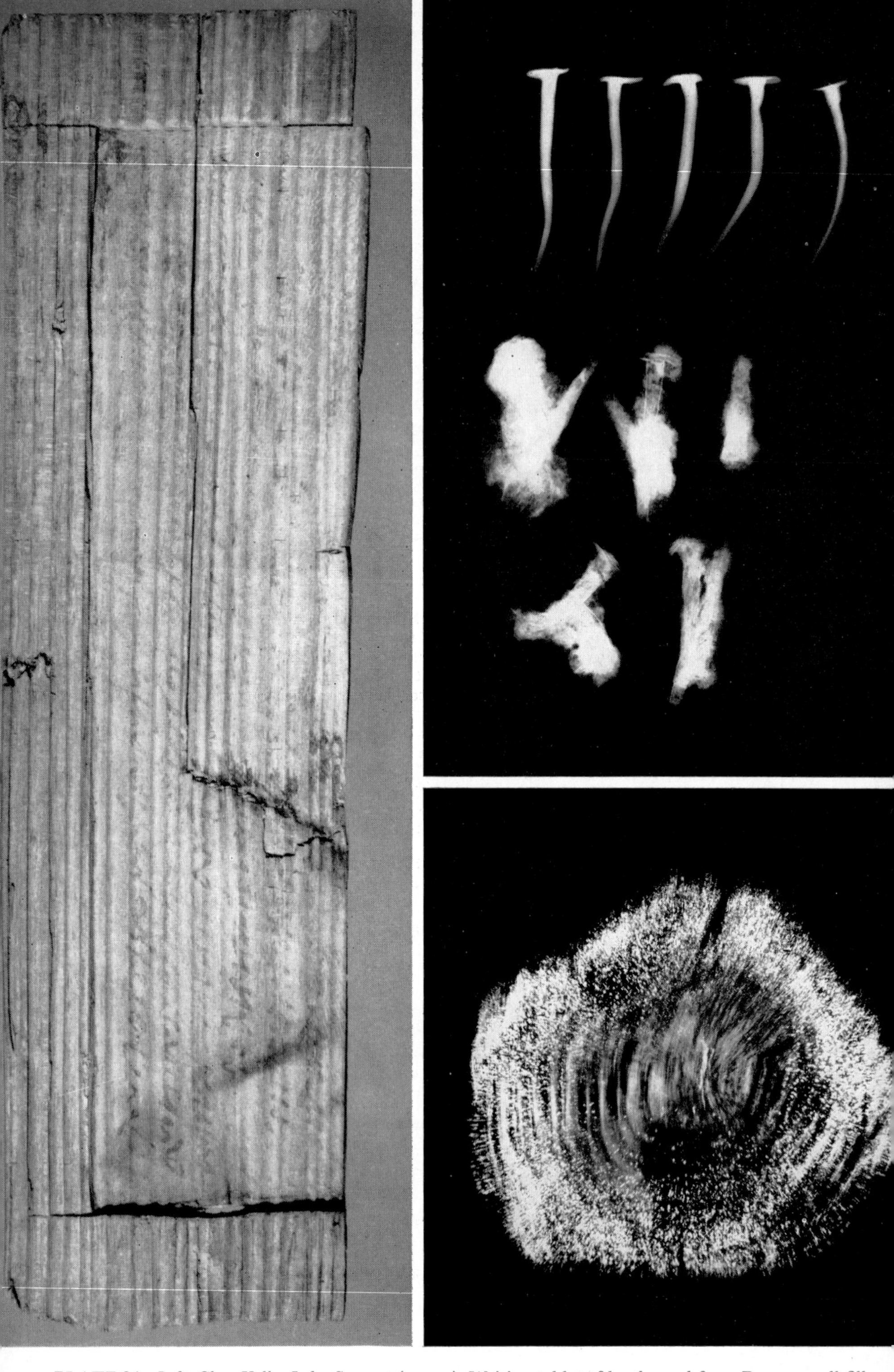

PLATE 24. *Left: Chew Valley Lake, Somerset* (p. 145). Writing tablet of larchwood from Roman well filling, treated. Top edge on left ($\times 1\frac{1}{2}$). *Right: X-radiographs of objects in Colour Plate II, facing. Upper:* Park Street, St. Albans, Herts. (cf. *A*, p. 133). Groups of Roman iron nails as found together in a hypocaust. Note livid outline of, e.g., central nail ($\times \frac{1}{2}$). *Lower:* Roman pit prop from Cyprus (cf. *B*, p. 126). Note distribution of copper as metal (bright specks) and salts (diffuse) ($\times \frac{2}{3}$).

II—*A*, *B* See pl. 24. Note red and blue in upper nails (*A*), metallic copper and bark (*B*). *C–F* Copper with more (*C*, *D*) and less tin/zinc (p. 161). *G–M*, *O* See Ch. Six (blue iron, *vivianite*). *G*, *M* Lead (left) and iron found waterlogged at Hungate (*G*) and Petergate (*M*) in York. *H–L* Chew Valley Lake: Copper alloy (*H*, *J*, *L*) and iron (*K*, *L*) found outside well (*H*), in top (*K*) and at bottom (*J*, *L*) of well filling. *N* Thetford madder pot (p. 105). *O* Iron found, but not buried, under water, unlike twigs from lower mud.

tablet (pl. 24). It had been written on in ink and about half the message was still legible. The wood was soft and cheesy to the squeeze but otherwise "in good condition".

The jug was studied at the National Chemical Laboratory by T. W. Farrer and colleagues. The copper seemed to be of good quality and so did the iron, but the solder turned out to be almost pure tin; the body had been beaten, and the handle wrought, with considerable skill, yet the soldering was clumsy. "Kettle fur" was found on the inside surface.

With Hungate very much in mind, the corrosion workers then turned their minds to the conditions which had evidently made it possible for the copper, and particularly the iron, to survive in such a truly remarkable state. Both in quantity and quality the Chew iron far surpassed the Hungate finds and remains the most fabulous collection I have yet worked on, although the London Walbrook finds appear to be richer still.

More incredible at first sight, the state of the copper is actually less difficult to understand. In the absence of air and in neutral solution the metal and its alloys are unlikely to suffer more than a superficial tarnish. But attack on the iron had clearly been inhibited once again, and the iron handle was of particular interest, since iron in contact with copper normally corrodes far more rapidly even than in isolation (p. 119). As at Hungate, sulphate reducers were present but not active.

This time tannins proper were looked for in the silt but could not be detected. I have already touched on possible reasons for this (p. 65). However, samples of the half-dozen different types of brushwood from the well were found by T. White and his staff, then at the Forestal Central Laboratories, still to contain detectable traces of such tannins. At the same time, as usually happens, there seemed to be another factor: a component in the silt that also exhibited desirable bacteriostatic activity. It was tracked down so far at the National Chemical Laboratory, mainly by absorption spectrography which showed it to have some similarities to a protein. But in the end there was not enough left and the search had to be abandoned.

Among the tannin-containing pieces of wood was a tiny fragment no different from the others in that respect. But in two other and most important ones it was. C. R. Metcalfe, of the Royal Botanic Gardens at Kew, with his assistant F. Richardson, had dutifully examined hundreds of pieces of wood from the well, and all of them with that one exception had been from normal types of hardwood such as oak, ash, hazel and elder. But this and a second small fragment, as well as the main tablet, were of larch, and other tablet fragments of silver fir. Both are conifers and classed as softwood timber, and neither is thought to have been growing in this country in Roman times (pl. 19).

The other great difference lay in the state of preservation. Superficially all the wood appeared to be in much the same condition, but when examined by R. D. Preston at Leeds University, in his words "the difference was dramatic". On the basis of the kind of investigation detailed later (p. 241), he found the submicroscopic structure of three hardwood species to have been completely disorganized. Silver fir, on the contrary, was "in such a perfect state that it was quite indistinguishable from modern wood except that it had an unusually high degree of crystallinity. . . . I can say with certainty that the fragment was taken from a tree which, at the time, was at least fifty years old". More recently, some of the brushwood from the well has been further examined at Leeds, and an approximate date of A.D. 300 has been assigned to the material.

Other work, at the Forest Products Research Laboratory (D.S.I.R.), showed that some wood-boring insect, probably the common furniture beetle, had attacked the tablets, clearly before they were thrown down the well, and that there had also been some fungus present and bacteria were there in force. But it was not possible to say if the fungus had in fact decayed the wood although bacteria seemed to have etched the surfaces of some of the cells.

The tablet fragments responded well to a comparatively short dehydration treatment at the Ancient Monuments Laboratory. After soaking in acetone for a week, and then in ether for a week, they were dried of the ether under vacuum, without undergoing any change in shape. Following this test, the main tablet was similarly treated with equal success.

Unfortunately the result did not reveal any more writing for

E. G. Turner to decipher. This Greek scholar had had little difficulty, even with the wet tablet (though with the aid of infra-red photographs), in describing the text as part of a certain type of Roman legal document connected with land transfer.[T11] But although the treated tablet was of course much easier to handle, and the improvement in clarity gave certainty to the readings, it was obvious that the significant section—giving details of parties and property—had been irretrievably lost in the well.

As for faint suggestions of writing on the other tablet fragments, there was no help even from the bleaching action on the wood which resulted from tests on the ink. These tests, by *not* bleaching the ink, confirmed the infra-red evidence that it was not based on the usual iron tannate and must thus be assumed to be carbon ink, of the Indian ink type.

The scientific work on the Hungate material had led to some results of benefit to the excavator, though not many; in the main, its value lay in establishing the nature of the conditions. But in building on these results, the work on Chew was at the same time able directly to be of use to the excavators in a far more specific way. Thus the copper jug became a kettle and two phases of work on it were clearly suggested—with an altogether more homely flight of fancy: could it have been that a well-wrought and possibly even imported piece of metalwork was allowed to boil dry and come "unstuck", and was someone then persuaded to "do it himself" in getting it together again?

Further—some seventeen centuries ago a larch tree is felled somewhere on the Continent. Either the timber, or a tablet cut from it, finds its way across to Somerset. Somewhere in between, perhaps about A.D. 220, a legal document is written on it with pen in carbon ink. It is thrown away or lost, and sooner or (more probably) later—after it had been eaten out of by an ancestor of our furniture beetle—half of it finishes up at the bottom of a well, before this is filled-in about a century after the writing of the message. For sixteen hundred years it helps (however humbly) to preserve ironwork in the well—provides food for microbes but in some respects changes hardly at all. When we find it, it has kept its surface, and on it—directly on it—about half the text. Apart from its immediate value, all the work greatly helps us to conserve the evidence for posterity; indeed, it alone makes possible at all some understanding of the processes of degradation and treatment that are involved.

Many other interesting things came out of the work on the material that was found in the well. In one way or another—and this has, of course, been one of my main points throughout—they do seem to hang together. But in following the particular thread I have here chosen I must leave them on one side with a mere mention, only, of a very few that would seem perhaps the most relevant.

For example, some fragments of rope (pl. 21) were found by T. H. Soutar at the British Jute Trade Research Association to consist of a vegetable (bast) fibre whose origins could not be traced with specific certainty (see p. 245). Although I had especially asked them to look out for any signs of bacterial attack, in view of that on the other (woody) cellulosic material from the well, the analysts could find none, and in fact thought that the undoubted degradation they could see was due to effects of "heat and pressure". Unless scorched beforehand—and that is of course a fundamental disability of this kind of evidence (p. 189) since we cannot ever be certain of the state of the material before burial—the rope was, according to the excavator, most unlikely to have suffered from either effect in the well. Nor was the "heat" effect consistent with frictional causes that might appear in use.

Cellulose was also present in the form of the earliest piece of cotton thread to be found in this country. But here it was shown quite plainly at the Shirley Institute that bacteria had caused considerable tendering. How are we to relate the evidence of bacterial attack on cellulose? Was the cotton *hair* more liable to it than the bast *fibre* (p. 128)? But then how about the woody *tissue*? Perhaps the surface becomes (chemically) opened up enough for such attack—and there is indeed some evidence that under aseptic examination no bacteria can be found in waterlogged heartwood.

But then what about the rope? And here is the archaeological reason for such detailed scientific investigation: should we compare the condition to that found in wood from Rotterdam piles some five hundred years old,[V3] and described as "on the way to lignite" whose formation is generally thought to involve heat and pressure? Or did the rope suffer heat and pressure before entering the well—lying under some weight near the kitchen fire? And how much happens to floating wood before it sinks? We have at the moment no positive evidence. But any correlation of the various states with effects of burial in the well seems quite unjustified. On the contrary, the thread and even the rope had far more probably come near to their present state before they reached the well.

As for the better preservation of softwood, there are possibly three main factors that might be responsible. Softwood has a simpler structure, is richer in resinous matter, and contains slightly more lignin. In general, less highly specialized systems are not so vulnerable as more complex organizations. Resins would increase water-resistance and have some "antiseptic" properties.[W17] Chemically speaking, lignin is normally far more persistent than cellulose, especially under water where analyses[B3, S10] have shown that after prolonged burial the original ratio can be almost reversed, so it is reasonable to assume that loss of lignin has in fact been negligible. It is with the influence of tannins that I am particularly concerned in this chapter—here, there is evidence that some resins are built up from, and break down into, compounds closely related to tannins both in structure and (? therefore) retarding influence on some biological agents of degradation.

The enormous number of bones found in the well would throughout have provided all the phosphate that the water might hold under the given conditions, and enough also for the vivianite which was again very much in evidence, distributed indiscriminately as before. The pH varied slightly with depth and, despite the considerable quantities of limestone fragments, appeared in places even to be somewhat on the acid side (fig. 4).

We have never looked back since. Waterlogged deposits have turned up regularly on a great variety of sites all over the country; indeed, excavators have been asked as a matter of routine to look out for, and report any, such deposits as early as possible so that they can be adequately dealt with. There is a standing arrangement whereby the specialists concerned with the study of these conditions are quickly informed of their discovery. As a result the general pattern has been confirmed in detail, and something new has been added every time.

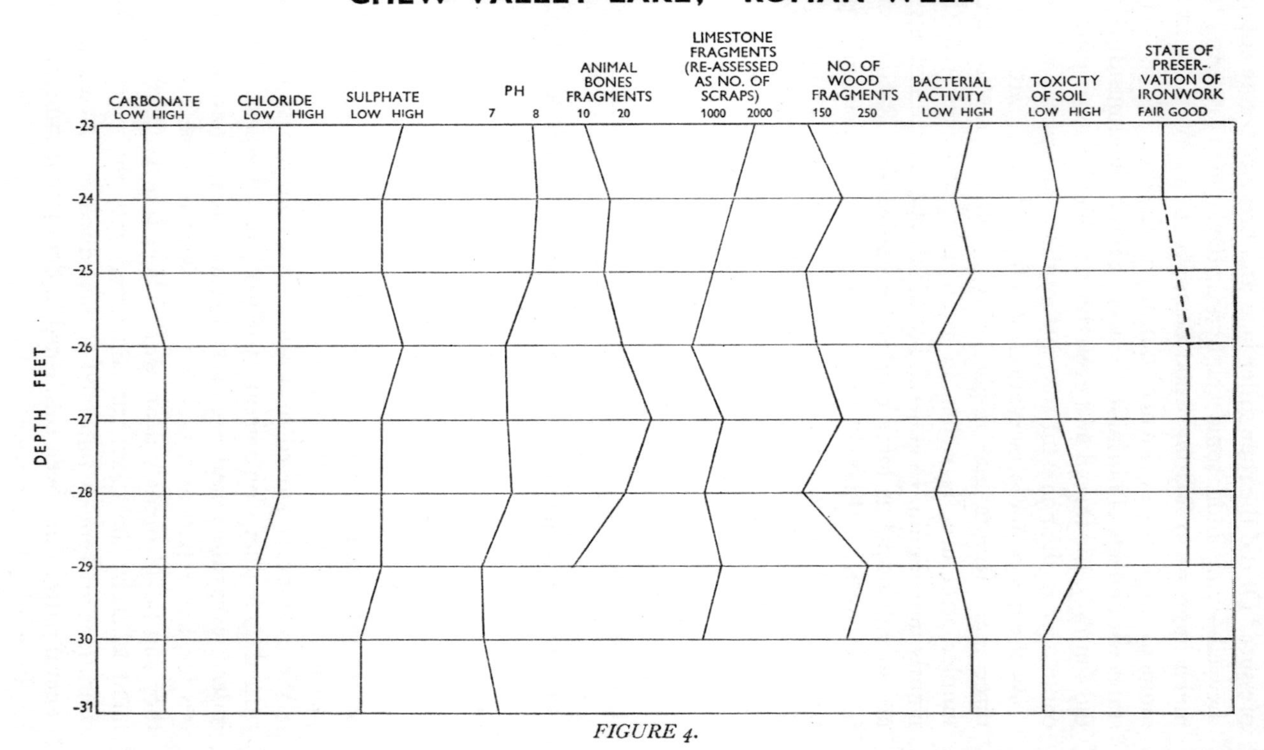
VARIATION OF FACTORS WITH DEPTH
CHEW VALLEY LAKE, ROMAN WELL
CARBONATE
LOW HIGH
CHLORIDE
LOW HIGH
SULPHATE
LOW HIGH
PH
7 8
ANIMAL BONES FRAGMENTS
10 20
LIMESTONE FRAGMENTS (RE-ASSESSED AS NO. OF SCRAPS)
1000 2000
NO. OF WOOD FRAGMENTS
150 250
BACTERIAL ACTIVITY
LOW HIGH
TOXICITY OF SOIL
LOW HIGH
STATE OF PRESER-VATION OF IRONWORK
FAIR GOOD
DEPTH FEET
-23
-24
-25
-26
-27
-28
-29
-30
-31

FIGURE 4.

Apart from field tests designed to see how well tannins would perform to order, as opposed to what they had seemingly done of their own free will, in preserving iron in aggressive soils, our experiences also brought a fresh stimulus in another direction. Tannin wash pre-treatments had been tried before on iron exposed to the atmosphere, in modern times at least as early as the twenties; they had then not been found satisfactory enough. Meanwhile tannin chemistry had made much progress, and as a result the excessively complex mixture of materials usually described as tannins had become better understood and up to a point more easily resolved. This meant that more specifically standard products were now available, with properties that were more certain in their reproducible activity, and that given tannins behaved very much better, for instance, in protecting iron. Although at first sight an entirely different mechanism, the action of tannins in preventing atmospheric corrosion of iron was thought once again to be worth further study.[K3] Tests at the National Chemical Laboratory suggested that other metals such as silver and lead could also be protected by tannin in wrappings.

A little later I came across some work[B21] which dealt with the movement of iron in soil water, downwards and away from the level and form normally most useful in plant husbandry. It appeared that in the laboratory certain plant leaf extracts could be made to pick the iron oxide coating off the sand grains at the top of a column and drain it away with them to a lower horizon where it was re-deposited. Although specific tannins were not then identified in these extracts, it was clear that their constitution was predominantly polyphenolic. Clay was similarly mobilized in some cases; where the fluidity of clayey and muddy materials is important, as in ceramics and oil drilling, such deflocculants can, of course, be at a premium.

At about the same time I was visiting Oxford to discuss in general certain scientific points raised by an excavation at Portesham.[T7] There, one of the most remarkable pedological phenomena so far to be found in this country was revealed as a by-product of sectioning a Bronze Age barrow. It showed quite clearly how a podzolic profile—that is, one in which iron is moved in a definite manner down into the subsoil and redeposited at a greater depth—could be formed in (archaeologically) measurable time in subsoil heaped on the surface of a mound.

In the process of discussing podzolic action, I was given a table of plants arranged according to their apparent connection with the podzolic or other soil profile on which they normally grew. The practical interest in these matters at the Commonwealth Forestry Institute centres around the possibilities of regenerating unproductive heathland for, and to some extent by, afforestation. At the same time, work is in progress there on the relation between vegetable litter and humus. By a process of elimination, the persistence of complexes formed between vegetable protein and polyphenols has emerged as the most important single factor.[H2]

The next day I went from Oxford to Cambridge to discuss the work carried on at the Food Investigation Laboratory, in so far as it related to tannins in plants. My attention had been drawn to it at Kew, where I had discussed the silhouette burial of Bishops Waltham (p. 181) which we saw in terms of an accumulation of mineral matter on the site of organic residues. It was the concept of accumulation which, by way of the action of tea leaves spread on the soil, led to a discussion of the Cambridge work.[B5]

At Cambridge, a turn in the conversation made me show the table I had brought away from Oxford. To my delight it elicited both great interest and surprise, since its division of plants corresponded to a large extent with what had been found at Cambridge about the tannin content of those plants. This information was written into the table which is shown, thus annotated, in pl. 18.

Gradually all these various fragments began to coalesce into the foreshadow of a pattern. Meanwhile came a most heartening instance of a "double return" which seemed to vindicate all the time and effort spent on the connecting game. When the roof of the clock tower housing Big Ben came up for repair in 1955, my advice was sought on the protection of the refurbished metalwork. The cast-iron tiles were in very good condition after a hundred years and there was no question of their serious corrosion even if left unpainted for the next hundred. But some war damage had to be made good and the general appearance was to be improved, and kept in good condition without maintenance which it would be impracticable to carry out at normal frequencies.

In the circumstances it was worth going to some trouble. The exceptionally thorough pre-treatment and resistant paint system seem on the whole to have been successful. After the mechanical cleaning of all surfaces, on the advice of L. A. Jordan (then Director of the Paint Research Station) the first stage was to apply—tannin. The wheel had turned full circle.

By the time this work was finished, the general pattern had taken on a recognizable form. In October 1956, a Symposium on Polyphenols was held. The important role of polyphenols, not only in leather chemistry but also in plant and soil metabolism, was for the first time approached with a strong resolve to integrate its various aspects. It was a strenuous and exhilarating day. At the end of it I tried to relate what I had heard to my experience of the archaeological record.

The whole business is complicated by many factors whose real nature remains obscure or equivocal. At bottom, it is beset by the multiplicity of combinations in which polyphenols appear, are metabolized and transformed, and disappear into related but no longer truly polyphenolic compounds. The conditions under which some reactions seem operative differ very little from others that may favour totally different mechanisms. Perhaps the most serious grouse is that of the organic chemist who has great difficulties in isolating, purifying and characterizing the components of naturally occurring mixtures of polyphenols without changing them in the process.

All the same, enough evidence appears to have been generally accepted now to allow the very general and crude integration which follows. In putting this forward I must stress the limitations to which such an undertaking is inevitably subject. But I believe that the emergence of the general picture which it suggests is worth the risk of misleading by oversimplification. This risk, though normally the most dangerous in my work, can here be kept within bounds quite easily by reference to the sources which are quoted.

This is not the place to discuss polyphenols as such.[P7, S18, W15] It is necessary, however, to divide them very roughly in two ways.

First, the same simple, basic type compound may combine with itself or other similar units to different degrees, giving a series of multiple-unit polymers. Secondly, a basic molecular type unit may be attached to one or both ends of an otherwise (relatively) "inert" chain, which itself can exist in a homologous series, increasing by one or two carbon atoms per molecule. Both these concepts are familiar from plastics, and the reactions which take place are essentially variants of the same kind of mechanism.

From work described in October 1956, and subsequently, it seems that we can now trace the life cycle of polyphenols fairly confidently and continuously in some respects. Precursors are formed especially in young growing leaves and the cambium of woody tissue.[H13] Simple polyphenols responsible for characteristic colours appear in late leaves, flowers, fruit, and sapwood.[P12] They can precipitate (dead) plant protein but will not tan (dead) hide. Under suitable conditions they will move iron down a soil profile.[B22]

More complex polyphenols are found in bark and heartwood.[H4] These are capable of tanning hide to give leather, of moving iron in soil rather more effectively, and of interfering quite decisively with the enzymes of some micro-organisms.[P12] To some extent they may be formed from the simpler polyphenols by oxidation, and they can indeed be regarded in some ways as doing more strongly all that the simpler ones do. But in some important respects this greater intensity can be so decisive as to change virtually into a difference in kind.

For the plant this is a crucial change. The particular oxidation and/or polymerization stage seems to be vital for protection. Thus a deliberately induced superficial wound may be able to cope with a virus infection, whereas an injection of the same virus into the sap is too much.

When the vegetable cell dies its protein is tanned by the plant's polyphenols. Here the kind and amount of polyphenol become decisive.[H2] If it is of the "condensed" type and can effectively deal with all the protein in the year's litter, it will tend to favour a *mor* type of humus and a soil in which nitrogen from such protein is not so easily available to growing vegetation. This in turn will encourage the kind of plant that will make conditions even worse in that respect, and micro-fauna normally producing a good turnover of nitrogen will be proportionately discouraged. The comparatively low oxidation state of the resulting soil seems, once again, to be important.

From this we can move in two directions, the most important single factor being drainage. If an area with quick drainage is involved, and there are polyphenols to spare over and above what is required for fixing the litter, then such "podzol formers" (see pl. 18) will move iron down and away from the growing surface rapidly enough to deplete it, and the vegetation will begin to tend towards heathland.[D10]

On the other hand, if drainage is slow and standing water is the rule, a different type of vegetation will be favoured which can grow better under such conditions; and this will almost always involve a faster rate of growth than of decay, the excess polyphenols accumulating near the surface and making the situation more stagnant still. Again, oxygen content is very low; this is characteristic of a state of affairs which tends towards bogs and peat, and is clearly also produced by human "interference" in deposits such as those at Hungate and Chew. Intermediate, oscillating conditions produce iron-mottled profiles such as "gley podzols" and "peaty gley soils".[K6]

If, however, conditions are relatively "dry" and there is more protein than effective polyphenol in the litter—two factors which may well be intimately connected—then a *mull* type of humus will tend to develop, giving rise to a soil in which nitrogen is more readily available to the growing plant. Such soils are better aerated and consequently populated with a copious microfauna which will tend in turn to preserve them.[R9] The connection between aeration, "dryness", polyphenol nature and content, and *mull* may lie in this, that even any excess polyphenol might be inactivated by oxidation in dry conditions rapidly enough to leave litter protein available.

The parallels with leather chemistry are throughout very close indeed. During tannage, a great part of the tannins remaining in the hide do so physically, as opposed to the rest which are chemically linked with the protein. The physical part is normally removed quite quickly during use. The chemical part can also be leached out over longer periods, and even made to tan about as much hide again, under suitable conditions. All the same, this particular protein-polyphenol complex is, in effect, leather; and its stability, as in the case of litter, determines the fate of the buried material. Leather is preserved on burial in waterlogged and particularly in peaty deposits, but decays in measurable time in well-aerated and relatively dry soil unless artificially preserved, as by the presence of copper (p. 124).

The next oxidation stage sees the disappearance of polyphenols as such. In both litter and soil tests, "keeping with air" appears to decrease the activity of the vegetable materials. The polymers thus formed, as in some other connections (p. 154), seem to become too large or complex to carry out any of their proper functions as polyphenols, except in mobilizing clay, where only higher molecular weight fractions seem to play a part. Oxidation also proceeds underground, even under the kind of waterlogged conditions with which I have been particularly concerned; only here it may largely by-pass the "heavy" stage and lead straight to breakdown. Bacteristatic activity is thereby unimpaired, chiefly (one suspects) owing to the greater acidity which ensues, and may even be enhanced.

No work has been done on the isolation of these breakdown products, to my knowledge, because unlike the litter and soil problems it has not yet been recognized as of value to any activity that is economically important. However, we do know that when tannins are put into the ground under such conditions they can no longer be detected there by the ordinary tests after some eighteen months—the shortest period so far between burial and re-excavation. On the other hand, there is clear evidence here, as in ancient deposits, of the presence of materials that might well be oxidized, broken-down tannins. This is our present limit. The general pattern of connections is now beginning to be proved.[C20, K4]

Work goes on all the time, of course, and I try to keep abreast of this aspect, not only the most fascinating but also the most universally permeative as far as my own work is concerned. This is made easier for me in that a Plant Phenolics Group was formed following the Symposium in 1956.

The organizers consider problems in the following fields as falling within the scope of the Group:

Fruit and vegetables (horticulture, genetics)
Plant physiology and pathology
Forest products and pedology
Food preservation and processing
Beverages (tea, coffee, cocoa)
Fermented beverages (wine, cider)
Soft drinks (fruit juices)
Tobacco
Tanning materials
Animal physiology and pharmacology.

The range of activities is very wide; yet every one of them touches my work at some point, and many at several. Keeping up with them is of course also made more difficult as, with characteristic disregard for accepted notions, each new result fans out into fresh complications. Thus detailed connections are being established between polyphenols and root initiation, bean metabolism and even beer haze.

The more detailed approach to corrosion mechanisms constantly moves the surfaces, at which the really significant things are supposed to happen, from one plane to another.[B23, F9] In the same way, emphasis is shifted from one factor or level to another. It may well be, for instance, that we shall soon have to reconsider the role of phosphates in preserving buried iron,[B24] and even a protective effect of (normally corrosive) sulphide at certain concentrations. Similarly, we are now coming to regard the action of tannins not so much as wholly anti-bacterial, in this case, but partly as one of the most convenient ways of keeping the soil too acid for bacterial comfort, and partly as interference with certain co-ordinating centres which control just the cycle directly involved in corrosion—perhaps by starving the organism of vital trace elements that may prefer polyphenolic attachments. At the same time there is no doubt that tannins can, in suitable circumstances, deposit on metallic iron an adherent and protective film—above ground or below. Again characteristic intermediate states are found, as for example in aerobic waterlogged deposits; here the higher oxygen content prevents both bacterial and polyphenolic activity (col. pl. II).

I have briefly traced the most remarkable influence of one material throughout the whole fabric of my work. It remains to extend this systematic approach in outline to all the different kinds of investigation that are possible on archaeological evidence as a whole. In the process their close material interrelation will once again become quite clear.

CHAPTER SEVEN

Co-ordination—Advance

FORTIFIED BY waiting and watching and connecting, the interpreter is ready to take the initiative. When the opportunity arises he finds he can take it in his stride because all the groundwork has been done. And take it he must, in order to subject to the "ordeal by synthesis" all his observations which have been purely analytical.

Once this "synthetic" start has been made, however, a further crop of analytical results becomes available. These are in a sense more reliable because they have been obtained under controlled conditions, and have come out in answer to specific questions. In this way the cycle of inquiry is set in motion. The next observations on antiquities or in the field will be made against this background of additional and firmer experience.

Such an advance on a broader front can begin only very slowly. Several factors contribute towards an opportunity. The observations must have been comparable enough to provide some continuity, and sufficiently weighted in favour of some feature to make it noticeable. Reflection on this state of affairs must have matured to a certain stage. After that, it might be said, almost astrologically, that matters depend on a conjunction of suitable material, time and (later) specialist help.

The advance, like the connecting game (p. 116), takes place at various levels. Probably the first progress to occur is in the general run of cleaning and conservation. Here the material aspect is more important than might have appeared from what I have just said. One needs a fair quantity of objects of the same kind, buried and found at the same time and place. Though not rare, such material must be waited for. It cannot be picked, as it might perhaps have been in other connections, from large and well-known or attested collections of a suitable nature, or even prepared, like modern test specimens. It must occur. But the interpreter must be ready. Ideally he should be there when it is found and not lose sight of it until his tests are complete.

Initial experiments are of course possible under less stringent conditions. They can indicate well enough, for normal purposes, which of several techniques in general use seem to be better than others. Such a test was carried out on *Some methods of protecting cleaned iron objects*.[B12]

A collection of iron keys, of various dates but in much the same condition, was recovered from one place by the Corporation of Great Yarmouth, in Norfolk, and given to the Ministry for exhibition at the Merchant's House there. Some two dozen specimens were selected so as to give scope for testing about a dozen techniques and materials on a large and a small item in each case.

The pieces were all cleaned together in the same solution to a certain condition. They were then treated in quick rotation to ensure as far as possible that the only difference between the various groups, in the end, would be that due to the different protective measures under test. A selection of other material, as well as modern mild steel specimens, passed through the testing procedure at the same time (see also table 8.1).

The keys were then all "exposed" at the Merchant's House, the other specimens in a laboratory store room. Conditions of cleaning, protection and exposure were deliberately chosen to give a compromise between strict control and approximation to normal museum conditions. In the circumstances, differences began to show after some eight months. All the factors that were thought to be significant, including cost and ease of application and renewal as well as purely protective qualities, were considered together in the production of an order of merit for the various methods. The exposure tests are continuing, but so far the standard material in use at the Laboratory seems to be slightly better than the others tested.

A similar experiment, in which the method of cleaning was also varied, has been carried out with a hoard of Roman bronze coins. It was hoped that such a comparative run would show which overall treatment gave the "truest" colour to the metal, but there was not enough material. The problem is clearly an important one.

There is no point in exchanging the green patina for something else that is as misleading. Plainly, too, there can be significant differences simply due to composition (col. pl. II*C*, p. 73). A lighter colour in both cases probably indicates a higher tin (and/or zinc?) content. For the coins, this was taken to be negligible. The results (col. pl. I*A*) clearly reflect differences in treatment (see table 8.2).

Another kind of problem, entirely, concerns the conservation of wood found waterlogged. Various methods have been studied but they all have certain drawbacks and the search continues for a technique that will with certainty, but no change in shape, consolidate such objects quickly, safely, permanently, easily and cheaply. Large quantities and sizes are often involved.

A material already exists that will mix with and replace water, and set even throughout a fair thickness of wood without distortion.[O3] Possibly with some oscillating "encouragement"[H10] and other development, time and temperature of treatment could be reduced. A urea-formaldehyde resin was used by us in a somewhat similar way with apparent success, although the *Wooden bucket restored*[B16] was comparatively dry when received.

Enough suitable material for proper tests came from the Roman well at Chew Park (p. 144) and an opportunity is awaited to carry them out. The ideal method would be based on replacement of the water by some other material, such as an organic solvent, which could afterwards be removed without shrinkage of the wood if, as often, the object were wanted quite dry. The ideal impregnant would—apart from satisfying colour, stability and other obvious requirements—set rapidly from a mobile, penetrating liquid to a solid without change in volume or application of heat. But first some fundamental work must establish the precise nature of this "wood"; really no more than a rather firm 15–20 per cent gel of cellulose–with–lignin in water.

The interpreter's interest then widens, to some extent leaving pure conservation, and moves towards the systematic consideration of the materials and methods used in antiquity. At this level, outside specialist help is required far more extensively. Having found out from authentic examples what was used, and how skilfully, we can assess more directly the status of the makers and demonstrate it more convincingly.

The rings (with thread remains) on the balance arm and pan from Dover (p. 118) were found in a fragile state. The fracture made me wonder whether corrosion alone could have produced such (almost "cast") porosity in this clearly wrought bronze object. Metallographic structures (and, hence, properties) are known to be modified at ordinary temperatures, spontaneously, in the case of (very pure) copper,[C15] silver[T6] and gold,[T4] simply as a result of an "ageing" effect.

RICHBOROUGH MAIL
CLOSED RINGS

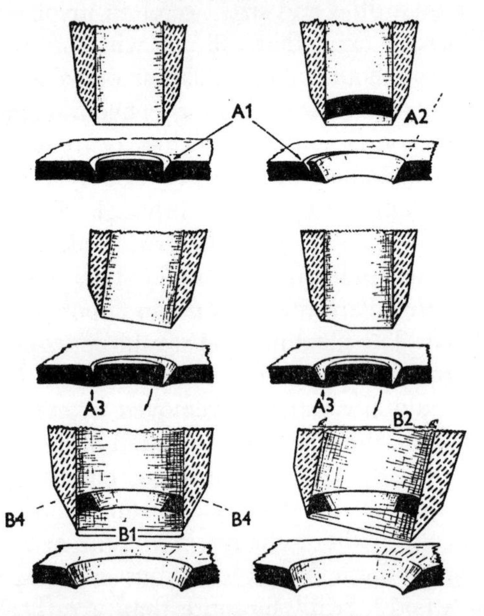

FIGURE 5. Probable method of manufacture suggested by J. W. Anstee. **A:** *Small hollow punch strikes out flan, thus forming inner edge of ring:* **1.** *Failure to penetrate at first strike.* 2. *Double strike.* **3.** *Angled or faulty punch. Note* angle *of inner edge, even with vertical strike, due to* outer *edge of punch. All these marks are retained on the ring.*

B: *Larger hollow punch strikes out the ring's outer edge:* **1.** *Perfect ring.* **2.** *Angled strike.* **4.** *Note characteristic section with* straight *outer edge due to* inner *edge of punch.*

While studying these rings, we were struck by their similarity to others in the mail fragment from Richborough (pl. 21; also p. 73) then also in the Laboratory. Certain markings and features were found which could be reproduced by punching such rings out of suitable metal sheet (fig. 5). Again, the porosity of the fracture seemed odd.

These observations gave us the final impetus to action—we asked for a small series of analyses (table 2). Not one of the pieces contained more tin than zinc, and the mail was a pure *brass*. The porous fractures were thus explicable in terms of "de-zincification", a well-known phenomenon in the corrosion of brasses which

TABLE 2

Chemical analysis of selected "bronze" specimens.

(*By courtesy of the Director, Tin Research Institute, and Dr. J. W. Price*)

No.	*Object*	*Site*	*Period*	*Percentage of*	
				Tin	*Zinc*
1	Scale pan ring	Dover, Buckland	Jutish	3½	4
2	Ring	Wroxeter	Roman	3½	18
3	Bracelet	Dover, Buckland	Jutish	7½	20
4	Chain mail	Richborough Castle	Roman	nil	21
5	Scale armour	Corbridge	Roman	2	13
6	Chain	Wroxeter	Roman	½	13

behave notoriously worse than bronzes under such conditions. Clearly, also, the use of brass was far more prevalent than is generally recognized, and the common level of zinc far higher. Some *Fragments of Roman "bronze" scale armour from Corbridge*[A11] (and see p. 121) of comparatively low-zinc brass with very little tin were evidently the result of mass-production of national importance. Split up into semi-mechanical unskilled operations, most of them performed possibly by women and children, this would produce a shirt of some 14,000 scales weighing about 7¼ lb.

Table 3 contains the results of analyses carried out on certain metal objects containing tin and lead. Nos. 1 and 2 represent two similar objects of the same period and from the same site, but made from diametrical extremes of the same type of alloy.[R15] No. 1 is harder and more brittle, a feature of considerable importance in cleaning, as also clearly recognized in antiquity and reflected in the technique. Other important effects of composition include differences in reaction to corrosive environments, and to heat. Where other cleaning methods would leave insufficient metal to make the object hang together, gas reduction (table 8.3) might be ideal. But accurate knowledge of the melting point, and hence of the composition, is essential.

TABLE 3

Tin: Lead ratios found in various objects

No.	*Object*	*Site*	*Period*	*Tin*	*Lead*
1	Brooch	Hungate[R15]	Pre-Conquest	Very high	Low
2	Brooch	Hungate[R15]	Pre-Conquest	Low	Very high
3	Jug	Chew Valley Lake[R7]	Roman	High	Low
4	Bowl	Chew Valley Lake[R7]	Roman	*c.* 25%	*c.* 75%
5	Jug	Baconsthorpe Castle, Norfolk	16th cent.	High	Low
6	Platter	Baconsthorpe Castle, Norfolk	16th cent.	High	Low
7	Dish	Thistleton[G15]	Roman	Low	High
8	Dish	Chalk[J6]	Roman	Low	High
When required, high purity lead was clearly available even in Roman times; e.g.:					
9	Fragments of water tank	Denton[G14]	Roman	Trace	99·6%

The tin: lead ratio appears to vary at random throughout period as well as function (table 3). Ignorance as a cause is argued with some conviction for Chinese bronze coins up to A.D. 1000,[H3] where numismatically homologous groups seem to have a fairly constant ratio only for copper to tin-plus-lead. But even the Romans could clearly exercise close control, and when late Roman lead-filled small change turns up persistently adulteration is virtually certain.

Sometimes there might be an intermediate explanation or a mixture. The makers of Roman speculum mirrors possessed the necessary knowledge and skill to a remarkable degree. Yet up to about five per cent of lead is often found in these alloys. Although not harmful, it has no specific advantage.

The Greeks certainly knew (e.g. [S3]) that lead makes the casting of bronze statuary easier, and a "speculum" was also used for coinage. It might be that the principle of lead dilution had been transferred, quite naturally if erroneously, or that only this particular alloy was commercially available.

The transference of method from one application or material to another may be of great diagnostic value—like finding iron "ore" collected as a curiosity by a people who clearly did not envisage its possibilities[F6]: availability as an asset must remain potential until significance is realized and skill developed.[C7]

Similarly, high temperatures achieved in certain pottery do not automatically indicate use of the kilns for metal smelting operations requiring similar conditions. And yet this becomes highly likely once economics and skill reach a certain stage.[C14]

In such ways minor details of technique can be of great chronological importance. All this, and evidently that other most human capacity of doing things right for the wrong reasons, enters into the kind of consideration which follows. In 1951 an iron pattern-welded sword of the ninth century came into the Laboratory for cleaning. Its method of construction stimulated research over the years which culminated in the reproduction (at Reading) of a full-scale weapon of the same type in 1956[A12, B14, D3] (pl. 23).

The very complex technique seems to have consisted in piling and twist-welding thin strips of iron into composite rods of which several were hammer-welded together into the bar that formed the core of the sword. This core was subsequently cutting-edged with plain metal and the whole suitably ground down and polished. Plate 22 shows a type specimen demonstrating all stages in the manufacture. A similar specimen has been shown to us, by A. Chiesman, of so-called "damascene" sporting-gun barrel manufacture, 1928.

Metallographic examination of the ninth-century sword showed clearly that the pattern need have nothing directly to do with the product's reputed excellence in antiquity. Although the twisted gross structure of the crystals' "fibrous grain" is important, on the microscopic level which determines properties the result is no different from plain wrought iron of similar quality. But it was probably impossible to produce, at that time, a plain sword of similar quality.

Iron, unlike copper, was won only in relatively small, brittle and spongy masses full of slag (p. 137). Although in the plain forged sword the surfaces might come to look satisfactory, a great many imperfections would remain and the metal would never be worked sufficiently right through. At best, each mass would be thinned out to the length required, and the resulting strips would be piled on top of each other and forged together in that position. Pattern-welding now clearly seems to have grown out of this piling refinement; for all that had to be done was to twist such a bundle of strips before any welding was begun, thus in effect thickening the metal up again. The rest would have followed almost as a matter of course, however slowly and laboriously.

In this manner it has been possible to shed some light on one of the most intriguing and typical processes of the Dark Ages—the result, as so often, of transcending one limitation and gracefully accepting the next, and thus producing a work of art that is at the same time of superb functional excellence. How was it superseded? There are magnificent examples of swords with strongly carburized cutting edges as early as the Iron Age.[P1, R11] But what must have been found is a comparatively simple way of getting a fair proportion of carbon evenly distributed throughout the body of the weapon. This alone could have displaced pattern-welding.

It is a curious and lamentable anomaly about this kind of work, as a whole, that pottery, which is still the principal single factor in archaeological evidence (p. 45), has not been scientifically examined nearly as much as many other materials. The excavator doubts if it could tell him more than he thinks he can say on typological grounds; the analyst shudders at the prospect of the comparatively difficult and tedious processes involved.[S8] And yet, because the great importance of such work was recognized early, there is in the United States even a laboratory concerned just with ancient ceramics.[S11]

Occasionally something does happen to the pottery fabric in the ground. Some of it may be the "wrong" colour when found, yet give a matching fit with the rest. Such a case was brought to me in

1952 from a Roman site in the City of London (col. pl. 1). The black variety was supposed to represent the original intention. Clearly something more (or less?) had happened to the other piece. Was it possible to say how they were related, and whether the red was, in fact, accidental?

By pure chance I came across some German work which had dealt experimentally with almost precisely the same problem.[D6] There the black form was thought to have been produced (and was reproduced by the workers from the red) inside a large quantity of charcoal in a sealed clay chamber; and the red form was due to strong and (almost certainly) accidental re-firing "in air".

Put very simply: other things being equal, the colour of a fired ceramic of this kind depends mainly on the iron (oxide) content of the clay, the amount of organic material in it, and whether the firing conditions were ultimately oxidizing (i.e. freely aerated) or reducing.

For a subsequent study of the same problem in a different context some analytical work [B19] was done on the iron oxides present, but this aspect remains complex. However, for our present purpose only two generic types are important: *magnetite*, producing an overall grey tone; and *haematite*, the bright red of bricks and flower-pots.

When enough air is present in the end, the pottery will be fired red—in a grey "core" magnetite has persisted unaffected by air at the surface—or it may be buff to white if it contains little or no iron, or brown if the temperature is low. When the kiln is full of charcoal and the air supply is limited, the resulting pottery is black mainly because the organic matter in it is charred.

Viewed against this background, our problem was practically solved. It only remained for the Clay Products Section at the Building Research Station to help us by cutting the small black sherd in half and re-firing one portion in an oxidizing atmosphere. As expected, this turned it red and confirmed that the rest of the German work also applied to our specimens.

A similar problem was posed at Verulamium (St. Albans, in Hertfordshire) (col. pl. I).[L8] So-called St. Rémy ware, among the earliest types of Roman or indeed European glazed pottery, carries a yellowish-green lead glaze. Very briefly, the lustrous pieces and parts could have been accidentally re-fired, this time under reducing conditions, acquiring a surface of metallic lead suspended in a siliceous matrix. Alternatively, the glaze might have been attacked in the cold, by the rather aggressive (and also reducing) environment often found in rubbish pits. This would expose its lead oxide to agencies transforming it into the very metallic-looking sulphide. Analysis alone can discriminate, but there is little difficulty, and the answer in turn clearly indicates the fate of the lustrous pieces.

Tests carried out by T. A. Read at the Associated Lead Manufacturers' Research Laboratories "on a fragment of the 'black' glaze showed that this could be readily converted to the amber colour by heating for a short time in a muffle furnace with an oxidizing atmosphere at a temperature of about 700°C, and conversely some of the amber colour glaze heated in a reducing atmosphere readily became black. . . .

"There is no evidence of exposure to sulphide since examination showed that the black material was present right throughout the thickness of the glaze, indicating that the glaze was in a semi-molten condition when reduction occurred."

On pottery recently found by Miss H. Frost in a Mediterranean wreck, however, there is some evidence for discoloration due to "cold" reduction.

All this leads directly to a simple general method for comparing basic pottery fabrics. Some such analyses have been carried out for us by F. J. Watson. Because they mainly reveal any difference between the clays that was masked in the pottery they are, of course, closely related to similar analyses of soil samples described on p. 223. Representative sherds are each broken into two pieces, one of which is re-fired under known conditions (col. pl. 1). Some differences remain, others are revealed or disappear. All the same, variations are not great and it was possible here for Watson to suggest, from his intimate knowledge of the deposits, that all this pottery could have been made from local clays.[W1] In addition, soil samples I took during excavation were made up into little pots and fired by him as well, and these made it possible to be a little more precise in suggesting the most likely raw material for some of the excavated sherds.

In almost all cases, grit could only have been added intentionally and consisted in the main of angular flint chips. Such pottery must clearly have been hand-made since any throwing on the wheel would have played havoc with the potter's hands.

In this connection, the question of other forms of reputedly deliberate inclusion in some other kinds of pottery was also considered. Terms like "shell-gritted" and "calcite-gritted" ware have passed into the archaeological literature but no fundamental work appears to have been done to link these concepts with what is known from modern pottery practice; nor has the true identity of the particles been established in a sufficient number of cases to justify much of what has been said about the pottery.

Shell grit, where it truly is such, might clearly be part of the very kind of estuarine clay which has in places been traced to some limited range of possible origin. If deliberate addition could be distinguished this would be of great value.

Further, one would expect shell fragments to decompose at temperatures above 900°C, although there might be some variation according to the firing atmosphere. Chalk, pure calcite, limestone and other forms of calcium carbonate would behave similarly, and the grit may either drop out or (on cooling) gradually expand and severely disrupt the fabric. Lime burning, and "popping" in plaster, are examples on a larger scale.

On this basis, a series of re-firing tests—though not in an electric kiln—will quickly indicate the maximum original kiln temperature for such pottery. Shell-gritted or other "calcareous" pottery could never have been fired much above about 850°C, except perhaps in an atmosphere very rich in carbon dioxide. This is surprising, as is also any deliberate use of shell to the modern potter. Satisfactory pottery can be made at temperatures even below 800°C.[W6] Yet a further 200° produces an enormous improvement in many ways and is known to have been attainable. Does the underfired, and thus cheap and simple, ware indicate unstable conditions and the use of makeshift firing facilities, possibly by itinerant potters?

Even such simple firing tests and a projected spectrographic survey of glazes should give us greater confidence in talking about the technological details of the pottery we find.[T3A]

The concept of repair and maintenance would appear as something tedious and temporary—a necessary evil. Yet several million people, from lawyers and picture restorers through all the trades and professions to chemists and engineers, spend their entire working lives on conservation.

It is difficult to convey the extent of the difference such an outlook can make. On first hearing, the word "corrosion" strikes a chill note: damage, loss, failure and decay. But the continuous attempt to prevent and cure it leads to such a wealth of unexpected experience that the activity can become a permanent joy.

Once general feelings of irritation and frustration have been overcome, a detailed study of causes becomes a fascinating occupation; the concept of discovery is extended to this part of the work as well. The primary object of the exercise ceases to dominate the scene yet receives in all its aspects the benefit of the whole activity in terms of fresh ideas, new materials and novel methods. The idea of co-ordination almost of itself impresses its connective tissue on the whole of experience. It is this which makes advance possible.

We start simply by wanting to clean and conserve. Clearly we can improve as we know more of what exactly we are dealing with. Causes are sought and found, in increasing detail. Related but fresh problems appear, relationships begin to crystallize. The results of research in one field are applied to problems in another. We discover that what burial has added may be of greater importance than what was originally buried. But now we come to see an even wider view. We step behind the actual instances and regard them as special cases of more general relationships.

So we become independent of all other considerations. We rearrange all the pieces of our jigsaw in a different plane. We are no longer concerned with typology, chronology or even shape, function, purpose, but solely with fate. Beyond that, the material itself takes second place and the primary criterion is the condition of exposure.

From this angle, looking across formal and material divisions, we consider the effect of "natural" agencies: what happens in such and such a medium? Not so much to any particular kind of thing, but to anything and everything that may there find itself.

This approach has two distinct but complementary advantages. It trains one to look at the evidence from a given section or level as a whole, materially speaking—within the limits of the particular conditions. Conversely, but for the same reasons, one comes to reconstruct from such evidence in a given case not only the particular conditions—even without having seen them *in situ*—but also as far as possible the original circumstances and the events before and after burial. Most important of all, one learns what state of material to look for, or when not to expect visible traces.

Here I must explain my use of "natural". I have throughout meant phenomena that one might expect on earth even though it had never known man. Yet today very few localities apart from deep sea bottoms and other inaccessible places would qualify in such terms (pp. 172, 175), and even they are beginning to register the results of our very latest games with the basic natural forces. And that, conversely, is just it: although we may no longer be able to study a truly natural condition, we can actually do nothing at all without having recourse to natural agencies. This is another form of our universal paradox.

In archaeological practice we do, of course, usually know quite well what we mean by the term. If, say, an "exotic" whetstone is involved, then the question is plainly whether it could have got to the locality naturally—that is, by glacial drifts or in alluvial deposits, or some combination of them—or whether we must invoke human purpose and transport.

This general consideration is of basic importance to the whole range of our inquiry (p. 67), especially to the study of many features in the ground itself which, unlike artefacts, have no clearly recognizable shape or function. Sometimes it is possible to coax some significance out of them; yet we must always start from what could have happened without any direct intervention by man.

As in space, so also in time difficulties arise; should our definition exclude a certain wholly natural—if long-term and residual—effect of human activity? It is good to look at the scene as so much food for metabolism—and here, of course, it does not matter whether the food itself is man-made or man-modified, or independent of his activities. But its provision at a given time to a certain set of elemental conditions, and even the conditions themselves, may be the result of human acts—directly or indirectly—or not. The distinction between a coin in a stratigraphically "sealed" pit and one silted into an adjacent ditch is plain enough. But even the deep soil profile into which pit and ditch were dug may be a natural result of forest clearance some three thousand years earlier (p. 221). All the same, we shall now be surveying from the natural point of view (fig. 6). It is fitting as well as convenient to do so in terms of the ancient elements.

Pure, cold, still *air* is innocuous in the main, although some things are sensitive enough to the oxygen in it. Such a situation is rare in the extreme but it does exist in places and therefore can affect our considerations, sometimes most unexpectedly. Thus I learn from the Geological Museum that there are today exposed at the surface, in the upper regions of some South American mountain ranges, metallic sulphide ores in an almost pristine condition. Normally they would since their first exposure (in geological time) have weathered into oxide minerals to a great depth, sulphide thereby becoming largely inaccessible to primitive metallurgists. Here they might have been easily seen and obtained. The question of such accessibility is important to students of early technology; it may not be relevant in the particular locality but is worth noting in principle.

But over the greater part of the earth's surface by far, and particularly in the now densely populated areas with which we are chiefly concerned, the air is of course not pure or cold or still; nor are conditions either dry or ever dark for long enough to affect this issue. For even in the open air, apart from the minor impurities which largely determine smell, weathering action and visibility, two other factors are indissolubly linked with the concept of "air"—moisture and light.

Once more we are caught up right away in a tangle of interdependence, for moisture in air goes with temperature, and temperature goes with "light"; yet all are separate in their several effects. We are in the main concerned here with their activities in concert, but there are occasions when we do not meet them together, as in mines and caves, which can be supremely important in this approach.

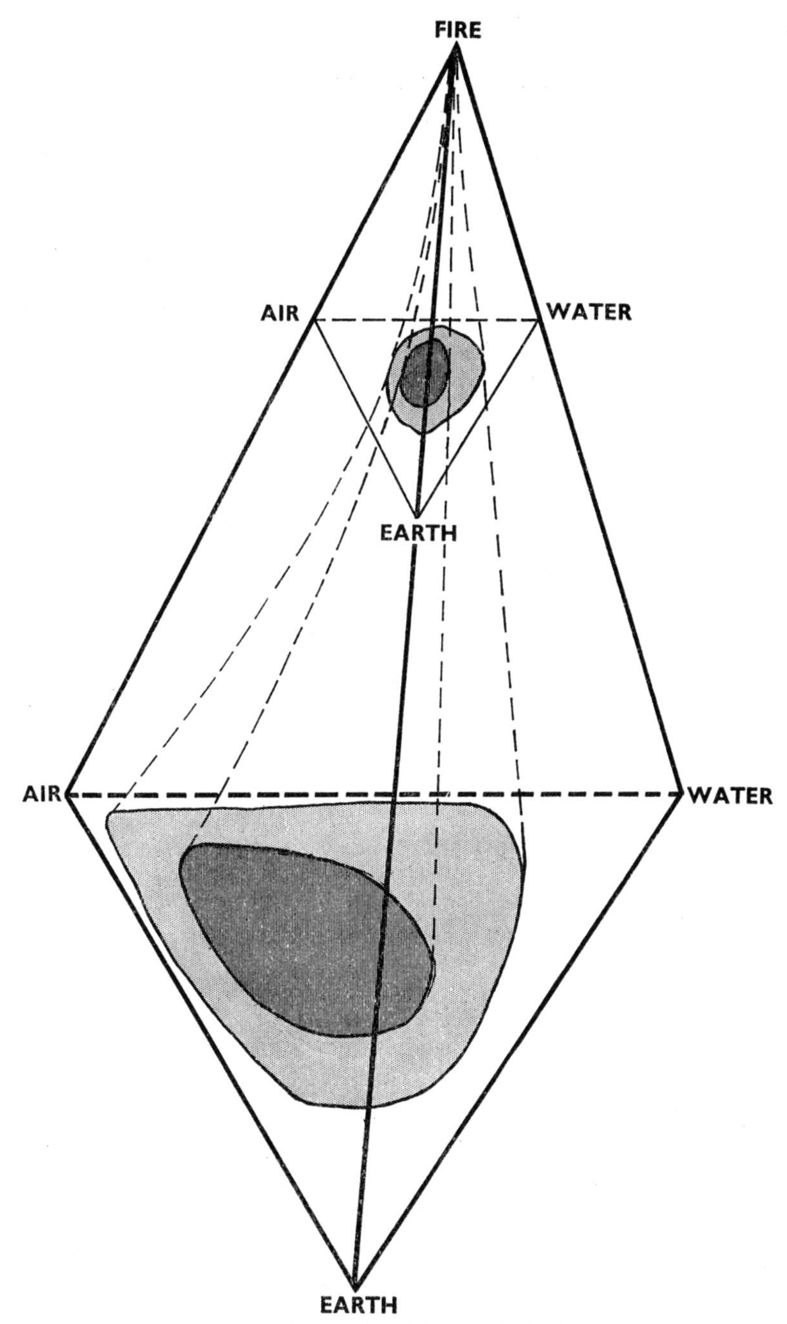

FIGURE 6. Effects of the elements. A highly generalized schematic attempt to indicate mutual influences in this "quaternary system". At apices, control by one element and effects minimal. The vertical variation in the "cones" of moderate (light) and severe (dark) deterioration shows how previous burning (without air) largely suppresses normal effects of burial.

Moisture in air, though destructive in its own right, too, is principally involved as a carrier for the impurities. Another result of its presence (even alone) is that air, however pure, will become corrosive, for example to iron, which only then is affected by oxygen at ordinary temperatures.

The two principal effects of light in this connection, as in thinking of colour, are perhaps even more difficult to isolate because light is so fundamentally tied up with everything we do in our waking lives. In the first place it raises the temperature: just as by "air" I meant our immediate atmosphere, so "light" means all that reaches us from sun and space by way of electromagnetic radiations. That includes the invisible ones we feel as heat or know to start chemical reactions and cause fading—and this is the second influence of "light-in-air". Again we must remember the separateness of the factors. Air filters harmful rays and therefore we would be far worse off in a vacuum, as for example in space. Also, we can of course isolate and control these effects ourselves.

As often in such cases, the results of exposure to air are normally additive so that degradation increases with time. In a sense the same applies to temperature; yet a warm sunny day will usually dry out damp places and may actually reduce deterioration. Probably the most insidious factor is the *oscillation* of temperature. Materials will distort and generally suffer wear over long periods, and the troubles caused by condensation are familiar enough.

When conditions become moist it is the water that locally takes control. In the pores of stonework, surface scales of exposed metal, and outer layers of fibrous materials such as leather and wood, generally what happens is determined by the physical chemistry of aqueous solution. But often in this micro-world of tiny droplets each remains discrete and therefore has a large surface for its size. The processes inside the droplets are therefore still much influenced by the huge reservoir of air which almost envelops them, and the vast majority of materials deteriorate most quickly and virulently under conditions of oscillating humidity.

Gradually we pass into the domain of *water*. But just like moisture in air, air continues to play an often decisive part in pure water, even when the material is actually submerged. The degree of aeration or "oxygen tension" of the water then still determines the amount of metallic corrosion, the decay of wood and other organic materials, and in general the type of biological activity by which such processes are ultimately affected.

As we have seen (p. 61), a sharp division appears between the condition in which materials are found after airless, deeply water-logged burial, and the distorted presence, or even presumed disappearance, of the same materials in water which has been continually re-saturated with air. But we must remember that this is a simplification in some important respects. Iron is corroded rapidly even in the absence of air by bacterial action, unless much organic matter is present (p. 143). Also the "excellence" of the state of preservation is a very relative, and often largely apparent, criterion. Although outward form may seem perfect, internal structure can be almost completely disorganized, as in the case of wood where water has replaced so much of the original matter as literally to be propping up all the remaining cells. Once more we need to qualify, for softwoods appear to fare much better than hardwoods, and some hardwoods better than others.

And even on a general plane—again, airless waterlogging is not normally encountered except in the presence of decisive amounts of "soil". No sooner do we think ourselves free of one of our elements in order to consider the effect of another in isolation than a third obtrudes itself. Not until we approach the mud at the bottom of a lake or river do we get a low enough oxygen tension to produce preservative conditions of this type. Even at the bottom of oceans only the ooze is truly anaerobic.

It is true that special conditions apply here. For one thing there is considerable movement to a great depth. Also the solubility of oxygen in water increases with pressure, and therefore with depth. The result of increasing darkness is more complex. Exceptionally conditions at the bottom favour such virulent bacterial growth that a large mass of water like the Black Sea may seasonally erupt with hydrogen sulphide, the black colour being due to iron sulphide. But normally, to produce fully anaerobic conditions even under considerable heights of water, it seems that we also need some depth of soil.

This is, of course, precisely what we have in suitable circumstances over the archaeological record, and very fortunate it is.

Wells get filled in; ditches, pits, estuaries, lakes and other depressions where the water table continues high—they can all silt up while remaining waterlogged almost continuously. The prime examples, marshes, fens and bogs, are proverbial in this respect. Such a deposit, especially as it is by its very nature of fine particle size and therefore relatively impermeable, restricts considerably the passage of air from above. Consequent biological activity rapidly develops and soon air is effectively shut out altogether.

Considering the question now from the standpoint of our third element alone, we find once again that this is very difficult to do because so rarely valid. In Britain certainly, just like the mutual effects of water and air, there is always enough air and water in most *soils* and even subsoils to determine their behaviour very largely, from our point of view. Even when there is no air there must be water, and *vice versa*, until we get to relatively impervious rock. Conversely, in passing, ancient monuments exposed to the air are also affected by the earth in which they stand, by the water from it and by the things this water carries up from it into them. Again, even on the copper roofs of historic buildings surprising amounts of evidently windborne earthy matter have been found in the patina.[V4]

Nevertheless we must try to isolate once more. In Egyptian tombs we come nearest to dry and airless earth. The effects of burial under these conditions are, again, well known. Air in earth without water, in the Sahara and Gobi and Turkestan, produces its own peculiar though somewhat similar results. At best we in Britain have only poor transitional examples—occasionally, by a slight stretch of definition, perhaps something like an immured medieval silver spoon in perfect condition.[R6] Such specialized effects, like those on waterlogged sites, are always striking. Our nearest approach to dry earth is perhaps sandy well-draining soil in an area with low rainfall. But here the archaeological record is affected chemically to an extent which completely masks any preservative tendency there might have been due to relative dryness (pp. 180, 187).

However, once again, our principal concern is the ordinary set of conditions—moist aerobic soil and subsoil. Here the earth adds its own multiplicity of most vigorous factors, though most of them clearly depend on the water and the air. There is the purely mineral chemical activity due to the active components from the parent rock below. Salts move about, are absorbed and exchanged preferentially by different soils and subsoils, and have a profound effect on buried metallic objects in particular. There is the purely physical effect of pressure by considerable earth masses on deformable shapes.

Then we have complex results of biological activity, from bacteria to fungi, and from worms to rabbits, leading in turn to very pronounced chemical or physical metamorphosis of objects, strata and features. It is only fair to stress that these biological activities in turn affect the ambient earth, within limits, much as it largely determines them. There is usually a trend towards some equilibrium of all the factors involved. Of this equilibrium the archaeological record becomes an integral part. As in conservation (p. 93) it must therefore be so considered where detailed interpretation is involved. For when excavation disturbs this equilibrium changes must clearly take place and may lead to loss of evidence very quickly.

The tangible results of all this are of course a familiar part of the excavator's experience. He has come to see given conditions as the effects of certain causes. Similarly he is well acquainted with the more immediate results of our last element—*fire*. Charcoal, hearths, burnt clay, calcined bone, smelting pits and slag, kilns and pottery—they are always well documented because clearly recognizable, very persistent and in the main easily interpreted. But there are various forms of such evidence that are not so easily discovered (p. 133), and the search for them is characteristic of our final complication here.

There is always a temptation to ascribe the condition of a corroded bronze wholly to its final period in the earth. Yet sometimes there have been several changes in environment; only very rarely has there been none. Once again the principle is accepted as a useful aid where the effect is plain. Thus a reasonably well-preserved, worn coin is often of diagnostic value. Within a considerable period of circulation, perhaps, such an example serves to place the date of burial towards a later part of it.

In our present terms the coin has had some wear and corrosion in air before being buried in earth. In most cases this situation is by no means clear. Admittedly any previous deterioration other than wear might not be serious enough to affect the issue—unless the object had been exposed to the weather for some months or even years. But then, how often must this have happened, as it happens still today, rather than the clear-cut burial of a comparatively fresh object, as in a pagan grave. And in the case of iron articles this effect is far more pronounced (p. 189).

This sequence would indeed seem to be the most usual but all the other combinations are possible and some of them quite common. Thus remains of boats found preserved in earth will carry marks of action by water—if they had been used; and it is precisely this which it might be essential to discover. They would have had to be waterlogged during burial to have survived at all—a typical complication which underlines the need to study all the fine detail by which distinctions could be made.

In the same way we must consider certain dwelling places—originally dug out of the earth, exposed to air and in part to fire, and perhaps later flooded and by us found waterlogged; or the evidence on a block of stone: used in a building where it weathered in air, burnt in a fire, thrown down a well which then probably had water in it but is by us found dry and filled in with earth.

These are examples of orderly sequences, well defined and involving each type of exposure only once. But the possibilities in special cases are almost boundless—with the more permanent materials that were in constant demand, the discarding of worn objects and their subsequent re-use in other forms must have been the rule. It is a fascinating thought that there may still be some objects actually in circulation which contain (a small portion of) metal smelted in the Bronze Age, scrapped and remelted perhaps only the odd hundred times or two.

Of all the permutations, those involving fire as the final—and often decisive—stage before burial are the most obvious. Provided it has been hot enough, an object or feature rarely changes much afterwards in earth (or water, or air for that matter) although once again there are possible intermediates.

In this connection there is a link with much earlier events. I have already stressed the close relationship between our studies and geology, not only in stratigraphy and general approach but in the basic physics and chemistry as well. Igneous rocks, too, are often very stable in earth—or in the other two elements—but again not invariably. In so far as they may have been used by early man this is clearly of interest to our study of him. But even in other ways, less obvious and more uncomfortable, geothermal phenomena are of direct relevance.

In regions with red soil, as in Devon, for example, it would probably be impossible to recognize an area burnt in antiquity simply by the usual reddening effect. The parent sandstone is supposed to have been formed from deposits laid down under conditions resembling today's Mediterranean climate. Is plain reddening a reliable indicator of fire anyway?

I have already discussed this in another connection (p. 133) but there, of course, such redness would be due actually to dehydration, and although firing would produce it, so might much lower temperatures at very low humidity for very much longer periods. In any case, the nature of the colour is not always clear and may be due to particle size effects.

As in other cases—for instance with magnetometric prospecting (pp. 208, 236) which in itself depends on another aspect of the same effect of fire—the relative size of the "anomaly" might perhaps serve to distinguish a significant feature. But it is necessary always to guard against the temptation of transferring (especially negative) evidence from one set of conditions to another, without wondering whether the implicit premisses should not be modified.

As this elemental outlook matures (fig. 6), one begins inevitably to look ahead rather further than before. We know that general preservation is poor, under ordinary conditions, though there are exceptions. These are always of interest but seem usually to be the result of some retarding action, rather than of direct and complete inhibition of attack. Organic residues are not found unless "fixed" by fire or water, or protected by mineral matter in some way: by biocidal action, or fossilization in the widest sense.

While this can all probably be learnt simply by digging, there are several advantages in looking at it from such a generalizing point of view. The interpreter, by collating facts and circumstances for which the excavator has little time, can prepare a kind of reference collection of type conditions. To that extent he participates in all the excavations and can at any time give any one excavator the benefit of all the others' experience.

More important still, he can begin to supply excavators with information they can normally not get for themselves very easily. On the basis of a reason-seeking approach to the fate of antiquities, as a subject in its own right, he can do two important things. He can suggest negative evidence—that the absence of a certain material or feature, for example, might be significant; and he can to some extent predict, from the geological map and the vegetation, what is and what is not likely to be found in the way of material condition.

We know that bones are generally well preserved, even after some three to four thousand years, when they have been buried under normal conditions in chalk or chalky soil. It is assumed, on the other hand, that comparable inhumations in well-drained (siliceous) gravel or sand have been completely dissolved because no trace of the bones can be found. Special conditions, such as exist in the clean sands of the Northern Netherlands,[V1] show only "silhouette burials" remaining, though these are clear enough.

Let us take, for example, a certain type of Bronze Age barrow, of a given date range, built up mainly and regularly of cut turves to cover and mark in a monumental fashion the buried remains of some important person that are accompanied by characteristic grave goods. The variable is the type of soil into which the burial pits have been dug—from and on which the mounds were erected.

Even after such typological levelling the purely material complications assail our simplified approach as usual. Changes in climate affecting soils and vegetations, effects due to human agency, disturbance by robbers and burrowers—such factors must be taken into account where known, or allowed for. All the same, the comparative attempt must be made as simply as possible.

I have chosen excavations at Bishops Waltham,[A13] in Hampshire, as typical of the kind of advance that suddenly becomes possible. As I see it now, the central feature gave me one of those valuable intermediates (p. 122) between the two extremes that I had then heard of but did not physically meet till later.[T7, W2]

It was a somewhat ragged but recognizable silhouette burial in a "coffin" (pl. 23). C. L. Bascomb of Rothamsted Experimental Station was persuaded to take an interest in it. Surprisingly, he found that there was no more phosphate in the "body" than in the coffin or the "neutral" earth around (cf. [J5]). However, about ten times as much manganese was present in the chocolate brown body as there was in the light-brownish yellow clayey sand, and a hundred times as much in the almost black coffin sides.

It seems as if decaying organic material had acted as a manganese "accumulator". The quantities involved are far greater than any that would be present naturally in organic matter or soil except in some accumulation like a manganese nodule or pan. Such pans occur quite frequently where the soil is comparatively rich in manganese though they are not as common as the more familiar iron pan. No pans worthy of the name were seen at Bishops Waltham, but the silhouette itself might of course be regarded as a manganese pan. No comparable analysis is known to me and it would be interesting to see whether other, or indeed all, silhouettes are similarly constituted.[cf. A6]

If this were so, one might try chemically to "develop" an indefinite or even "invisible" silhouette. At Bishops Waltham it was only just there. At Little Ouseburn, near York, the stains did not cohere satisfactorily.[R5] There might also be some other material accumulated in the same way without a visible trace. Finding the burial is a matter of great importance to barrow diggers. When they cannot actually see one, or any sign of later disturbance where there might have been one, they can only assume that the burial had completely disappeared as a result of soil action.[P5] This is clearly not satisfactory. After all, the barrow might have been a token one and never contained a burial at all.

The findings also support the general assumption that the most important single factor in the destruction of buried bone is probably the pH of the soil—the measure of its acidity or alkalinity. The calcium phosphate of bone, insoluble in (neutral) water of pH 7, becomes slightly soluble even in faintly acid solutions of pH 6·8 while it is protected more or less indefinitely in chalk, with a pH of up to 8 and over. There is a corresponding connection between sour garden soil, acid and deficient in calcium, and the sweetening of it by addition of calcium in the form of lime.

pH values of the samples from Bishops Waltham ranged from 6·5 to 6·8. We must be careful here. It is possible that the pH has changed since the time of the burial, and if it has then it was probably more acid than now. More rapid attack under worse conditions, producing the silhouette as much as some two thousand years ago, perhaps, and followed by a slower process of equilibration, cannot be ruled out. Even some individual geological processes are now considered to have taken far less time than was previously thought.

At Sutton Hoo[B33] no body could be found. The age of the monument, only a third that of Bronze Age barrows, was here held to be insufficient for complete disappearance of all visible traces. Yet conditions were far more acid[Z1] and the evidence may well serve as a useful marker, underlining the possibility of faster rates of decay.

Until we find a medieval burial next to a Bronze Age one in this kind of soil we shall not be able to tell—and even then any climatic change during the interval would entail further difficulties. One must reach into the other evidence for help, yet is prevented by the conditions themselves. An analysis of the pollen from the buried pre-barrow surface would tell us, by recreating the vegetation, all we want to know about conditions at the time of barrow building; but pollen analysis is usually not worth trying on soil in these circumstances unless its pH is below about 5·5—otherwise pollen appears hardly ever to be preserved. Luckily, evidence from mollusca (only preserved in non-acid soil) can often be complementary.

Even taking the bony evidence on its own, we are now in a better position than we would have been without Bishops Waltham. For instance at Litton Cheney,[W2] where a Bronze Age burial had been perfectly preserved under one barrow (pH 7·4), and a probably medieval one similarly in a ditch (pH 7·3), we can say more firmly that a third one should have been preserved too, under another "barrow" (pH 6·7–7·4), had it ever existed. But there was no trace of it; on this and other scientific evidence it seemed sensible to demote that other barrow to a relatively modern spoil heap of gravel diggers.

Despite some pH values below 7, the influence of the Chalk was in general accepted as strong enough here to prevent dissolution of bone. At Bishops Waltham we were in clayey sand. What happens when, as at Row Down in Berkshire,[R3] we have a "barrow" reputedly sitting on the Chalk but on excavation it is shown actually to be on a little mound of clay and flint gravel capping, of (at least largely) natural origin, and with a pH of 5·0–5·8?

The situation was again complicated in various ways, including Roman potsherds and a robber pit where one would have expected a burial; in the end the supervisor decided to regard as Roman or later everything except a small section which he thought might be prehistoric. But he has no evidence for such a claim which must be judged solely by any scientific data the soil might provide.

There is some point, here, in looking for pollen; unfortunately there was no clear buried surface. Pollen, though present, was deficient in tree species. The slight but definite difference in vegetation it suggested, as between the known Roman and suspected prehistoric levels, could therefore not be made significant enough to allow a firm decision. It was a good example of the borderline: the evidence proved to be just insufficient. All the same, any burial in the "prehistoric" levels might well have disappeared without necessarily leaving any visible traces whatsoever.

Not far away, another more reputable barrow was dug by the same excavator at Farncombe Down.[R2] Again, no burial could be found. The immediate surface of the Chalk was once more complicated by spreads of clay. Here, however, this clay was found to be calcareous, and even the (clear) buried surface was full of shells—which were thus made to provide the vegetational picture instead of pollen. Wherever a body had been buried here, within the area of the excavation, the bones would most decidedly have been there still. Animal bones were, in fact, found in the buried surface, and even a human bone higher up in the mound (though this probably belonged to a later period)—all of them in good condition.

TABLE 4

Preservation of bone buried under barrows

From own experience, only, except where directly cognate; some modern figures[H16] *for comparison. Normal British conditions)*

Subsoil	*Ambient medium*	pH (*average*)	*Present vegetation*	*Moisture status*	*Preservation of unburnt bone*	*Cremation found*	*Period*	*Site*	*County*	*Salts*
Chalk	chalky		grass	med.	perfect	yes	Bronze Age	Arreton Down	Isle of Wight	
Chalk	chalky	7·8	arable	low med.	perfect	no	Bronze Age	Amesbury	Wilts.	
Chalk	chalky		arable	low med.	perfect	no	Neolithic	Earlswood	Wilts.	
Chalk	chalky		grass	med.	perfect	no	Bronze Age	Wilsford	Wilts.	
Chalk	clayey gravel	1. 7·4	grass	med.	perfect	yes	Bronze Age	}		
		2. 7·2 (3.)	grass	med.	none	no	presumed modern spoil heaps	} Litton Cheney	Dorset	
		4. 6·4	grass	med.	perfect	no	med.	}		
Chalk	clay		grass	med.	none	no	Bronze Age	Farncombe Down	Berks.	
Chalk	gravel	5·6	grass	med.	none	no	Roman and ?prehistoric	Row Down	Berks.	
*Chalk		8·4						Gog-Magog Hills	Cambs.	sulphate and carbonate high
Limestone	sand		grass	low	none	no	Bronze Age	Stroxton	Lincs.	
Limestone	clay	8	arable	high med.	good	yes	Neolithic	Seamer Moor	Yorks.	
*Clay		8						Rudston	Yorks.	carbonate high

Clay-with-Flints on Chalk	clay	5	arable	med.	none	yes	Bronze Age	Overton Down	Wilts.	
Sandy clay		6·8	grass	med.	silhouette	yes	Bronze Age	Bishops Waltham	Hants.	
*Sandy loam		6·3						Armthorpe	Yorks.	traces of salts only
Shaley slate	sand		grass	med.	none	yes	Bronze Age	St. Eval	Cornwall	
Shaley sandstone	sand	4·5	grass and bracken	high med.	none	yes	Bronze Age	Liskey	Cornwall	
Sandstone	sand		grass and arable	med.	none	yes	Bronze Age	Puncknowle	Dorset	
Sandstone	clay		grass and arable	high med.	none	yes	Bronze Age	Carvinack	Cornwall	
Siliceous grit	peaty clayey sand	4·1	grass	med.	none	yes	Bronze Age	Otterham	Cornwall	
Sand		5·4	grass	low	? silhouette	yes	Bronze Age	Little Ouseburn	Yorks.	
Sand			heath	low	none	yes	Bronze Age	Brightwell Heath	Suffolk	
*Sand		6·6						Durness	Sutherland	chloride high
Sand and gravel	sand	2. 4·6	grass	low	none	yes	Bronze Age	Swarkeston	Derbys.	
Sand and gravel	sand		grass	low	none	yes	Bronze Age	Swarkeston	Derbys.	
Gravel	gravel	4. 4·5	heather and bracken	med.	none	no	Bronze Age	Portesham	Dorset	

The existence of a basic relationship between type of soil, pH, vegetation and the fate of bone is clear enough. Its precise nature is not so easily defined. In an even more general sense, I have already dealt with some of the details in Chapter Six. The application to the present problem is shown along with the other information in Table 4. There is always a direct connection. In many cases there appears to be a strong mutual influence, almost a vicious cycle, involving the various factors (p. 154).

An important conclusion emerges. If the individual turves at the core of a barrow show the characteristic podzolic banding, then no bone is likely to have survived at all. If conditions have remained unchanged, the present vegetation is a good guide even before digging starts—for example, supervisors should not expect bones under heather.

Such over-simplification could be misleading. Throughout, this discussion has revolved only around unburnt bone (p. 133). Normally, burnt bone appears to be resistant to decay even where unburnt bone is dissolved away. Bishops Waltham provided a fine illustration in that the silhouette actually overlay, in the same coffin, a cremation that had materially remained quite well preserved.

All the same, the simplified statement provides a useful working basis. It has two principal corollaries: any bone that *is* found must be recent; also, there can be no chalk, limestone or other calcium-saturated subsoil near enough to influence the situation. Thus at Litton Cheney,[W2] although the pH was as suitable in places as at Bishops Waltham, the effect of the Chalk remained dominant and bone was not destroyed. "Near enough" merits a closer limit than I can give it now, but at Portesham[T7] (p. 151) the Chalk was exposed a matter of yards away, horizontally—supporting in significant contrast a typical lush grass—yet it had been quite unable to this day to affect the exceedingly severe conditions either on the gravel or on the barrow itself.

But where it is dominant its effect is plain. A turf mound under such conditions usually also shows a clear banded structure, though here it is due to the contrast between the alternate dark humus residue and off-white clayey chalk layer of which each turf consists.[R1, R2] But the "lime" in control both prevents the pH from dropping, and at the same time encourages the growth of vegetation which does not produce an excess of substances that move iron downwards and away from the surface.

In between these two extremes—broadly speaking, heathland and the Chalk downs—there seems to be an almost continuous gradation of conditions. As always there are the exceptions; some are inexplicable, others for the present remain obscure and therefore intriguing. But in the main almost all sections of my interest in such phenomena have fitted into this general pattern.

In the establishment of the pattern Bishops Waltham[A13] played an important part. But several features about the excavation were also responsible, directly or indirectly, for other advances made in the Laboratory. The precarious condition of the pottery fragments led to the development of *A new impregnating chamber*.[B13] The condition of the two bronze daggers—reduced almost entirely to tin oxide stained copper-green, yet retaining their shape to a remarkable degree—provided valuable evidence of the fate of bronze.

As might be expected this reflects conditions in the same way as the fate of bone, preservation in chalk being invariably much better and often remarkable, although some corrosion almost always occurs. The shaped dark stains visible to the excavator in the soil, where one would have expected the handles, have stimulated attempts to characterize and develop such silhouettes also, and even to determine the original material. Handles are known from better-preserved examples to have been made of horn, bone, wood and antler.

But probably the most exciting find at Bishops Waltham, from the scientific point of view, was made in a sample of the material found to occupy the position of the coffin bottom. Most of this had presumably been wood at the time of burial. Although vestiges of shadow structure remain it is not possible to confirm this botanically or even to say definitely that the material was of vegetable origin. Some vegetable debris was indeed present but it was so well preserved that it must have been recent, possibly from roots (p. 106).

Among the upper layers of that "structure", however, there was a great number of microscopic bodies which could be identified with some certainty. In Plate 23 a few are shown together with some near modern counterparts, the teleutospores of *Puccinia graminis*. In other words, they would appear to be a certain type of spore, namely that which is in action during the late summer and early autumn, produced by a cereal rust fungus.

Such spores are of course carried by the wind. From its quantity and position, however, interleaved as it was between remnants of what had once probably been vegetable tissue, this material was taken to have been introduced into the coffin while attached to leaves or stalks of some plant, with which the bottom of the coffin had evidently been lined to receive the cremation. This concept of deliberate preparation was reinforced by the presence of a thin layer of finely divided charcoal between leaves and coffin bottom.

What a wealth of circumstantial information! Some four thousand years ago, already, cereal rust may have been active in much the same way as today. Such rusts can live on wild grasses, but we may be nearer the truth if we imagine a cereal plant being collected and spread on the bottom of the coffin, in the late summer or early autumn. We feel a fleeting wave of annoyance that the evidence should give us the season so precisely and the year not at all. And yet, though perhaps basically a nutritional effect, the size of the teleutospores as of flax ultimates (p. 122) may in due course provide some sort of time scale, at least for agricultural development.

At the same time, the opposite set of conditions and states of preservation due to waterlogging had been providing complementary experience (Chapter Six). Another site in York[W10A] produced a crop similar to that from Hungate (col. pl. 11); the corrosion products on a "bronze" needle included minerals of the same tennantite–tetrahedrite type which has been studied as possible "ores" (p. 221). Here, also, various intermediate states have been observed. In York again, ironically enough, yet another site proved at first rather disappointing.

In excavations which revealed part of the South Corner Tower of the Roman defences[S24] conditions were met that were in many ways similar to those at Hungate. The waterlogging was there, and the depth, with a vengeance. Much organic material was found in a good state of preservation, including a series of early medieval shoes and much botanical residue of all kinds. Yet what little ironwork there was had been badly preserved. A solitary brass stud was in excellent condition; most of the few lead pieces seemed to have been buried in an anaerobic medium, but they had corroded, to some extent, however gently.

Two features about site conditions here seem important. Although in the main they conformed quite well, showing vivianite and black and grey colours, the iron objects also carried areas of ordinary rust. Also the pH was on the alkaline side throughout (7·9–8·2).

Such conditions might perhaps be due to a fair degree of aeration in the groundwaters carrying some components of the underlying Magnesian Limestone in solution. They might indicate that waterlogging was intermittent, or occurred some time after the burial of the ironwork—and again, possibly the iron was already rusted when it came to be buried (p. 148). There are no comparative pieces here by which we might tell.

But all else apart, polyphenolic compounds would be less effective in protecting iron both in a slightly aerated and in a somewhat alkaline environment, as they are fairly rapidly altered, though differently, by either condition. Sulphate-reducing bacteria were present, and in most cases active to some extent, in the soil samples that were analysed. We may well have to reckon with a similar, if more abrupt, gradation here as in aerobic media.

All the same, there is no mistaking a thoroughly and continuously waterlogged site. When we heard of the Roman well at Chew[R7] (p. 144) we knew what to expect and to look for. The tremendous variety of problems and quantity of material strained our resources well beyond their limits, particularly in the matter of specialist goodwill. But I felt, as never before or since, that here was a magnificent chance and challenge. We simply had to regard the strain as something that would ultimately enlarge our scope, and hope for the best.

In the event I believe we were amply justified and rewarded beyond all expectation. The site presented us in effect with a microcosm of an entire valley, being a fairly far-flung complex

TABLE 5

Organization schedules for material from Chew Valley Lake complex

(Copy of field programme, 1954; × = material present)

(*A*) *All sites*

	Chew Park	*Herriotts Bridge*	*Nunnery Moat*	*Ben Bridge*	*Barrow Mead*	*Moreton*	*Stratford Mill*
TREATMENT AND EXAMINATION							
Metals							
Copper	×	—	×	—	×	×	×
Iron	×	×	×	×	—	×	×
Lead	×	×	×	×	—	×	
Pottery	×	×	×	×			
Wood	×	×					
Leather	×						
Rope	×						
Shale	×	×					
SPECIALIST INVESTIGATION							
Slag							
Iron	×	×	×	×	—	×	
Lead	×	×	×	×			
Coal	×	×	—	×			
Soil	×	×	×	×			
Whetstones	×	×	×	×	×	×	
Animal bones	×	×	×	×	—	×	×
Charcoal	×	×	×	×	—	×	
Burnt clay	×	×	×	×	—	×	×
Stones	×	×	×	×	—	×	
Mortar, etc.	×	—	×	×	—	×	

(*B*) *Chew Park Villa*
(Breakdown)

Area	1 *Villa*	2 *Hearths*	3 *Postholes*	4 *Furnace*	5 *Well*	6 *KILNS* *Rom.*	7 *Med. I*	8 *Med. II*	9 *CORN* *drier*	10 *grinder*	11 *Ditches*
FINDS											
Iron	×	—	—	—	×	—	—	—	—	—	×
Copper, etc.	×	—	—	—	×	—	—	—	—	—	×
Lead (-base)	×	—	—	—	×	—	—	—	—	—	×
Pottery	×	—	—	—	×	—	—	—	—	—	×
Wood	—	—	—	—	×	×					
Leather	—	—	—	—	×						
Rope	—	—	—	—	×						
Shale	×	—	—	—	×						
Bone	×	—	—	—	×						
Glass	×	—	—	—	×						
INVESTIGATIONS											
Wood	—	—	—	—	×	×					
Charcoal	×	×	×	×	×	×	×	×	×	×	×
Seeds, fruit, etc.	×	—	—	—	×	—	—	—	×	—	×
Shells	×	—	—	—	×	—	—	—	×	—	×
Archaeomagnetic	—	?	—	?	—	×	×	×	?		
Mortar	×										
Lime	—	—	—	—	—	×	×	×			
Stone	×	×	—	—	×	×	×	×	×	×	×
Water	—	—	—	—	×						
Soil	×	×	×	×	×	×	×	×	—	—	×
Bones, etc.	×	—	—	—	×	—	—	—	—	—	×
Burnt clay	×	×	—	×	×	×	×	×	—	—	×
Slags	×	—	—	×	×						

with a wide range of material, period and condition. Had there been time enough, a great deal more could have been done. The work is not complete yet, and its scientific repercussions will continue to be felt for a long time.

The highlights were described in Chapter Six. My working charts, shown in table 5, give a purely qualitative impression of the variety. The excavators' chart of material from the well (table 6) shows how much was found there alone. Chew is indeed still giving us a good opportunity to test many aspects of our general approach and to learn an apparently infinite number of fascinating new things.

The last lap of the interpreter's progress brings him, albeit gradually, not only abreast of work in progress but even in advance of it. Clearly it is in the long run even more economical in every respect to plan ahead for a particular problem.

As part of the complex operations recently carried out at Stonehenge,[B2] where everything had to be worked out to fine tolerances and planned to the minute, I was asked to arrange for a preliminary examination of one of the fallen stones which were to be re-erected. Might it be too badly cracked as a result of its fall? Some major clefts were actually visible to the unaided eye but it was not clear how deep they were, nor whether they might affect the strength of the stone.

Owing to the gigantic dimensions of the specimen—the shortest side is some five feet long—it looked at first as though it would be impossible to do what was required. The most likely instruments, ultrasonic flaw detectors of the type used on concrete, did indeed fail to produce any results. Although the (siliceous) material of the stone was not in itself nearly as opaque to X-rays as, for example, limestone would have been, normal radiography was clearly out of the question.

But it so happened that a certain radioisotope, extremely useful for just such a purpose, had lately been used in the United States for the first time with some success. My request to Harwell was therefore taken up with considerable interest. They were in fact eager to try out sodium-24 on something worthy of its power.[H15]

The examination had to be made at short notice, within a

limited time, and in the face of various other difficulties. The time factor was decided both by the progress of the general operations and by the rapidity with which the radioactive source decayed. The other main anxiety concerned the radiation hazard during the examination which had to be continued for two nights and a day.

Had there been time to carry out preliminary tests, or even to repeat the procedure after the first exposure had been made, better results could probably have been obtained in certain respects. As it was, the hazard area was roped off after the surroundings of the stone had been excavated, by both archaeologists and engineers; the specially irradiated source was rushed from Harwell to Stonehenge and put under the stone, which carried the films stuck down to the top of it. A continuous watch was kept on the area to prevent any unauthorized entrants from coming to harm. That was about all.

Much has been, and more could be, made of the various ironic contrasts involved—between the ancient methods and the present work; between the shaving stick of a source and its tremendous power even at a range of yards; between the sizes of the stone, the source and the barrel full of lead in which it had to be handled throughout; between the innocuous washing soda of the source material and the deadly crystals into which it was transformed in the Harwell pile; and finally, between the amount of trouble taken, and the purpose and the result.

The purpose as such is irrelevant here, but I have briefly discussed the general principles which are, of course, basic to all this work (pp. 17, 41). The result was very useful to the architect responsible. It helped to set his mind at rest on a matter that required a far-reaching decision in the full glare of nation-wide publicity and involved a series of operations for which there was in a modern sense really no precedent. Widely reported at the time, the result seemed to indicate that there were no major cracks in the plane in which they might have been dangerous.

The small proportion of gamma rays which got through the stone, and blackened the film, produced a picture that was just definite enough to show that they had met much the same resistance in all the directions investigated—in other words, that there

TABL

Chew Par

Depth, feet	Freestone	Gravel	Lias blocks	Lias lumps	Lias scraps	Pennant	New Red Sandst. blocks	New Red Sandst. lumps	Conglomerate	Tufa	Bones	Wood—twigs and branches	Oyster-shells	Whelks	Snails	Cherry-stones	Plum-stones	Leather scraps	Soles or part-soles	Charcoal	Bucket eyes	Bucket handles
1				Soil	only																	
2	2	3	35			10					5											
3, 4 } 4	4	3	15		6	7		3			2											
5, 6 } 6		5	19	26	30	8					4											
7		6	6	12	34	5					20											
8, 9 } 9			6	11	32	4					20											
10			10	20	12	2		2			22											
11		4	3	33	8	5	1				400											
12			8	26	28	16		3			250											
13			4	43	22	10	1				100											
14		7	4	45	50	16		2			30									Major Quantity Throughout		
15			8	27	28	20					39	2						6				
16			3	20	60	40			2		15	15					1	50	2			
17			5	30	20	8					20	60			6			100	2			
18	R.C.1		4	20	30	20		1			1	83			11		1	50	2			
19			1	20	45	30					10	100			5			12	1			
20		3	1	30	100	40	27				25	100	5			1		50	6			
21			3	30	36	20		12			20	90	6	2				20				
22			3	22	200	12		25			12	200	4		20			30	4		1	1
23		1	18	15	100	18	4	3			10	100	8		1			4			1	
24			24	35	200	25		17			16	200					1	6			2	2
25			6	34	30	12		2			10	120									2	
26			3	12	90	22	2	2			20	150			2	7					2	
27			8	23	200	21	10	18		3	26	200	8	1	10	6	2	6				1
28			4	20	200	6			25	1	20	100	3			20	1	6	1			
29			7	25	250	10		6			7	250	4		4			4			1	1
30		1		19	600	5		4		1		200									1	
Total	7	33	208	598	2,411	391	45	90	27	5	1,104	1,970	38	3	59	34	6	344	18		10	5

Vell 1954

Cut-wood	*Bucket-hoops*	*Pot-lids*	*Rope*	*Pottery sherds*	*Whole vessels of pot or metal*	*Coins*	*Glass*	*Nails*	*Hazel-nuts*	*Beans*	*Horn-cores*	*Miscellaneous (see pls. 20, 21, 24 & col. pl. II)*	*Bucket nos.*
													—
													1–9
				2				2					}10–25
				5							9		}26–37
											1		38–43
													}44–50
													51–63
				1									64–77
													78–88
				8									89–100
				80									101–108
1 Fork		9		150	1 Olla							Bracelet, Bronze Ring	109–115
		1		70			Counter					Bone Bracelet, Iron Axe-head Whetstone	116–124
				100					1				125–130
1		2		25					6			1 Flint	131–147
		1		120					15		1	Comb Bronze Ring	148–179
1+1 Board				360	Pewter Jug		1	2	10			2 Combs, Pot Disc, 1 Piece Lead, ½ Whetstone	180–222
1+1				30				2	2	1		1 Comb, Counter	223–241
				100				2	17			Bronze Ring	242–262
6				40	Copper Jug				1		1		Rest marked by feet
7	1			160					20			Counter, Knife, Black Pebble	
8			2	122					6			Rope, 2 Bone Pins, Lead Plug	
12				96		1			6	3		Tablet (25 ft.)	
				166		3	1	2	10	3		Iron Ring	
6		1		17		1	2	2			1	2 Bone Pins, Bronze Plate	
				17					6			Iron Gouge, Loop, 2 Bone Pins, 1 Penann. Brooch (Iron)	
10	1							3	1			Flint, Pebble, Fungus	
54	2	14	2	1,669		5	4	17	102	7	13		

P. A. Rahtz & E. Greenfield

were no large gaps along which they could proceed unhindered. We must remember, however, that any uniform cracks in a plane at right angles to the gamma rays could not have been detected; nor was it possible to test more than a fairly small, if seemingly representative, portion of the stone.

The scientists from Harwell were quite satisfied, from their own point of view, and shortly after described the details at an international meeting concerned with non-destructive testing of materials. The test had added to the general experience of technique. One of the back-handed conclusions was that the particular type of stone could provide an effective screen even to such high-energy radiation!

Finally we reach the stage where the interpreter is well ahead of events, and on a large scale. Road development at Waternewton, near Peterborough, was about to cut across a stretch of country where Roman remains were known to exist, in great density over certain parts, but without precise details about locations within the actual development area. It was suspected that pottery kilns, always extremely valuable evidence (p. 45), were buried in the area and the primary objective was to locate and excavate these. The organization of the tremendous task from the archaeological point of view is described elsewhere.[W7]

As the stretch was some two miles long by two hundred feet wide, and resources and time were severely limited, some method of selection was clearly required. At a lecture some six months before excavations were due to begin, J. C. Belshé had described the use of a sensitive magnetometer in studying the physical processes which accompanied the firing of an experimental pottery kiln, built on the Roman model. The experience encouraged the hope that such an instrument could now be used in the field. It meant, in effect, that it was possible to go prospecting for fired structures buried down to a depth of six feet or more.

Graham Webster, who was organizing the excavations, was present at the lecture and seized on the idea. Aerial photographs by J. K. S. St. Joseph of some of the area were already available. It was hoped to provide the excavators, before they started, with a complete picture of where they should dig.

This ideal was not attained, but as a first exercise of such concerted scientific effort on a large scale the attempt was a landmark. In the general approach to the problem early and as a whole, it fully accepted the need for a tightly co-ordinated scientific reconnaissance. The Ministry's Land Survey Section mapped out the entire area in a fifty-foot grid. A recently developed commercial field magnetometer was borrowed by Cambridge University from Germany and operated on the site by Birmingham University. A specially adapted transistorized magnetometer was built and used by Oxford University, following a design pioneered at the Signals Research and Development Establishment, Christchurch. The Ministry's Engineering Test Branch, with some archaeological prospecting behind them, further modified and doubled their electrical resistivity equipment for use on the long straight runs.

The diggers profited in two ways. To some extent before they began, and more fully while they were at work, it was possible to indicate where digging was likely to be fruitless. Test holes sunk in such areas invariably confirmed these suggestions, and the whole section could be safely abandoned as most probably barren from the archaeological point of view. Large stretches were fairly quickly disposed of in this way.

On the other hand, certain definite features were picked up. Some were clearly of a geological nature, others represented human utilization of such "geological anomalies", in the shape of clay pits or stone quarries. Several kilns were actually found, and mostly excavated with very useful results. But all of them were outside the surveyed area, if only just, and all except one were discovered by the road workers along the stretch just behind the survey. The odd one was located by the Oxford magnetometer; cautious preliminary tests[A2] have indicated that in all probability a kiln lies buried there, but as it is not threatened by road (or indeed other) development no excavation is contemplated.

There was another feature of great interest. In the middle of a field inside the road area, the air photograph had indicated a crop mark running straight across. As part of the survey this field was covered by both the Ministry's electrical resistivity team and the Oxford magnetometer. Contours of anomalies obtained by both methods were plotted, and when superimposed they coincided not only with each other but also with a projection of the aerial crop mark.

One might be tempted, at first sight, to minimize the importance I have attached to this result. There are some discrepancies between the electrical and magnetic contours. The aerial projection is not quite in the same place as the others. Anyway, general agreement is after all only what one would have expected. But such comments can be answered quite simply.

There is a fundamental difference between the electrical and magnetic methods. Although both will show up deviations from the normal, only the former will also clearly discriminate between (denser, drier) masonry walls or banks and (looser, wetter fillings of) ditches or pits. The other method will therefore show all disturbances in terms of only one kind of anomaly, and results must look different in the transitional zones (p. 208).

As for the projection of the aerial crop mark, it cannot from an oblique photograph be much more accurate than shown. Yet the overall correspondence is very close, and the first practical demonstration has a fundamental value far beyond its immediate return. In addition, the proton magnetometer had clearly had a field day and shown considerable prowess at picking out ditches and pits. Spectacular results have since been reported from other sites.[A2 (b2 and 3), A3, A4]

At Waternewton, all that remained was to dig. Unfortunately the field was drilled immediately after the survey and had to be harvested before excavation. Subsequently, the area became waterlogged and last-minute digging could only suggest part of a ditch-and-bank enclosure before it was swallowed up in the road works.

The interpreter has now arrived. He begins to feel more of a grasp of the situation, knowing to some extent both what is about to be done and what he should expect from it, materially speaking. Out of the thinking and connecting has grown a general scheme, diagrammatically shown in Figure 7. On to this framework are woven together all the threads from the meticulous attention to detail which I have been describing. In this way there emerges as a matter of routine, for each individual excavation as well as on a

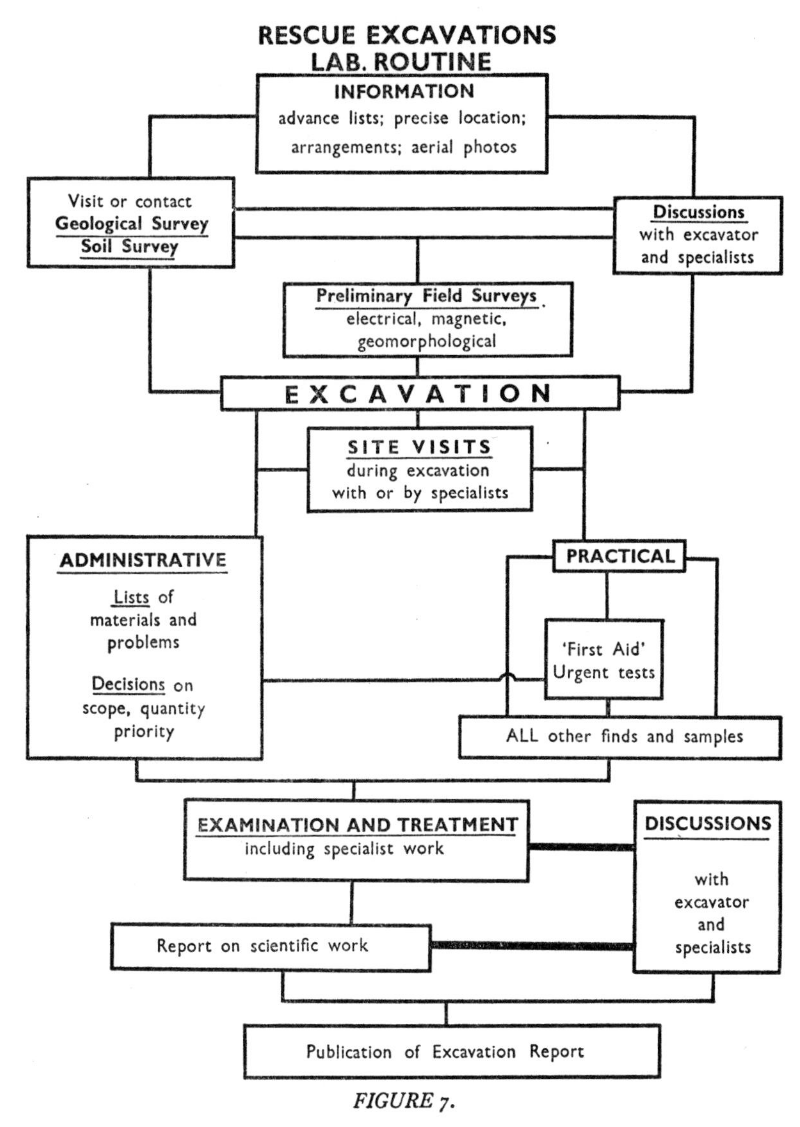

FIGURE 7.

wider scale, a pattern from the scientific interpretation of the totality of evidence.

As a result the interpreter can deal more easily and quickly with the new problems which constantly arise. He can give better service to the archaeologist direct. He becomes more likely all the time to provide the scientific specialists with the kind of material and information that they really want. They in turn are then more interested to participate in archaeological work which thereby benefits immensely and immediately.

The conservation of antiquities has been compared often enough to medicine. The patient in need of treatment (particularly when overdue), diagnosis and cure, routine examination and specialist consultation, prevention and research—all these concepts are directly applicable. Bronze disease and tin pest speak for themselves.

In such terms the interpreter is a G.P. He can often deal straightaway with the ordinary complaint. If he cannot he should know the appropriate specialists, and they should know him. For they get many of their interesting cases for study and research from him. But it is he who sees the cases through from the start—even anticipating and preparing for their arrival—until they have come to be known and understood and cared for to the best of our present ability, and he is responsible for arranging that they should continue to be well looked after.

There are the obvious differences. The objects are not alive in the most immediate sense. Yet they have all led a very varied existence; this insistently reflects in part the true life of previous ages, and in part the sub-animate metabolism of the soil which among other things nourishes that life.

To the extent that they are not alive, though, they also have a kind of relative immortality; not so the features in the field. Here discovery and study, especially in rescue excavations, involve rapid and certain destruction. Conservation simply does not enter into this picture and the detective aspect of the interpreter's approach becomes dominant. The watchdog turns tracker. To be effective he must be, in the material sense, ahead not only of the excavation but also of the excavator. No scent, old or new, should escape him, because once exposed it does not remain for long and then has gone for good.

Every G.P. inevitably has some limited area of particular interest. When I started, a certain problem thrust itself at me, not only through bitter experience but also by being nearest to what I knew (table 8.2).

In the standard museum method for cleaning sound bronze objects, direct electric current is passed through dilute caustic soda solution from a steel plate to the object, which is normally the cathode (negative).[F4, P9] One might expect to finish with something very slightly smaller but otherwise like the original. Instead a rough and pitted surface usually appears on the remaining metal, coloured a more or less smoky dull grey-black.

Most of this dark film consists of metallic iron. Although highly unlikely, the phenomenon was shown to be real enough by a close study of our electrolytic bath. My search for technical advice brought only mild interest and slight incredulity.

There was nothing for it but to find out for myself.[B17] From the practical standpoint the effect is most obnoxious. A group of articles can be left for reduction unattended in the bath; twenty will take no longer than one. But each then requires a period of individual, tedious and continuous, manual attention to remove by brushing a deposit very largely put there by the very cleaning process itself.

The process, though grossly inefficient, continues to be widely used because it remains the simplest way of cleaning bronzes nevertheless. But with the vast number of objects now coming out of excavations improvement is clearly needed, especially as the steel plate furs up into the bargain, so that in time the bath is running at about one per cent efficiency anyway.

Fundamentally, the reactions between iron and oxygen in alkaline solution have been left well alone because they are among the most complex of their kind. But at least one can see the entire process here, instead of having—as normally in our work—some of the products only. Applying the same type of principle as I have been illustrating throughout, I have tried to separate the various interconnected factors which seemed important.

It seems that under our conditions the steel is unable to stand the strain and gives up a steady, if slow, stream of charged iron particles (ions) to the solution. Although not normally capable of taking up such ions in a simple or big way, the caustic soda appears to carry enough, in a more complex form—and in the wrong direction. Caught in the blanket of hydrogen formed around the object, they are reduced along with it.

As a result, iron is actually moved in plain dilute alkali significantly from positive to negative electrode and deposited there. At the same time the (positive) steel itself is filmed over by the oxygen evolved there; the skin grows and slows down the whole process until it has ceased altogether. Both statements will make every good electrochemist's hair stand on end.

For a certain range of current density there must be fierce competition at the steel surface—between the chemical and physical effects of the oxygen bubbles: between film formation and disruption. But at a certain stage film rupture is predominant, and then the bath works best; though clearly, if unfortunately, the greatest efficiency thus coincides with maximum iron deposition.

Most similar and otherwise suitable materials seem to behave in much the same way; it is thus not merely a matter of using another electrode material. Also there is usually enough iron in the caustic soda and the corroded bronzes to produce a sufficiently serious effect alone. The answer is, of course, to trap the iron in the liquid and prevent it from ever reaching the metallic surface of the object.

But this is a difficult business; for a start, iron is supposed to be insoluble for all practical purposes in the very caustic soda in which it swims about so freely. Complexing and sequestering agents only smooth out both the process and the deposit. The use of platinized titanium in place of steel, though expensive, seems successful and removes the principal source of iron. But the trapping problem remains.

When this work is complete it should become possible simply to put a whole basketful of corroded bronzes into the bath, to transfer this basket after reduction straight into a rinsing chamber, a washing bath, a drying chamber, a resin bath and a final drying chamber without any individual attention. The objects would then go in at one end as found, and come out clean and protected at the other—literally untouched by hand.

Every interpreter must have some such speciality which absorbs his interest and energy to an extent where he feels that he has added something to the general fund of knowledge, on his own as far as is possible nowadays. Without this feeling, I believe, his general position would not be tenable for very long. There simply must be something, however slight, about which he knows more than anyone else.

In some measure this is of course true of us all, but perhaps it applies with particular stress to the interpreter. He has to acquire in some respects the qualities of a hard-rubber covered ball so as not to be crushed by the astronomical pressures of knowledge developed in that ball-mill of specialisms in which he is constantly ground.

If he manages to grow a thick enough skin of his own little specialism, he can learn to resist the otherwise flattening thrusts that bear in on him how extremely little, after all his efforts, he actually knows. Only then can he really accept, as he must, that scientific research for archaeology is carried out at scientific research institutions. All the interpreter can hope for is to get to know the specialists, their requirements and facilities, and to supply them with suitable material. But the actual research can be done only by them. My final chapter is a brief outline, I hope both palatable and nourishing, of the various types of work and method which are currently being developed.

CHAPTER EIGHT

Scientific Research for Archaeology—Consolidation

THE NEED for permanent co-operation between archaeologists and scientists can be seen to be vital and urgent for both. As outlined in the Introduction and then self-modelling throughout, such a concept is clearly bound to have wider connotations, and they will reflect into it any developments which they may undergo. There is thus a dynamic equilibrium involving mutual encouragement reactions of the sort today most familiar from the plutonium self-feeding reactor. But I am here concerned solely with the narrower aspects of our particular field.

All along there are two principal types of activity, with intermediate stages well represented as usual. There is the inclusion in a research project, be it humble or ambitious, of some specifically archaeological theme—such as the development or variability of certain anatomical features in man over a given period, or the study of land surfaces buried under barrows from the pedological or botanical point of view. These researches, carried out in Faculties of Science, are the most valuable and inevitably also the rarest so far.

At the other end—as it can only be part-time—is the collection of data from archaeological excavations. Thus a research worker in some particular scientific field will over the years take an interest in evidence that is of the same generic type as his subject, even though it may not be directly relevant to his own study. He is not paid to study archaeological material and his efforts must needs be intermittent, however keen he may personally be, and however much indirect benefit he and his subject may ultimately derive from his extra-mural activities.

Such work, while in itself extremely valuable and luckily somewhat more frequent, cannot but suffer from a lack of continuity and tradition. All the same, it is to such efforts that we owe the present rapid development of archaeomagnetic dating services in Britain (p. 230) and some detailed studies in the anatomy and histology of certain animals (p. 247).

In between, many varieties of activity and usefulness may be found. Workers at either end, while having temporarily (or even perhaps altogether) left the archaeological aspect out of their practical work, can remain valuable advisers for a long time. Certain discoveries may be made in a branch of a scientific study not hitherto archaeologically minded or connected; such advisers or their colleagues may spot an obvious application, and this may lead to specialized development in both directions, scientific and archaeological.

Throughout, such distinctions of form have here been disregarded, but they are clearly responsible for the large amount of unevenness which exists in scope, depth, facilities and manpower between the different kinds of scientific research for archaeology. An analysis of such factors from a complementary point of view was made in Chapter 4 (p. 84). There, as elsewhere in this book, information was implicitly used that is here specifically acknowledged, because the present chapter was inspired by it and by subsequent discussion and work arising more or less directly from it.

In 1953 it had become clear to me, as a result of my experience in this field, that two kinds of potentiality had been imperfectly realized—in all senses of the phrase. On the one hand, digging archaeologists knew far too little about what to do in specific cases, or what had lately become possible as a result of rapidly developing scientific techniques. On the other, archaeologists and scientists in general knew next to nothing of each other or of each other's aims, methods and requirements.

Partly—but only partly—in my selfish quest for more information in every way, I suggested to the Council for British Archaeology that a nation-wide scheme might be operated for archaeologists in general, on the basis of the much smaller model that was then beginning to take shape in the way I have described. A

Scientific Research Committee would be added to the Period Research Committees of the Council and would be responsible for organizing and maintaining a steady flow of material for analysis, generally acting as a clearing-house for ideas that were likely to prove of mutual benefit.

The Council agreed to consider the suggestion in principle, but first the views of prominent scientists active in this field were to be sought at a Conference on *Archaeology in the laboratory*. The proceedings of this Conference, which was held in April, 1954, served also to bring together in an informal and fascinating way accounts of the state of knowledge in the various scientific disciplines which concern themselves directly with archaeological material.

It was, I believe, for all those who attended, a memorable occasion. A private joke which still delights me is the spectacle, repeated several times, of specialist colleagues from different fields who had hitherto only corresponded, or talked over the telephone, meeting here for the first time. A summary of the proceedings appeared in *Nature*.[B11] The Scientific Research Committee was duly set up. It has recently completed the revision of *Notes for the guidance of archaeologists to expert evidence*, a slim pamphlet produced by a less permanent forerunner, the Natural Sciences Panel of the Council, and in many respects inevitably quite out of date.

But the full proceedings of the Conference were never published and, although in some ways common knowledge in their own spheres, such specialist descriptions are here brought together for the first time in a comprehensive manner. For permission to use this material, as well as additions and modifications now necessary and other cognate ideas thrown up during more recent discussion, I am very grateful to my friends and colleagues and to the Council. Where I have felt it necessary to provide some basic introductory remark they have generously vetted it.

Only a brief and superficial account is possible within the framework of this book. For details the abundant specialist literature should be consulted, until the general textbook on this subject appears for which the need was postulated in my Introduction and underlined by what has followed.

In the discussion below I have confined myself to the basic purpose, present situation and any special developments of each type of investigation. Other details are given in Table 7. General remarks made at the Conference have in some cases been incorporated elsewhere (pp. 79, 90) but a brief summary appears at the end of the chapter.

Additional specific information, subsequent or extraneous to the Conference but germane to the subject, is here included in the appropriate place, although a reference to the source is given in the normal manner to distinguish it from Conference material. The latter is followed by the name of the speaker, in any given paragraph. I have throughout observed the "evolutionary sequence" which naturally imposes itself in any such overall consideration, and whose value in establishing the pattern of investigation will by now be abundantly clear (p. 55, figs. 7 and 12, and table 7). For easy reference, various threads of information begun earlier are drawn together here (See also [U1]).

Preliminary Surveys

Especially where a large area has to be excavated in a limited time, some idea of the scope of buried remains and concentration of larger features—more detailed than on aerial photographs—is very valuable to the excavator in planning his work before he starts digging. Nothing may be visible on the surface but any disturbance of the soil and subsoil in antiquity has altered the properties of the affected parts significantly and permanently in certain respects, relative to the general earth mass.

This is made use of in various forms of *geochemical and geophysical survey*. The former is essentially soil analysis (p. 223) on a scale that has hitherto rarely seemed economical; but with recent improvements in aerial crop spraying, sampling and rapid large-scale analysis [B8, N4, R19b] its possibilities should not be ignored.

The "megger" method has already been mentioned (p. 28). The recent refinement by the Ministry's Engineering Test Branch, as used at Waternewton (p. 197) and since, incorporates a battery-operated A.C. instrument [B9, N1] and special switchgear for use with about two dozen electrodes "simultaneously", successive quartets being presented in rotation.

This means that cranking is no longer necessary—one (skilled) operator merely presses a button, turns a knob and records on specially prepared paper the reading shown on a dial, while preferably two (unskilled) others move spacing rods into position along a surveyed grid and shift the electrodes from points at which measurements have been made to others, well in advance of measurement in progress. The continuously recording operator moves from one set of electrodes to the next simply by switching over.

Such a team can advance along a strip fifty feet wide, with their electrodes spaced five feet apart—that is, reading to a depth of five feet—at the rate of about an acre every three hours. The result is a grid of the average electrical resistivity at intervals of five feet. Contours can be drawn and evaluated in the normal manner. Various other refinements are possible. [B9]

Surveys giving substantially similar results in some respects can be carried out also with magnetometric devices. The *transistorized proton resonance magnetometer* built early in 1958 at Oxford [A4] interprets disturbances of soil and subsoil in terms of the consequent anomalous fossilized magnetism which they exhibit. The instrument consists of a polythene bottle—containing distilled water or methyl alcohol and wound with a coil of wire—and a battery-operated electronic circuit carried in a rucksack. Recent developments have reduced the weight of the latter to some four and a half pounds.

With the bottle on a tripod over a given spot, once again the skilled operator presses a button, thereby energizes the coil and makes the hydrogen atoms (i.e. protons) in the water demonstrate the fact that they are the primary magnets. Their behaviour will be affected by anything with magnetic properties between them and the earth's core but in practice, depending on the size of the anomalous feature in the ground, that means down to about twelve feet deep. Once again, contours of anomalies can be drawn.

Magnetometric devices are particularly useful, and were in fact developed, for detecting pottery kilns and other areas of burning where the fossilized magnetism is very strong. This is explained later (p. 230) in its proper context of archaeomagnetic dating where the first work of this nature was carried out. But for some reason, which has not yet been satisfactorily demonstrated,[L3] magnetometers also pick up ditches and pits and other buried disturbances.

The speed of working is of the same order as for the resistivity survey; in favourable circumstances it can be about twice as fast. Although the instrument is simpler to handle it does, of course, record only spot readings, whereas average values are given by the electrical method.

Both types of survey are sensitive to non-archaeological features such as buried telephone lines, water pipes, bedsteads and other scrap iron; the magnetometer is even severely affected by wire fencing around fields, nearby trolley-buses and electric railways, and by traffic on adjacent roads. Although these are likely to remain permanent disabilities, being inherent in the basic principles of the methods, astounding results have been produced in this manner, very rapidly in certain cases.[A3]

In general these techniques are certain to prove of great value wherever they are employed by experienced operators—provided their shortcomings, and the geological character and drainage pattern of the subsoil, are properly taken into account. Many other methods are potentially useful, from mine detectors to sonic prospecting.[B9]

A totally different kind of survey, which has not so far been very prominent in this context—but will, I hope, soon become as much of a routine as the preliminary inspection—is a *geomorphological examination*. Indeed it should go with the preliminary inspection. No instruments are required, only the geological six-inch map (if there is one) for the area and a specialist with considerable field experience, preferably of the region involved. For the study of how given basic earth features produce certain fundamental landscapes, and of how these interact with human activity throughout (after all, archaeological) time, has become a new and most exciting specialism[C10, D14, S22, T9, V6, W18]—I mean that only in its factual sense here: a specialist is required to interpret.

An experienced field worker in this line will be able to suggest to the intending excavator which part of the site would have been more likely to contain springs, and therefore wells, perhaps, even though none may now be marked on the map. He may quickly distinguish between natural and artificial features from his knowledge of landscape building.

He will at once point to areas which for various reasons would have been preferred for settlements proper, or for specific activities such as pottery making or metal smelting. To the extent to which his training has made him capable of seeing the landscape as it was, he will see it also in terms of the needs and desires of the men whose activities we are trying to understand. This sphere of interest he shares with the geologist whose presence is often as valuable early as later (pp. 27, 211).

The next specialist who ought to appear regularly on the scene at this stage is the *ecologist.* He should come in again later on when all the various biological and other natural history identifications are to hand, to tie them up neatly and present the excavator with a compact picture of what life was like there at the time. But it is good for him to see the site now.

Some of the details will suggest certain relationships between vegetation and animals, and between herbivores and predators, which might have applied—and which the excavator might with advantage look out for as they will help to establish his general background. Riverside, moorland and lakeland, as well as marine and heathland sites, are among the most likely to be served usefully in this way. The ecologist can also go on to extrapolate from the geomorphologist's picture.

But at this stage probably the best service the ecologist can render the excavator is to encourage his humility. An archaeologist will—and must, of course—be primarily set on finding human activity. But it will do him good to be reminded that there are many ways of observing life into which man enters not at all—except as observer.

On such a basis it will be easier for him to accept, as again he must, the enormous pressure of environment on early man. He will then be able to understand more fully the very direct relationship which existed, for example, between neolithic man and his sheep, their grazing and his pottery, his climate and birds and weeds and wood-cutting tools and clothing.

Similarly, the excavator should seek and accept the equally modifying evidence of the *soil surveyor*—who must also come and see for himself even before the dig has begun, as of course most certainly afterwards, too. His bias is highly ecological. Often a near-by exposure or preliminary test-hole will provide the required profile, and the excavation may be deeply influenced by his interpretation of it. Soil maps are useful, where they exist,[G17] but confirmation in detail is always required from a soil surveyor.

From this point onwards I have limited myself almost exclusively to details that cannot be fitted into Table 7, either because they are too individual, or because they would remain too obscure in the space there available. Also I have given greater prominence to the simpler methods in constant use at the Ancient Monuments Laboratory, as well as to the newer developments, to the more recent applications—in this field—of scientific techniques, and to methods and aspects that have seemed to me to be somewhat more abstrusely connected than most with the archaeologist's immediate purpose. The hierarchical order of what follows is thus not at all determined by its importance to the archaeologist but rather by its relative unfamiliarity.

Table 7 itself can be no more than a very general survey of the main possibilities (see also Table in [H1]). It is not meant to be comprehensive in all respects but should be seen rather as an attempt to stimulate fresh investigations and a wider comparative outlook. The craftsman's contribution has been stressed in only a few places but is of course implicit in all artefacts, [S9] especially where primitive methods are little changed (see e.g. [C8]). All the appraisals are inevitably biased by my own experience, although I have tried to make the last three columns of indices as strictly comparable as I could.

Aids during and after Excavation

The simplest way in which a *rock* may be completely characterized, where its composition and structure are sufficiently well defined to make this possible, is by a study of a thin section under a microscope by transmitted light. Idiosyncratic combinations of minerals may occur that are as unique, in many cases, as fingerprints. In the normal "slicing" method a thin slip is cut from the specimen right across the longest axis; this is polished on one side,

TA

Comparative analys

Material	*Basis of investigation*	*Main branch of science*	*General types of method used*	*General level of results*	*Use to excavator*	*Present accuracy*	*Normal drawbacks*	*Basic suitability of material*	*Requ in m*
STONES Objects (especially axes, etc.)	Regional character of rocks	Geology	Petrological Palaeonto-logical Physical methods X-ray diffraction X-ray spectro-scopical Optical spectro-scopical	Good	Provenance Trade routes	Very good	Tedious (matching)	Good	Easy
Whetstones	,,	,,	,,	Fair	,,	Fair	,,	Poor	,,
Building stones	,,	,,	,,	Good	,,	Good	,,	Fair	,,
	Weathering Environmental effects	,, *also* Chemistry Physics	,, *also* Proximate analysis	Very good	Interpreta-tion of conditions	Good	Limited experience	Fair	Fairly string (X)
Minerals	(Regional character of rocks) Specific nature	,,	,, *also* Mineralogi-cal	Very good	Provenance Trade routes Skill	Very good	Insufficient evidence Tedious (statistical)	Very good	Easy
COAL	Regional character at outcrop	Geology (Biology) (Chemis-try)	Palaeonto-logical Proximate analysis of coal and ash	Variable	,,	Limited	Very tedious and often unrewarding	Fair	Easy
SOIL	Environmental effects and residues from human activity	Pedology (Biology, ecology) (Chemis-try, physics)	Chemical and physical including micro-methods (preliminary ignition)	Good	"Fossil" soils for "dating" and environ-ment, nature of deposits and residues	Good	Tedious in part	Good	(C) bu (X) al always
BURNT CLAY Incidentally affected, mostly exposed to relatively low heat	Effects of fire on macro- and microstructure	Chemistry Physics	Mineralogi-cal, chemical and physical including X-ray diffrac-tion and radiography	Fair	Type of activity and skill	Fair	Tedious if full ex-amination	Fair	(C)
	Magnetic deviation	Physics	Magneto-metric	Good	Dating	Good	Lack of dated material between A.D. 400 and 1400	Very good	(X) *in situ*
				Very good	Prospecting	Very good	Metal and electrical installations	Very good	(X)
FIRED CLAY Pottery	Regional characteristics of clays Effects of firing on macro- and microstructure	Chemistry Physics	Mineralogi-cal Chemical and physical Optical spectro-scopical Neutron activation (Preliminary ignition)	Fair	Provenance	Fair	Tedious	Fair	Easy
					Skill	Good	Limited experience	Very good	,,
	Magnetic deviation	Physics	Magneto-metric	Limited	Dating	Poor	Limited experience	Poor	Easy

(C) = Field control essential. (S) = Specialist sampling esser

ntific investigations

ments ma-	Serial No. (*see also other investigations*)	*Particular method used in development*	*Dependence on*	*Availability of*	*Prospects for*		*General service for archaeology*	*Index of*		
			standards or comparative material		*method*	*worker*		*Actual value (see fig. 2)*	*Exploitation = actual value × use*	*Development = actual / potential value*
	1 (5, 8, 14, 21, 23)	Petrological: microscopical and field work	Complete	Adequate for most purposes	Fair	Poor	Yes	Medium	Medium	Medium
	2 („)	„	„	Poor	Poor	„	No	„	„	High
	3 („)	„	„	Fair	Limited	„	No	„	„	„
tant	4 (7, 8, 9, 15, 30)	Physico-chemical	Slight	Poor	Improving	„	No	„	Low	„
	5 (8, 11, 14, 21)	Mineralogical microscopical and field work	Strong	Good	Good	Fair	No	„	„	Medium
	6 (1, 8, 32, 33)	Micro-palaeonto-logical Chemical Petrological	Strong	Fair	Limited	Poor	No	„	„	„
nt	7 (4, 8, 30, 39, 54)	Pedological Chemical Physical	Complete	Good	Good	Fair	No	„	„	„
tant	8 (5, 11, 14, 21, 23)	X-radiography	(Complete)	Adequate	Good	Poor	No	„	„	High
	9 (13, 15)	Magneto-metrical and field work	Complete	Improv-ing	Very good	Good	Yes	„	„	Low
	10 (16)	Transistor-ized proton magnetometer	Slight	Adequate	„	„	„	Medium	High	High
	11 (1, 5, 8, 14, 21, 23)	Mineralogical Neutron activation	Complete (proven-ance)	Poor	Good	Improving	No	Low	Low	Low
	12 (14, 21, 23)	Practical potting	Slight (skill)	Adequate	Very good	Very good	No	High	„	Medium
tant	13 (9, 15)	Magneto-metrical	Complete	Improving	Poor	Poor	Yes	Low	„	Low

= Specialist field examination essential.

TAB

Comparative analysi

Material	*Basis of investigation*	*Main branch of science*	*General types of method used*	*General level of results*	*Use to excavator*	*Present accuracy*	*Normal drawbacks*	*Basic suitability of material*	*Requi in m*
Bricks Tiles	Regional characteristics of clays Fired structure	Chemistry Physics	Mineralogical Chemical and physical	Fair	Provenance Skill	Limited	Tedious	Fair	Easy
	Magnetic deviation	Physics	Magnetometric	Limited	Dating	Fairly good	Lack of dated material (A.D. 400–1400)	Poor	(X) *in situ*
				Very good	Prospecting	Very good	Metal and electrical instruments	Very good	(X)
MORTAR, etc.	Local variation of natural grading in aggregate Composition	Chemistry Physics	Chemical and physical Microscopical	Good	Comparison of structures, Skill	Fair	Acid-soluble aggregate, limitation of assumptions (statistics)	Fair	(S) pre
GLASS, etc.	Regional characteristics of constituents Composition Structure	Chemistry Physics	Chemical and physical X-ray spectroscopical Optical spectroscopical Neutron activation Microscopical	Good	Provenance Skill	Limited	Laborious Statistics	Fair	Easy
	Weathering	,,	Microscopical	Seemingly good	Dating	Very good	Limited to certain climatic conditions?	Limited	(X)
PIGMENTS	Regional characteristics Specific nature	Chemistry Physics	Microchemical and physical	Very good	Provenance Skill Use	Very good		Very good	Easy
METALS Extraction (and SLAG) Iron	Regional and smelting characteristics of deposits and aids	Metallurgy (Geology) Chemistry Physics Engineering	Microscopical: X-radiographic Petrographical Metallographical Optical spectroscopical X-ray spectroscopical Neutron activation	Limited	Provenance	Doubtful	Limited experience	Poor	Easy
				Very good	Skill	Very good		Very good	,,
Copper	,,	,,	,,	Very good	Provenance	Good		Good	
					Skill	Very good		Very good	,,
Lead	,,	,,	,,	Fair	Provenance	Good	Limited experience	Poor	,,
					Skill	,,	,,	Fair	,,
Other metals	,,		,,	,,	Provenance	Fair	,,	Fair	,,
					Skill	Good	,,	Good	,,

(C) = Field control essential. (S) = Specialist sampling essen

ntific investigations—*contd.*

...ments ...rma- ...n	Serial No. (*see also other investiga- tions*)	*Particular method used in development*	*Dependence on* standards or comparative material	*Availability of* standards or comparative material	*Prospects for* *method*	*Prospects for* *worker*	*General service for archae- ology*	*Index of* *Actual value (see fig. 2)*	*Index of* *Exploitation = actual value × use*	*Index of* *Development = actual / potential value*
	14 (1, 5, 8, 11, 21, 33)	Mineralogical Practical brickmaking	Complete (proven- ance) Very slight (skill)	Poor	Fair	Poor	No	Medium	Low	Medium
	15 (9, 13)	Magneto- metric	Complete	Improving	Very good	,,	Yes	Low	,,	Low
	16 (10)	Transistor- ized proton magneto- meter	Slight	Adequate	,,	Good	Yes	Medium	Medium	,,
...nt	17 (1, 4, 5, 7)	Chemical Physical Microscopical	,, (for internal comparison)	,,	Fair	Fair	No	,,	Low	High
	18 (1, 5, 21)	Spectroscopical Microscopical Chemical Physical Microprobe	Complete (proven- ance) Very slight (skill)	Poor	Fair	Poor	No	,,	,,	Medium
	19	Microscopical	Slight	Adequate	As yet unknown	?	No	Low	,,	Low
	20 (1, 5, 8, 18, 23, 30)	Microchemical Microprobe	Very slight	Adequate	Very good	Fair	No	High	Medium	High
	21 (1, 5, 8, 11, 13)	Petrographical	Complete	Fair	Limited	Good	Yes	Low	Low	Low
	22 (7, 8, 14, 24, 29)	Chemical Physical X-ray spectroscopical	Slight	Very good	Very good	,,	Yes	High	Medium	High
	23 (as 21)	,, *also* Optical spectroscopical X-ray spectro- scopical	Complete	Fair	Good	,,	No	Medium	Low	Medium
	24 (as 22)	,,	Fair	,,	,,	Fair	No	High	Medium	High
	25 (as 23)	,,	Complete	Poor	Poor	Poor	No	Low	Low	Low
	26 (as 24)	,,	Fair	Fair	Fair	,,	No	,,	,,	Medium
	27 (as 23)	,, *also* Neutron activation	Complete	Improving	Good	,,	No	,,	,,	Low
	28 (as 24)	,,	Fair	Poor	Poor	,,	No	High	,,	High

...= Specialist field examination essential.

TABL

Comparative analysi

Material	*Basis of investigation*	*Main branch of science*	*General types of method used*	*General level of results*	*Use to excavator*	*Present accuracy*	*Normal drawbacks*	*Basic suitability of material*	*Requir in ma*
Fabrication	Effects on macro- and microstructure	Metallurgy (Geology) Chemistry Physics Engineering	Metallographic Chemical and physical	Very good	Technique Skill Use	Very good	Laborious, but improving	Very good	Easy
Corrosion	Environmental effects on macro- and microstructure	„ also Microbiology	Chemical and physical Microscopical X-ray diffraction X-radiographic	Good	Use, nature and fate (environment)	Good		Good	(C) soil (X) pre
WOOD	Anatomy	Botany	Microscopical	Very good	Nature Environment Use	Very good	Tedious	Very good	Easy
		Physics Chemistry	Submicroscopical	Good	Dating	Good	Limited	Good	(Contin waterlo only)
	Decay due to fungi	Botany	Mycological	Good	Environment Fate	Good	Tedious	Good	(S) bu (X) b
	Result of attack by animals	Zoology	Entomological Marine biol.	Good	Environment prior to burial	Good	State of specimen	Good	Fairly stringer
	Natural radioactivity	Physics	Chemical preparation Atomic radiation counting	Good	Dating	Fair (B.C.)	Complex Expensive	Very good	Very stringen
CHARCOAL	Anatomy	Botany	Microscopical	Good	Nature Use	Good	Tedious	Good	Easy
	Natural radioactivity	Physics	Chemical preparation Atomic radiation counting	Good	Dating	Fair (B.C.)	Complex Expensive	Very good	Very stringen
GRAIN, etc	Anatomy	Botany (Ecology)	Microscopical	Very good	Nature Use Environment	Very good	Tedious	Good	Importa
POLLEN	Anatomy	Botany (Ecology)	(Chemical preparation) Microscopical	Very good	Environment, date range, cultivation rating	Very good	Very tedious	Very good	(X)
FIBRES (see also TEXTILE)	Anatomy Composition	Botany Chemistry	Microscopical Chemical and physical	Good	Nature Use	Good	Condition of material	Good	Easy
PAPER	Anatomy Composition	Botany Chemistry	Microchemical Microscopical	Good	Provenance Nature	Good	„	Good	Easy

(C) = Field control essential. (S) = Specialist sampling essent

tific investigations—*contd.*

nts a-	Serial No. (*see also other investiga- tions*)	*Particular method used in development*	*Dependence on* standards or comparative material	*Availability of* standards or comparative material	*Prospects for* method	*Prospects for* worker	*General service for archae- ology*	*Index of* Actual value (*see fig. 2*)	*Index of* Exploitation = actual value × use	*Index of* Development = actual / potential value
	29 (22, 24, 26, 28)	Neutron activation Practical metalworking	Very slight	Very good	Very good	Good	No	High	Medium	High
)	30 (4, 7, 8, 18, 20)	Metallo- graphic Chemical Physical Bacteriological	,,	Good	Improving	Improving	No	Medium	Low	,,
	31 (36, 39)	Microscopical (mechanical improvements)	Slight	Adequate	Fair	Poor	No	High	High	,,
ged	32 (6, 7)	Electron microscopical Biochemical Microbiological	,,	,,	Good	Poor	Yes	Medium	Low	,,
	33 (6, 7)	,,	,,	,,	Fair	Fair	No	High	,,	,,
t	34 (43, 44)	X-radiographic	,,	,,	Limited	Limited	No	Medium	,,	,,
	35 (37, 54)	Radiometric	(Nominal)	(,,)	Very good	Very good	Yes	Medium	Medium	Low
	36 (31)	Microscopical (mounting)	Slight	Adequate	Fair	Poor	No	High	High	High
	37 (35, 54)	Radiometric	(Nominal)	(,,)	Very good	Very good	Yes	Medium	Medium	Low
	38 (31)	Microscopical	Fair	Adequate	Good	Good	No	,,	,,	High
	39 (4, 31, 36)	Microscopical	Complete	Adequate	Very good	Very good	No	High	,,	Medium
	40 (31, 50)	Microscopical	Strong	Poor	Fair	Poor	No	,,	Low	High
	41 (31, 40)	Microscopical	Slight	Adequate	Limited	Limited	No	,,	,,	,,

pecialist field examination essential.

TA

Comparative analys

Material	*Basis of investigation*	*Main branch of science*	*General types of method used*	*General level of results*	*Use to excavator*	*Present accuracy*	*Normal drawbacks*	*Basic suitability of material*	*Req in*
INKS, DYES	Specific character of colorant and medium	Chemistry Physics (Botany, zoology)	Microchemical Absorption in u.v. and i.r.	Fair	Provenance Skill	Good	State and amount	Fair	Eas
ANIMALS Mollusca	Anatomy	Zoology (Ecology)	Conchological	Very good	Environm't Economy	Very good	State of specimens	Very good	(S) (X)
Insects and miscellaneous	„	„	Entomological, etc.	Very good	Environment	Very good	State of specimens	Very good	Eas
Vertebrate remains (most)	„	„	Osteological	Very good	Nature Use Economy	Very good	„	Very good	Eas for resu
	Blood group patterns	„	Serological	Promising	Provenance Distribution	Fair	Limited experience	Good	Eas
Bird bones	Anatomy	„	Osteological	Very good	Nature Economy Environment	Very good	Tedious Limited material	Good	Eas
Ivory, horn	Histology	„	Microscopical	Good	Nature Economy Environment	Very good		Good	„
LEATHER	Specific characteristics of hide and tanning material	Zoology Chemistry	Microscopical Chemical and physical	Good	Nature Economy Skill	Very good	State of specimen	Good	Eas
HAIR, FUR (including WOOL)	Histology	Zoology	Microscopical	Good	Nature Economy	Very good	State of specimen	Good	Easy
TEXTILE	Weave	Textile technology	Textile examination	Very good	Skill	Very good	„	Good	
MEDIA	Specific composition indicating source	Chemistry Physics	Microchemical Chromatographic Physical	Good	Nature Skill	Very good	Limited amount and poor state	Good	(S)
HUMAN REMAINS Description	Anatomical and pathological characteristics	Human anatomy	Osteological Pathological Physical anthropology	Very good	Individual (age and sex) pathological and "racial" features Environment Economy	Very good	Large amount and poor state	Very good	Easy thou best often
Dating from condition	Chemical characteristics and natural radioactivity	Chemistry Physics	Microchemical Microscopical Atomic radiation counting	Fair	Dating Environment Comparison	Good	Limited amount	Good	(C) best (X)
Blood groups	Family and "racial" characters	Biology	Serological	Promising	Relationships between individuals and groups	Good	Limited experience and amount Tedious Statistics	Promising	Easy

(C) = Field control essential. (S) = Specialist sampling ess

tific investigations—*contd.*

nts --	Serial No. (*see also other investigations*)	*Particular method used in development*	*Dependence on*	*Availability of*	*Prospects for*		*General service for archaeology*	*Index of*		
			standards or comparative material		*method*	*worker*		*Actual value* (*see fig. 2*)	*Exploitation = actual value × use*	*Development = actual / potential value*
	42 (31, 34, 44)	Microscopic Special photographic, chromatographic	Fair	Adequate	Limited	Limited	No	High	Low	High
	43 (7, 34)	X-radiographic	Fair	Good	Very good	Good	No	,,	High	,,
	44 (7, 34)	,,	,,	,,	Limited	Limited	No	,,	Medium	,,
or ts	45 (47, 53)	,,	Fairly strong, especially for early material	Limited for early material	Very good	Good	No	Very high	High	,,
	46 (55)	Serological	Complete	Poor	Good	Fair	No	Low	Low	Low
	47 (45)	Osteological	Strong	Improving	Good	Poor	No	High	High	High
	48 (40, 45, 49)	Histological and microscopical	Fair	Fair	Limited	Limited	No	,,	,,	,,
	49 (31, 45)	Microscopical Chromatographical	Slight	Adequate	Limited	Poor	No	,,	Medium	,,
	50 (40, 45, 48)	Microscopical	Slight	Adequate	Limited	Poor	No	Low	Low	,,
	51 (40, 50)	(,,) Practical weaving	,,	,,	Good	Poor	No	High	High	,,
	52 (42, 45, 49)	Chromatographic Microchemical	Complete	Fair	Good	Fair	No	Medium	Low	,,
or lts	53 (45)	Anatomical (measurement) Dental X-radiographic	Fair	Limited in some respects	Good	Good	No	High		,,
	54 (5, 7, 20, 35, 37)	Chemical (especially fluorine) Microscopical X-ray diffraction Radiometric	Complete	Internal	Good	Fair	No	High	Low	High
	55 (46)	Serological	,,	Poor	Very good	Good	Yes	Low	,,	,,

pecialist field examination essential.

mounted, and then ground and polished on the other down to the required transparent thinness. More recently, in order to do as little damage as possible to the specimen, a modification of this technique (for archaeology) utilizes the material cut instead from a much smaller oblique notch or nick. Other, less specific examinations are carried out direct on suitable flakes or crushes of the material. Some twenty groups of stone axes are clearly recognized; in many cases the localities and sometimes even the "factories" from which they came are known. New finds can now be fairly easily matched with any known group, wherever they may come from, but the characterization of new groups is likely to prove a more tedious and lengthy business (F. W. Shotton).[S12, S27] Nothing can yet be made of amber or flint.[S6]

Apart from the use of the other methods mentioned in Table 7, some problems might turn out to be susceptible also to a partial solution, at least, by a determination of their trace element patterns, as described below for ores, pottery and metals. But very little work (cf. [E6]) has been done, to my knowledge, probably because there is no economic need for it.

As with other geological deposits, the fossil content of *coal* varies with the age of the seam. Unfortunately, although the distribution and nature of British coalfields are for obvious reasons extremely well known, this knowledge itself does not help the archaeologist a great deal. Many seams are very extensive in their distribution, others may be near-contemporary though present in several coalfields far apart, and the very distinction between the fossils—principally microspores, tedious to extract and examine—may turn out to be less specific than some workers had hoped. Nevertheless some useful work has been done, especially where a group of seams appearing at the surface could clearly indicate distinct working sites.[B37, R7] Establishment of the use of coal from "coke" and slag residues may be significant.[R7]

The great disparity in knowledge, in Britain, between ferrous and copper extractive metallurgy is due to the fact that copper is no longer smelted here while the iron and steel industry patently flourishes. It is thus comparatively easy to get help in working out the details of an iron-smelting furnace, cinders and blooms, *ores* and refractory lining, and all the rest of the refinements (p. 239). But it is almost impossible to catch someone with comparable practical experience in winning copper. By contrast, copper ores tend to be somewhat more clearly defined, and it is really this—almost alone—that has made feasible the relatively small amount of practical work which has so far been done.

Such work is intimately linked with the older, more extensive and intensive study of metal artefacts and concerned mainly with the provenance of their metal (see below). There is some hope for copper sulphides, as recent work on the lead and zinc minerals has shown,[E4] of making spectrographic "trace impurities patterns" into "*tracer* patterns" by relating them to conditions of mineral formation, and thus within limits to certain localities.

Analyses of possible "ores" are rather more complicated than for metals and work in England has only recently begun. At the same time, it has already given some support to the suggestion—based mainly on the metal analyses—that the earliest artefacts in Britain could have been made from metal won by, or with the aid of, skilled foreign metallurgists, from complex sulphide ores rich in arsenic and/or antimony[B15] (see also p. 188 [W10A]).

Apart from the obvious features, there are several things about *soil* profiles and deposits exposed by excavation which appear to be indirectly significant in terms of human activity. Thus the deposition of iron in pans has been seen in some cases as the result of trampling on what was at the time a land surface. But in some similar cases it is equally clear that this could not have been so, and that in fact there is no evidence whatever of any disturbance of the profile in archaeological time. Nevertheless, it seems very probable that even such pans may be the result of human activity after all—only indirectly: activity at a time perhaps some thousands of years earlier and not actually touching the soil, but removing the forest cover and changing the land use.[D10]

Other features again, similar or not, lines or stains or deposits, can of course be wholly natural, and only the specialist, if anybody, can provide the answer. Field work is but one aspect of his activity, it is true, and he must often work from samples supplied to him by the excavator if anything is to be done at all.

The fact remains that his field visit is vital, to the extent that samples not taken by himself or on his express instructions are almost always suspect, and often not even worth starting on as they may produce misleading results. Sometimes only visible differences in the soil profile need to be sampled, or perhaps no sampling at all may be required (the undisturbed profile must always act as a guide). At other times it may be essential to have a great many samples within a very short vertical distance in order to interpret some close succession of deposits or find an invisible feature. The specialist alone can decide; but even he cannot provide an answer unless the archaeologist asks a question (F. E. Zeuner, I. W. Cornwall).

Once the sampling has been properly carried out and the problems have been clearly stated, there is a great deal that laboratory work, and experience gained in other contexts, can do for the excavator in this respect. Ecology is clearly significant: "forams" will fix marine transgressions (p. 248) under suitable conditions, and certain (macro) plant remains indicate brackish silt.[G10] It is true that soil science as such—"soil mechanics" notwithstanding—tends to be concerned largely with soil proper, that is, the stuff in which things will grow; and this may sometimes be directly useful in unexpected ways. Naturally, in the study of the nutrient status of a soil, the subsoil will be of great importance, but it is as well for the archaeologist to remember that his use of "soil", as referring to the whole of the environment out of which he digs his finds, is almost entirely restricted to archaeology.

I stress this partly also because there is no reason to be despondent if a given soil scientist seems unenthusiastic about some particular problem; it may be a peculiarity of the *sub*soil with which he might not normally be familiar. Furthermore, there are a great many valuable details that could be worked out which have nothing to do with soil in the narrow sense, if one had the time to think them out in terms of subsoil—things like the stresses due to various types of buildings and other structures such as wells, roads and bridges—and indeed earthworks, as the experimental ones are aimed to show (p. 226). Specialist aid has hardly been tapped here. It could easily provide some good reasons for certain possible forms of construction, and quickly dispose of a number of ill-founded hypotheses.

Even soil science proper is of course not only an activity of many parts but inevitably also one that uses the techniques of many other sciences to a particular end. Thus the analyses carried out by the soil chemist or physicist are basically chemical or physical analyses done on soils. They are to that extent selective but otherwise no different from such analyses carried out elsewhere for other purposes. Similarly some of the soil microbiology is essentially the same at an agricultural station as in a corrosion laboratory.

Three points emerge from this. First, if one knows the problem exactly, it need not be tackled at a soil research establishment, should that be inconvenient at any time. Then there is a whole range of techniques which could be brought to bear on any given problem; once again, several of them should always be used together. Finally, any particular combination is not necessarily exclusive to a given soil problem—the same formation of scientific forces might well be deployed equally in attack on problems of deposits on pots, colouring matter in murals, or corrosion products on metals.

In practice, the two features in a soil profile that are of most immediate importance to the archaeologist are the relative amounts of *iron compounds* and *organic matter* present—both in the succession of layers down the section, and in any less regular and well-defined lines and stains. For various reasons which are more or less well understood, and in some cases quite plain even to the layman, the straightforward colour of the section, as found, is a most unreliable guide. Once iron and organic matter have been properly "developed", many problems are clarified sufficiently and most others become much simpler to tackle.

A method which rapidly and visually develops a section in just such a way has been in use at the Ancient Monuments Laboratory for some years now and has proved most useful and effective. It consists simply in *firing* suitable samples under specific conditions. In one run, air has free access, in the other it is virtually excluded. The first was adapted from a similar method developed by

Dimbleby[D10]; it is, of course, like the second, a straightforward application of fundamental principles to specialized experience, and both types of run have had their counterparts in tests on pottery and other materials for some considerable time.

The value of the oxidizing run lies in the fact that normally, at a dull red heat, any iron oxides present will be dehydrated and oxidized to the bright red, haematitic colour which we associate with bricks and flower-pots, where it is of course due to the same cause. At the same time any organic matter present is completely burnt away. The results of this run therefore give in the depth of the red hue a direct, if approximate, measure of the relative amounts of iron distributed through a section or feature.

The reducing run suggested itself (paradoxically and typically) because it simply happened, during my first attempt at an oxidizing run—a mild mistake turned to considerable profit. Here, any organic matter will char, i.e., be turned into carbon black. At the same time, any iron oxides present will be dehydrated and reduced to a cement-grey colour, familiar in stoneware and grey clays. The results of this run will therefore indicate relative amounts of organic matter, provided due allowance is made for the small contribution of the pale iron oxides to the depth of the greyish-black hue.

Together, the two runs provide a formidable preliminary tool for opening up the soil profile in the search for fossil soils and indications of past conditions, as well as for unsuspected relationships between various strata, and also between soil and pottery (see p. 168). In the (rare) absence of organic matter, or presence of oxidizing agents (probably mainly manganese dioxide), the reducing run gives anomalous, oxidized colours; but these are conspicuous and thus indirectly significant, too. Normally the results are quite an accurate enough measure (Fig. 8) and it seems safe to interpret features within such limits—always provided that adequate controls are available among the samples: perhaps the most cogent reason for the specialist's visit to the site. On the other hand, it is doubtful whether similar results obtained by more precise methods are in many cases worth the far greater trouble and longer time, and whether they really justify the rather elaborate hypotheses which are sometimes built on them.

Further tests are often necessary and many specialized refinements are possible. Some, such as pH measurements, are not likely to become much simpler than they are at present, requiring as they do a minimum of instrumentation to be accurate and reproducible enough for the general comparison which alone can make them really useful. Others, like tests for nitrogen and phosphorus, are possibly capable of being simplified sufficiently while remaining good enough for our purpose.

It is intended at the Ancient Monuments Laboratory to utilize the newly installed kiln also for controlled routine soil tests of various kinds and on a large scale, apart from its primary use for examining pottery, glass and metal. At the moment, however, the preliminary tests on soil consist of nothing more complicated than the firing on a gas ring in open ceramic boats (eight at a time) for the oxidizing run, and singly in small ignition tubes (relatively long for their diameter) for the reducing run.

Apart from these more specifically chemical tests, perhaps the most useful general examination of a physical property is a *particle size* analysis. Again, it is possible to do a most elaborate piece of work and in this case the results may often be well worth the considerable trouble. For instance they may show up—as nothing else will—the presence of a pronouncedly windblown deposit that may be of vital importance in establishing the status of the land during a given period.[P3]

But, at the same time, it is often useful to carry out a simple sedimentation run on a set of samples which will quickly reveal in a relative way, much as for the firing tests, any gross distinctions and obvious similarities in ultimate texture. The present method at the Ancient Monuments Laboratory (much as at the Soil Survey) consists in simply shaking or stirring equal, small volumes of soil in up to ten times the volume of water for a few minutes and then watching the manner of separation on settlement. As with the firing tests which it usefully complements, and with chemical analysis, the degree of refinement adopted must bear some relation to the economics of the result (fig. 8). Much the same holds for morphological examination in thin section, as advocated by Kubiena,[K6] and for de Geer's[D6A] clay-varve counting, under special conditions.

It is obviously important literally to reconstruct certain types of ancient earthwork whose weathered remains we excavate today. Most welcome, therefore, is the emergence of a committee—under the auspices of the British Association, and following a stimulating paper read at their Glasgow Meeting in 1958 by Jewell[J3]—to study "by experiment the denudation and burial of archaeological structures". Among its aims one is "to build simple structures, such as a ditch and bank, laid down to precise measure-

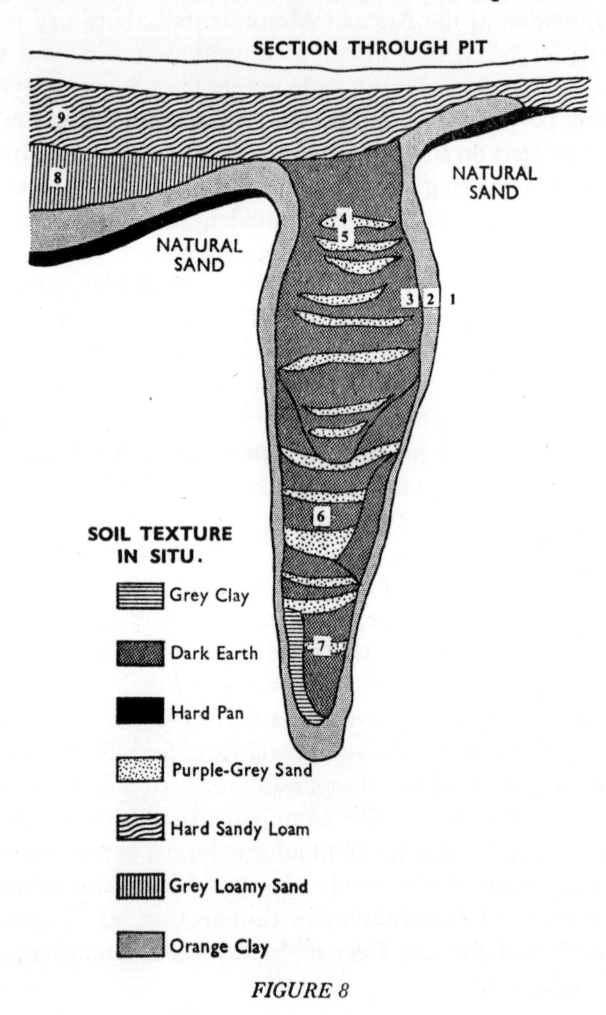

FIGURE 8

ments, and then to follow (over several decades) the rates of ditch silting, denudations and spreading of banks, turf formation and soil compaction". The first earthwork was built in 1960,[J3] the second, just completed, 1963.

From our present point of view, the production of *pottery* and other *ceramic material* may be regarded as the firing of "soil". Hence the same primary methods of examination apply[H7, K5] and

RESULTS OF SOIL TESTS

CALKE WOOD, WATTISFIELD,

SUFFOLK, PIT 1

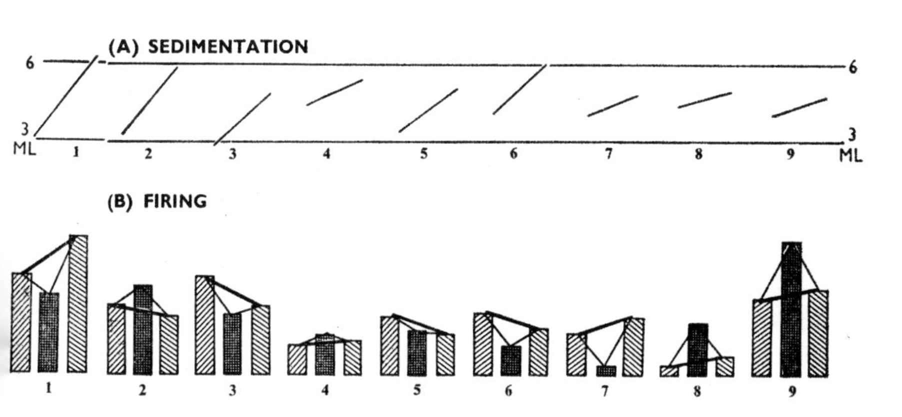

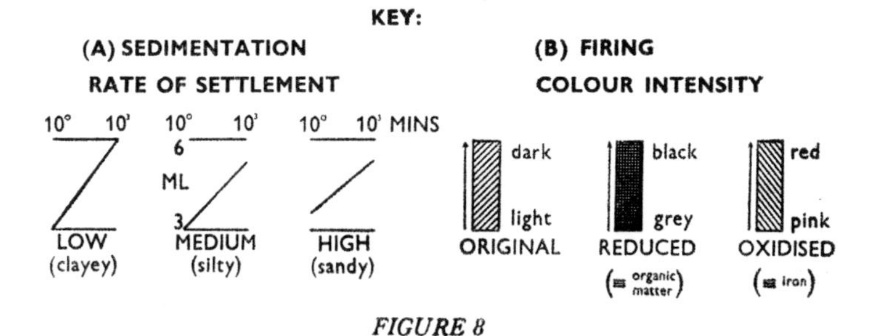

FIGURE 8

indeed provide a most useful basis for comparison (p. 168). From the results of re-firing portions of selected sherds under accurately known conditions of temperature, time and kiln atmosphere, it is possible quite simply to consider pottery in a manner that is independent of the normal typological considerations. "Coring" in different colours, the common black usually due to rapid firing, and other features add refinement to the interpretation.

It is hoped shortly to see more clearly also in the matter of the various inclusions ("grog", "backing" or "temper"), whether natural or artificial, which may reflect on locality or skill[S11] (p. 169). Here, too, the importance of experiments on a larger scale is clearly realized and kilns have been built and fired at Wattisfield[W6] (p. 168) and more recently at Boston in Lincolnshire.[M2A]

At the other end of the scale, pottery may be treated as an aggregate of complex minerals and examined in thin section much as rock specimens (p. 211). While we can thus express the nature of a ware with a remarkable degree of precision for purposes of comparison,[S11] the number and variety of clay deposits, even in a restricted area, are so vast that even fine distinctions are of limited value in assessing likely provenance of pottery or bricks, especially as little is known in this sense about the deposits (H. G. Midgley). As with other raw materials, surface deposits may have been exhausted in antiquity, and may have been different from present (deeper) workings on this site. Where such data are available, however (as for example for certain clays of the Hastings Beds[B36]), or well-defined local material was used (pp. 168–9), a direct comparison is of course possible, and extremely valuable whatever the outcome. X-rays can be helpful in revealing the potter's "sweep" in terms of the voids left by fired-out grass-temper, also opaque mineral grains and sometimes the nature of any glaze.

Recently, attempts have been made to correlate ware with origin of deposits by *neutron bombardment*—at least, the ware has been so analysed, and certain groupings have seemed justifiable on the basis of the results, and on that alone.[E6, Y3] In time such work will become extended in both scope and depth, and attempts at correlation will become a routine matter though some difficulties are likely to remain.

The method does not, of course, extend our range significantly beyond what is already possible (as for ores and rocks) by means of the optical spectrograph.[R14] Also it suffers (at least at the moment) from having to be carried out in an atomic pile; "neutron generators", though they may prove adequate before long, are not yet powerful enough. On the other hand it is in some respects very much more sensitive and also (on specimens smaller than one inch in diameter) completely non-destructive, even though a given safety period must be allowed to elapse after examination: a certain amount of radioactivity is induced in the material for the purpose of analysis, and this is left to decay below hazard level before the object is returned.

Attempts have also been made[A2, A4] to date pottery by the archaeomagnetic method, described below for fired structures found *in situ*. But this is only just becoming refined enough to be valuable and its use will always remain limited, in any case, to well-defined and specialized types of ware for which the basic assumption—that they were always fired dead upright, or in some other fixed position—may strictly be taken to apply.

Material extraneous to the ceramic object, but found in some way attached to it, is examined under the various heads where it may possibly belong. Generally, as will have become obvious, this process is of course standard routine. But there is probably a greater variety of material found, for several reasons, attached to pottery than to anything else; thus it seems the proper place here to stress the point in general. Examples could probably be found of nearly every category—I will only mention the more significant ones in my own experience; even so, the list is impressive.

First there are the many vague and "unknown" stains, accretions, deposits inside and out, efflorescences and discolorations unconnected directly with the process of pottery making. Then we have concretions of vivianite, for example, nothing to do with the particular sherd but of great importance as indicators of the general soil conditions. Similarly, fragments of crucibles for melting glass, with residues remaining; glazes and pigments, the latter both in decoration and as contents; slag and bits of metal dross with fragments of bone, fired and stuck on to the pottery, and impressions made in the "green" clayware with tooth of beaver—all these are searched for automatically, and examined separately where found.

Perhaps the most consistently valuable extraneous evidence, however, is provided in the shape of accidental impressions of material that is, at the same time, archaeologically significant and highly perishable. To this category belong the well-known impressions of various kinds of textile, which have permitted us to determine the weave—and sometimes even the fibre—used at a time and in a place from which no actual textile remains.

Similarly there are imprints of leaves, stalks and other kinds of important botanical material, in particular of seeds and cereal grains: sooner or later one of these is sure to be found on a precisely datable cuneiform clay-tablet document, which would thus accurately (if again unconsciously: p. 108) record the current state of agriculture for us, as well. Finally we have the persistence of a normally fugitive dyestuff (p. 105).

The *archaeomagnetic dating* of structures found *in situ* depends on two principal physical facts. First, the true magnetic bearings of any given point on the earth's surface vary slightly but significantly with time. There has over the past five hundred years been (from documentary evidence) a change of about ten degrees for every hundred years in London measurements of declination—that is, the angle between a freely suspended magnetized needle and the geographical meridian (fig. 9). Secondly, any material which is heated to about 600°C and contains enough iron—chiefly in the form of certain oxides—will become magnetized to some extent as it cools down afterwards. The magnetization is relatively weak but, with modern methods, capable of being measured accurately enough. Furthermore—and this is the crucial point—such materials take on the earth's field as it is at that place and moment. After that, if they are not reheated, they retain the direction of this "remanent magnetism" for ever, although its intensity is thought to decrease somewhat.[T2] It follows that fired clay, soil and even stone features such as furnaces, kilns, hearths, or ovens—provided they are found, and can be given today's magnetic "fix", *in situ*—may, in the laboratory, be made to reveal the time of last firing by their "fossil" magnetism. At present, the date curve is only beginning to be established from otherwise closely datable material. It is likely, also, that the magnetic variation occurs along a cyclical path, so that one would always have to know approximately into which half-millennium, say, any given specimen should be referred. But it is hoped within such limitations eventually to produce a dating method perhaps accurate to something like ten years (S. K. Runcorn, R. M. Cook).

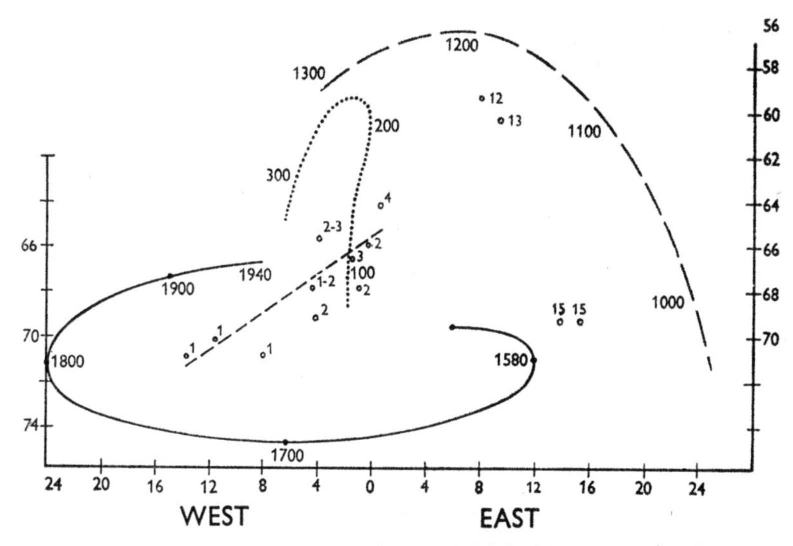

FIGURE 9. Magnetic variation with time for the period A.D. (———— from documentary evidence (London); ------ after Cook and Belshé[C16] .... *and* ———— *after Aitken*[A4]).

In practice a suitable area is chosen on the fired feature, carefully cut round without disturbing it and in such a way as to permit a special, standard-size frame to be squared over it, and then cast round with plaster of Paris which is allowed to find its own level. On this surface, accurately levelled when set, the present magnetic field bearings are marked. The block is then cut out and taken to the laboratory, where it may be suitable for direct measurement in a large, sensitive magnetometer, or may have to be cored to provide smaller samples suitable for the more robust, normal instrument.[A2a, A4, C16]

The more samples are available, the more confidently can any errors be calculated away. At least half a dozen samples are taken from any one feature, wherever possible, and both inclination and declination are measured. The dating angles are given by the difference, in each case, between the present bearings as measured in the field, and the fossil magnetism as found in the specially non-magnetic laboratory when the sample is set up again in precisely the same position relative to the present earth's field. The results are plotted as shown in Figure 9. The Roman period is fairly well covered now, but there is little known about the Dark Ages until about 1200.

Other aspects of *burnt clay* may be provided by all those rather vague materials from cob to daub which are made up for the construction especially of walls and roofs, though floors should also be included in the consideration. When they become fired, usually by accident, the results bear a clear family resemblance to the kinds of feature we have been considering—hearths and kilns. The temperatures here are mostly, though not invariably, much lower. Yet the similarity is real, and the same methods of examination apply.

Sometimes signs of firing may not be immediately clear; usually it is quite easy to make certain, for example by (re)firing. Here, also, important traces of extraneous material may survive, particularly impressions of the kind already mentioned (see p. 230), and evidence of the wattling and other organic matter used in the construction. As with pottery, X-rays are proving quite useful.[R7]

Of the remaining group of building materials a great variety of types is known in this country even from the Roman period,[D2] including hydraulic and pozzolanic mortars and "concrete" floors; there are also all the other, ordinary *mortars*, *renderings* and *plasters* made of lime, gypsum and cementitious mixtures, and used in flooring, wall construction and covering, roofing and foundation. Firing does not enter into the setting of these materials. Unlike the fired clay products they are used in the plastic form and are more closely related in this respect to daubing.

But firing does of course play a most important part in their manufacture. The raw materials are calcined in all cases, and subsequently used as a slurry with water. It is important to remember this because we always find the end product more or less fully set, but this does not mean that we can leave the matter there. In the case of a lime, for instance, the material may have been left as a contaminated putty by builders, or it may have been laid as a mortar floor; this floor may have been calcined in a severe fire and thereby turned back into lime, subsequently "setting" once again.

Sometimes we can distinguish between such alternatives. But in the main the work on these materials involves only their straightforward identification and description, except for lime-and-sand mortars and renderings and, of course, in a different sense also wallplasters.

It is possible quite simply to differentiate a wide range of *lime mortars* that may look similar even to experienced inspection with the naked eye. The proportion of lime to sand is rarely characteristic, though it may be helpful as confirmatory evidence. The main criterion is the grading of the "aggregate", i.e. the non-lime component—chiefly sand and gravel.

By "grading" I do not here mean to imply any deliberate sorting and mixing. This has clearly taken place at times in the past, but there the scale of distribution is rather larger and more definite. Although it may be helpful, therefore, artificial grading is on the whole less important—indeed, the basis of mortar analysis generally rather assumes that natural material was used.

Very roughly, if one imagines that ancient sand diggers predominantly worked shallow pits, and accepts that the distribution of the sizes of sand and gravel particles is then fairly uniform throughout the limited volume used for any one particular job—but different for various pits, or even for different parts and depths of the same pit—then it is possible to compare the aggregates in different mortars on that basis. Thus various walls, different parts of the same wall, or even spills from a robber trench, may be shown to belong to given periods or structures, if their similarity to other, datable, walls or features can be indicated in this way.[D2]

It can be little more than a suggestion, at this stage anyway. In practice, a sample of the mortar is carefully crushed, weighed, and taken up in dilute acid which dissolves away the more or less fully carbonated lime. The aggregate thus freed is separated, washed, dried and sieved through a grading train, and its separate fractions are weighed. The resulting proportions are plotted as shown in Figure 10.

A marked difference suggests that separate jobs are more likely; but they may have been separated by days only, perhaps. A close similarity suggests the same job—but it is possible that the same sand pit, or a long and uniformly graded section, was used for several centuries. On the whole, differences in grading are more valuable than similarities, and when set (in the same context) against similarities (within other groups) the overall evidence is taken to be fairly conclusive, especially where a (statistically) large number of samples is involved.

Sometimes there are peculiar inclusions in the aggregate, such as crushed wallplaster from a previous decoration, and this can make the particular mix readily distinguishable. The famous Roman *opus signinum*, a pronouncedly pink and very hard mortar, normally contains no sand or gravel but only crushed red tile. Occasionally crushed chalk is present. This is, like poorly slaked lime (now set in lumps) from which it is extremely difficult to distinguish, of course chemically identical with the carbonated lime matrix of the mortar itself and dissolved away with it by the acid treatment. Visual examination of a suitably smoothed section is then necessary. All these considerations become particularly important when the object of the analysis is not to help with archaeological interpretation but to match the original mix in some repair work to a standing monument.

As always, there are a number of pitfalls. Sea sand may have been used, indiscriminately. The whole of the "sand and gravel" may be oolitic or otherwise calcareous, and therefore soluble. There is then little that can be done. But even in the normal cases, acid or carbon dioxide in the ground-water may have leached out a proportion of the lime from a buried mortar. As is well known to every amateur repointer *malgré lui*, much can be dissolved out of the surface of an exposed joint even above ground. The degree of the chemical setting action—the carbonation by carbon dioxide from the air—is probably never uniform and hence not accurately determinable on the small quantities usually available for

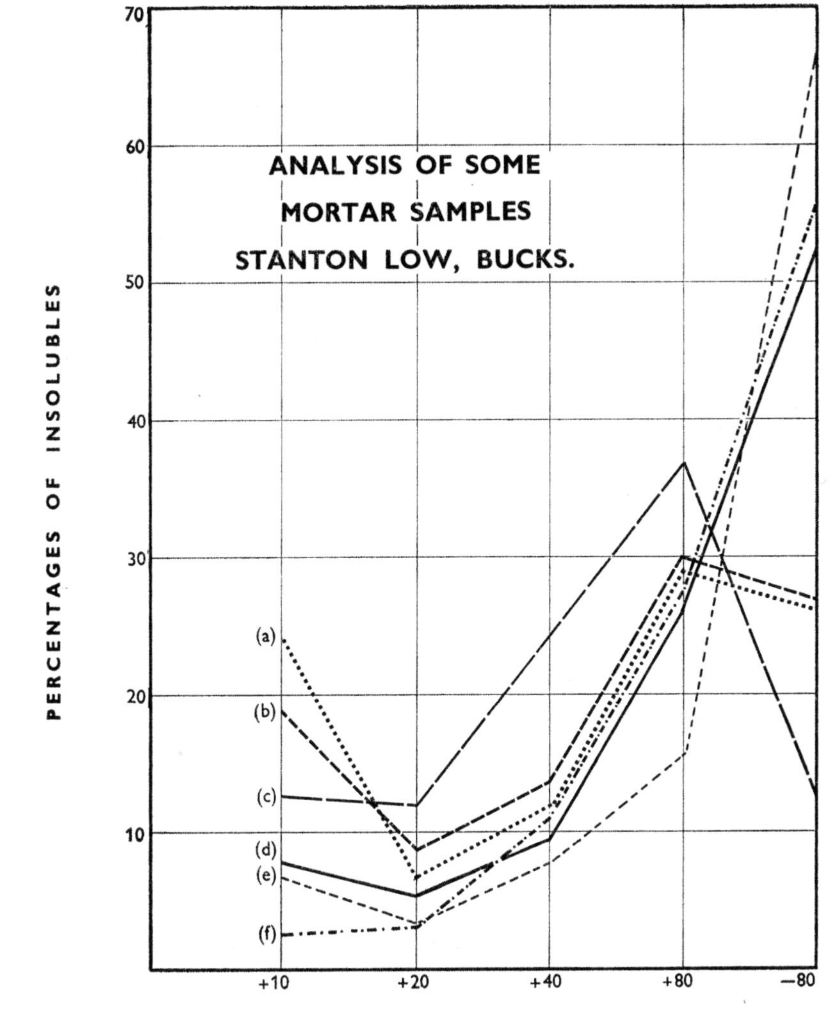

FIGURE 10. (a) *and* (b) *are clearly similar, and different from* (d) *and* (f); (e) *may belong to the latter group, but* (c) *is an outsider.*

analysis, nor will the purity of the lime ever be known. One can thus rarely be precise about the original proportions of the mix.

True, this does not usually matter very much—the acid-insoluble material is the most important. But for that aspect, too, it is essential that sampling should be adequate, careful and not from the exposed surface. Even so, it is still not fully realized that no analysis of a mortar, as such, can at present provide any kind of independent and absolute date for it (N. Davey). There is always the chance, of course, that it may yield a coin; or, in the future, accurate Carbon-14 tests on the very small quantities of charcoal it sometimes contains may become possible.

In the case of *wallplasters*, although recent work has suggested that its value here may be underrated,[J1] the study of composition and grading is of secondary importance. The main interest centres in the original surface layer, a few thousandths of an inch thick, where this has been coloured. Our concern at this point, in a rigidly material catalogue, is only with the *mineral pigments* (p. 245). For these, ordinary microchemical methods are normally adequate,[P10, Y3] though non-destructive refinements are possible by special photography or X-ray fluorescence (p. 237). This also applies when such pigments are found in any other form, whether as residues in some bone or pottery container, as paintings on a cave wall, decoration on pottery or as raw lumps.

Here again (as p. 229), to point a general relation in an obscure context, the same material may appear in various disguises in different places. Thus the iron oxide *haematite* may be found during our work in almost all the forms known to modern analytical science: as the ore; as a mineral in building stones; as polishing agent (jewellers' rouge); in burnt coal; in soils (?naturally, or) fired red; in pottery (the ware fired in an oxidizing atmosphere, or a slip or other decoration); in bricks and tiles and other forms of clay fired accidentally or on purpose, including those most valuable features suitable for archaeomagnetic dating (though the haematite itself is only a poorly magnetic material it acts as useful indicator); traces in fired mortars and plasters, and as pigment: various shades of red ochre; and of course in the "slag" embedded in wrought iron and as "fire" scale in corrosion products (p. 133).

In some connection or other, not always strictly relevant but often valuable, the oxide can also crop up with any of the materials not of mineral origin that are about to be listed.

But first, one relatively small yet important subgroup of a mineral nature remains to be dealt with. *Glasses* and *glazes* are for our present purpose synonymous, and (vitreous) *enamels* are also included in these general remarks. Methods of analysis and aims of investigation were usefully summarized at the British Association's symposium, *Technology of ancient glass and metal*, already noted[B14] (p. 165). Degree and type of weathering may provide a rough diagnosis even in Britain, and under suitable conditions elsewhere can seemingly be used as a possible firmer basis for dating glass[B26] and even obsidian.[B32] Of the more recent techniques—the non-destructive ones which are of course particularly valuable here—two deserve special mention.[C1A, T12]

The *neutron activation* method (p. 228) is to be tried on glass, where curious spectrographic results have opened up exciting possibilities: it seems (from a limited number of preliminary data) that chronology comes over more clearly than geography. "The tendency is for glass of a given period to have the same composition, no matter where it was made, throughout the ancient world. From time to time a new process must have entered in, because the overall analysis of glass noticeably changes. And one can see this change spread geographically over a period . . . of maybe a couple of centuries . . .".[Y3]

Also, the *X-ray fluorescence spectrometer* can be used to good and direct effect to make a fine distinction, non-destructively, probably impossible by any other means. The stylistically typical blue in Chinese blue-and-white glazes was examined for manganese content of the primary cobalt colouring. The series of wares fell fairly clearly into three groups of which one contained far less manganese, a circumstance associated with the (early) import from Persia of (superior) cobalt known to be poor in this element.[Y2] But no connection with art-historically appraised quality or date could be found. The method itself is probably the most remarkable contribution to analytical technique since Carbon-14, especially for archaeology and art history.

The only effect it may have is on certain glass-like materials—a (reversible) discoloration. Otherwise it is merely a matter of placing the specimens in position and switching on—just before going off for the week-end, say, although one analysis for one element only takes thirty seconds—and on return finding the results of a whole series all typed or traced out on graph paper, and the machine switched off (E. T. Hall)—the nearest approach so far, surely, to the archaeologist's dream.

In more precise terms, the concentration limits are now 0·01% and 100%, for most elements above calcium in the periodic table, and even the lower limits of both sensitivity and atomic number (i.e. element) are likely to be improved upon in the near future. Bombardment of the specimen with a beam of "white" (i.e. the whole range of) X-rays produces secondary X-ray fluorescence with wavelengths characteristic of the elements that are present. This secondary radiation is suitably separated and the various fractions are collected and counted, in turn, to give the proportions directly,[Y3] though calibration is necessary. Only the immediate surface of the specimen will be reflected in the analysis. The area actually examined at any time is about ¾ in. (1·8 cm.) in diameter but the size of the specimen chamber is about one cubic foot (*c.* 0·3 m^3), so that all of the external surface of a fairly large object can be scanned. The next logical step is the *micro-probe*[D13] which (though utilizing electrons) operates on much the same principle but examines a spot only 1 *micron* in diameter (= 1 millionth of a metre). However, at present it requires a specially mounted specimen of severely limited size (2·5 cm., i.e. less than 1 in., dia.) and is thus no longer strictly non-destructive except for very small items.

These methods are, of course, particularly useful also in the examination of *metal* objects where they have been employed to good effect, particularly on non-ferrous metals.[E5, S29] However, here the most widely and frequently used tool by far has been the optical spectrograph. Until quite recently, only the very earliest archaeologically datable material had been worked on in England, in order to keep to the minimum, or even exclude, any possible error due to the re-use of scrap. Analyses carried out all over Europe[C11, P6] have shown that it is possible to arrive at significant major groupings of artefacts on the basis of their impurities pattern (H. H. Coghlan), although the validity of sub-groups must remain in doubt until enough results are available (also for the "ores", see p. 221) to make statistical comparisons useful. More recent English analyses have also included material dated to the later Bronze Age.[B20]

This work shows plainly how very close the collaboration between archaeologist and scientist must be at every stage, for it is only the archaeologist ultimately who can say what series of implements would be worth treating as a homogeneous unit for statistical analysis. At the same time, it is only the laboratory worker who can say what sort of analysis is worth doing (E. M. Jope).

Many archaeologists still do not realize how far the whole battery of available modern techniques can decipher the record of manufacture which any ancient metal object must always carry in its sounder parts. Yet the value of such examination—mainly metallographic,[C12,R11] though supplemented to advantage in many cases by other forms, such as straightforward chemical, radiographic and X-ray diffraction analysis—has been demonstrated abundantly.

Similarly, though in a different way, the corrosion products carry evidence of the fate of the object that is of interest to scientists in several fields and may be suitably revealed by some of the same methods (T. W. Farrer, W. H. J. Vernon).

Clearly here, perhaps more than in any other field with the possible exception of pottery, there is an urgent need for experiment, for doing things again as we think they were done. Some work on iron smelting[T13,W20] and much on working[C12, P1] has been done, more is contemplated. There are plans for primitive copper smelting, with particular reference to the fate of trace elements. As for conditions of burial, modern exposure tests in corrosion research programmes—some of them now over forty years old[R17]—are likely to become increasingly helpful in future.

Petrographical or X-radiographic examination of a thin section has proved to be the most profitable approach to *ferrous smelting slags* and ancillary material. Chemical analysis can be very useful, especially to show variation (and thus level of skill) in a large series,[R7] or for glassy slags where it alone can help. It will also distinguish oddities, such as (cereal) grain slags, but should never be interpreted (or, really, published) without a (physical) description of the appearance, because there is a wide range of overlap: slags and cinders and even fused coal ash [G13] may be of similar composition, and equally some specimens looking much the same may be quite differently constituted. An analytical service for archaeology (originated by M. Davies and) developed by H. F. Cleere is now successfully operating through the Iron and Steel Institute, but *non-ferrous slags* are for various reasons less well known in Britain (p. 220). Yet copper slags in particular, though rare, are also very significant [S17] and very similar to iron slags at the same time.

In this systematic survey of materials a fitting transition between mineral and organic factors is provided by a group of activities which, though it is studied most often in connection with one or other of these materials, is becoming important in its own right. *Microbiology*, and in particular the result of fungal and bacterial action, is beginning to be recognized as a subject of supreme importance, not only in the decay of timber and textiles, in alcoholic and other fermentation processes, and in diseases, where it has been treated with proper respect for some considerable time, but in many of the spheres here discussed, from soil science to metal corrosion, and from various stains and discolorations even to some special cases of stone decay.

The time has come in archaeological studies, also, to consider on their own merits its many possible effects—especially under waterlogged or otherwise stagnant conditions (p. 155). It is probable that a fair proportion of puzzling field observations may be produced indirectly—and sometimes irrelevantly—by microbial activity. At other times (e.g. Winklebury,[M1] p. 122) there is a direct connection. It is certain that evaluation of archaeological evidence from this, and from the biochemical, point of view *as such* will in due course have a great deal to add to the general picture in many different ways.

What is perhaps the most important and certainly the most prolific organic material generally, *wood* in its various forms, provides a good example of the complete range of approach. As solid timber, in many cases it hardly requires even a hand-lens to be firmly identified—as a tiny fragment of waterlogged writing tablet, to be distinguished from a mass of apparently similar brushwood, it needs cutting and mounting for the microscope.

A large beam or pile, the fatter the better, should be cut at an angle of forty-five or even thirty degrees to its long axis, i.e. in a taper section, to give the best material for *dendrochronological study.* The evaluation of the relative thicknesses of tree rings, taken together with climatic fluctuations (known or hypothetical) can under suitable conditions be made to give a really precise date, to the year, after about A.D. 1100 in Britain.[S7] Much uncertainty remains for many localities,[G7] but a great deal of it is in the process of being cleared away.

At the other end of the scale there is crushed brushwood whose *submicroscopic structure,*[P11] magnified some 300,000 times or even more in an electron micrograph, will show significant evidence of a relation between decay and period of burial. In conjunction with results from X-ray diffraction methods and the use of the polarizing microscope, such evidence has suggested that under waterlogged conditions there might be some valuable connection. Amorphous cellulose disappears first, and subsequently the other, crystalline component is gradually broken down. This breakdown occurs in terms of a shortening in the ultimate cell wall units, the so-called micro-fibrils (pl. 3, fig. 1).

There are many reservations. The rate of decay varies, for example, for different types of tree—in particular, softwoods appear under these conditions to be incomparably more resistant than hardwoods (p. 146)—and even within a given tree the heartwood will behave differently from the sapwood. The position of burial may be important, and the adherence of bark may upset the whole business (R. D. Preston).

Within these limitations, nevertheless, the workers at Leeds have established to their satisfaction what amounts to an alternative and independent method for *dating* wood—(presumed) continuously *waterlogged wood* only. The extent to which microfibrils are shortened appears to be proportional to the amount of water that is taken up by buried wood. In other words, with suitable precautions, the wood is weighed wet at saturation equilibrium, dried, and reweighed. The moisture content thus found is a direct measure of the period of burial. It's as simple as that.

A curve has been obtained for material of various ages that are otherwise known, back as far as the Roman period, and the standard error seems small enough to make the method worth while exploring. The mechanism of degradation appears to be entirely chemical, without the intervention of any biological agencies such as fungi or bacteria. It is this circumstance which probably keeps the rate of decay so uniform, and thus makes the method possible at all.

The *radiocarbon dating* technique is most easily applied to wood, or better still charcoal. These commonly provide the highest density of carbon which was part of the life-cycle at the time of burial. But the method is of course equally applicable to other organic materials such as bone and antler, leather, horn, ivory, and even snail shells and, theoretically at least, probably also (short-lived) buried land surfaces—always provided they contain enough carbon.[cf. B29A]

Before any submission of such materials for radiocarbon dating is contemplated it is as well to have the carbon assayed, wherever possible, on a small fraction of the material. In bone it could be calculated from the result of a nitrogen test (p. 251). The carbon content, if high enough, will be a good introduction to the vetting committee—much as a previously found pH less than 5·4, for a mineral soil, is to the pollen investigator (p. 246).

Little can be said here about the method itself. First, of all such matters it has probably received the most attention in every way, scientifically and from the laity. The basic assumptions are, in detail, very complex, as is the apparatus whose operation requires rigorous precautions. A discussion that would do them justice is out of place here. There are several thorough-going appraisals which may be consulted for details (e.g. [B4]). The method has aroused much controversy. Sir Mortimer Wheeler gives a valuable layman's impression of this among other techniques.[W13]

But even if I wanted I should probably not be able to produce a satisfactory account of the whole method that would remain up-to-date for long enough to be of value. The technique is still developing too rapidly. I shall therefore limit myself to a few remarks on the latest refinements and practical difficulties as they affect the excavator and the interpreter.

One of the basic assumptions, that the ratio of ^{14}C to ^{12}C has always been constant in the carbon life-cycle, has been challenged on several counts recently. Following objections on (palaeo-) geomagnetic grounds, careful work carried out[D7, W16] on separate rings in substantial quantity, from trees of known and considerable age, clearly showed fluctuations of radioactivity in North-west Europe. These appear to agree with certain upper-atmospheric oscillations postulated for the (late medieval) periods studied. It seems as if medieval archaeology, already difficult enough to serve in this respect, is now even less likely truly to benefit from the method.

A great many of the initial snags, including the much vaunted modern contamination of the apparatus by fall-out from atomic explosions, have seemingly been overcome satisfactorily. Refinements in counting have reduced the standard error by some sixty per cent or more over the past few years. The time has probably come when—apart from the need to establish in the archaeologist's mind a clear understanding of this error and of the statistical approach (E. M. Jope, H. Barker)—one of the most important single factors has become the taking and packing of the sample.

It is here, perhaps, that the interpreter can help most. The excavator is clearly not able to keep up with the latest developments in possibilities and dangers. At the same time he may not always realize the critical difference which modern organic material might make: anything from straw or paper packing to the first-aid impregnation with plastic.

Finally, there is a very important point of which the laboratory worker may be unaware, if he does not himself take the sample or at least visit the site, and one which may also escape the excavator, preoccupied with other more pressing considerations, as he will usually be, or even unaware (in a different sense) of the circumstances. Contact with fossil organic matter, such as bitumen, may give far too old a date; or, in a highly organic and well draining or diffusing soil, there may be a significant amount of constant contamination by more modern organic material, with the result that the measured piece produces too young an activity (F. E. Zeuner).

In Britain, several radiocarbon laboratories (e.g. at the Royal Institution, the Department of Quaternary Research, Cambridge, and at the British Museum) have produced valuable results, severely handicapped as they have been by a lack of understanding of their requirements. It is good news that the status of this work has now at last been recognized here, as in some other countries (notably the United States, the Netherlands, and Scandinavia) it has been for some time. A "general store" type (p. 79) radiocarbon service has been set up at Teddington, for the Department of Scientific and Industrial Research. Results from there will carry the stamp of quality normally associated with the National Physical Laboratory in many other connections.

Although the various *media*[H12] from vegetable products, in effect mainly the drying oils, were not used until very much later as such, *Linum* was cultivated right from the beginning, primarily for the linseed as a food. Helbaek[H9] has traced the intriguing twin development along independent lines of this characteristically "beaked" seed, down to its appearance in Northern Europe in two different forms from different directions. Bast fibre was won and spun into linen from this remarkable plant very early on, too, but authentic remains are fewer, later and relatively less well preserved, apart from being almost uncharacteristic compared with the seed.

Other *seeds*, particularly cereal grains but also fruit stones and nuts, have been similarly studied and with equally rewarding results.[C23, H8] Following recent advances in techniques of submicroscopic examination,[N6] it is hoped to make it a routine to look at such and other botanical material (notably leaves) at this level, too, studying changes in structure especially with an eye on any connections useful for dating purposes.

Throughout, once again, the ecological aspect is ever present. *Mosses* (or even their spores) can be most valuable by indicating the microclimate that obtained, for instance, when the turf in which they were growing was cut and immediately buried in the heart of a rampart. They can corroborate the evidence from snails or even take its place, as they must in acid soils (p. 183). To the investigator of shipworm[C22] the timber itself is merely a background. An entomologist, on the other hand, may know more about *oak galls* than the man who knows all about oaks, whether he be forester or botanist. The latter regards galls as an irrelevant nuisance, even though they are part of the vegetable matter of the tree. The former is intimately concerned with the behaviour of the wasps which induce the tree to grow galls.

Another specialist in galls may be concerned with the ink for which they are traditionally used. Most *inks* and *dyes* in antiquity were of vegetable origin, and many of course still are. Perhaps the most striking exception was Tyrian purple, from the *Murex* snail; lac, cochineal and kermes, all insect dyes, are others. Whatever the origin, the nature of the colouring principle and action is now well understood.

This knowledge can be used successfully in the chemical or physical detection even of traces, provided enough has remained and is not too severely degraded. Mordant residues, almost invariably mineral in nature, may for that reason enable dyes to survive burial for millennia,[C1, L6] or themselves persist better than the dyes. Obliquely, once again, they will then be valuable virtual evidence. Although easier to capture analytically they are, however, far more akin to substances present in the soil anyway, and therefore more difficult to interpret.

The *fibrous substrates* on which the dyes and inks most commonly appear, from papyrus to cloth and paper or even wood, are once again mainly vegetable in origin. The exceptions are silk, vellum (or parchment) and wool which are quite distinct under the microscope. Vegetable cloth and paper, as also rope, are made mostly from the bast fibres in the woody tissues of plants. Although characteristic as bast fibres, they are not easily traced back to the plant. Certain tests will distinguish between flax, hemp, jute, and nettle, but only on fresh material; otherwise one has to rely on dimensions, but these overlap and are in any case subject to variation or at least doubt over the centuries (p. 122). Cotton *hairs*, on the other hand, are quite distinct (e.g. [S28, Y3]).

Perhaps one of the most striking contributions in recent years has come from *pollen analysis*, or palynology. Many trees depend on the wind for transporting their pollen. The outer membranes of pollen grains can be very resistant to degradation on burial and become, in effect, fossils from which conditions at the time of the various deposits—often many feet thick and accumulated over periods of significant change—can be deduced easily and directly.

Until very recently the only deposits generally regarded as useful in this connection were those seen in peaty or otherwise waterlogged sections, stratified and undisturbed. Work on these has become quite complex, extending the scope of interpretation[G9]—into methods of plant and animal husbandry, and more or less independently of the primary dating and climatic criteria—as well as the range of identification, bringing oil immersion lenses to bear on a great variety of pollen of herbaceous plants, besides studying the tree pollen with which the work originally began (H. Godwin).

In addition to this, some workers have now turned their attention to other types of deposit, notably to mineral soil profiles of a podzolic nature (p. 151) where the general organic content is relatively low, but the acidic nature of the significant horizons helps to preserve the pollen grains.[D10, V2, W5] In waterlogged deposits nearly all pollen will be preserved faithfully in all respects. In mineral soils a pH below 5·5 appears generally to be necessary—that means, for instance, that pollen is almost never preserved at sites directly on the Chalk—there may be considerable downwash (which is, however, clearly apparent from the complete pollen diagram), and there is always a chance that certain pollen may be preferentially preserved.

Nevertheless, analysis of suitable mineral soils is obviously of great advantage because they are encountered on archaeological sites more commonly than waterlogged sections. Such analysis is able quite precisely to place buried land surfaces, as well as giving them a sharply defined ecological background, a cultivation rating, and in suitable circumstances perhaps even a date range.[D9] However confessedly incomplete such a general picture may be—and in most cases it is probably quite adequate for our purpose—it is patently so much better than nothing at all.

The normal method of preparation—as developed primarily in Scandinavia, and in general use in Britain—involves removal of mineral material (by evaporation with hydrofluoric acid), followed by separation of humus (by acetolysis) and finally mounting of the insoluble residue—mainly pollen grains—for microscopical examination at about ×500.[F1]

As will have become abundantly clear, all study of vegetable matter from archaeological deposits, and of much of the mineral variety, is dependent on scrupulous microscope work. Apart from changes in microbiological cultures—paradoxically, clear to the naked eye—this is largely static inasmuch as it requires observation of structure and comparison with reference material. Much importance attaches particularly to the method and skill of preparation, which are often as decisive as experience in observation and availability of standards. In other instances, notably the examination of most zoological specimens, the microscope is almost unnecessary.

On a sound basis of comparative *osteology*,[C19, R13] the origin and movement of breeds of cattle and sheep can clearly be developed into factors of great importance.[B32, J4] Correlation with other evidence,[R22] about build, special characters, and ecological data, will inevitably enhance the general picture. The study of domestication and economy is obviously going to benefit from this development, but there are other more obscure ways in which it will be of value, such as geographical and climatic adaptation, and the cycle is completed by the reflection of such features back on origin and domestication. As with human remains (see below) blood-grouping has shown itself to be a potentially most useful tool.[E7]

Of great value in determining man's habitat during a given period of occupation is *conchology*—the study of mollusca, or just "shells" to the excavator. This term at once goes to the root of the matter here, as it is the minute specimens which the digger cannot see that are the most significant to the specialist—rather than the large species, although these may be food remains in some cases. Short of a visit to the site, the conchologist likes best a block of soil, about nine inches square, through a suspected surface or given level. This he can wash and sieve at leisure in the laboratory to yield the material which is of real interest to him and of most value to the excavator (F. E. Zeuner; and quoting the late A. G. Davis). Useful ecological deductions can be drawn only from a (buried) surface (e.g. [R2])—indeed, mollusca like pollen will indicate its precise position—and the excavator's selection only confuses the issue.[S23] On the other hand, evidence from mollusca has been used even to suggest certain pathological details in co-eval man.[B18]

Further down the vertical approach may be found the microscopic "shells" of the *foraminifera*, marine in origin, and of *diatoms* which flourish in fresh or coastal waters and cultivated soils. The former are amoeba-like animals with shells or "tests" of calcium carbonate; the latter, alga-like plants which have cell walls much strengthened with silica. Both exist in astronomical variety and in many cases provide most useful characteristic evidence. "Forams", like mollusca and other calcareous material, will disappear in acid soils. Diatom skeletons, on the other hand, like the silica bodies of grasses and some other plants, will of course persist—and (most important, see pp. 122, 188) will remain morphologically intact under most conditions.

Ecologically important, too, are *insect* remains since the chitinous beetle and pupa cases are among the most tenacious materials to survive, especially under anaerobic conditions where preservation is perfect even to the colours of the structural members.[B25] *Bird* bones have been listed separately because their identification presents a great problem at the moment: there are only a very few specialists in this field, rather surprisingly. For obvious reasons birds also require an entirely different ecological approach. The various kinds of *horn*, "tortoise shell" and ivory are less well served than animal bones, too, though adequately in the main.

Apart from its direct uses, like most of today's, there are other senses in which the study of *animal hair* is of value (e.g. for impressions, pp. 230, 232). The material includes fibres of various animals from beaver and rabbit to goat and cow, as well as sheep's wool and human hair. Like the chitin in beetle cases, keratin in animal fibre is relatively persistent and thus potentially useful.[S28]

The complex processes and materials involved in *leather* manufacture are coming to be understood at the fundamental level.[P4, S18, W15] This makes it easier to determine very small or badly preserved pieces. Unlike charcoal, charred leather is difficult to characterize; presumably owing to its flexible structure it is easily distorted by fire. Even so, microscopical examination of thin sections often shows the distinctive three-dimensional "weave"[B29] of the leather fibres clearly enough for us to be reasonably certain, and in an extreme instance a black treacly mass has been interpreted as a rawhide-plaited chariot platform.[L7] Recent work on dating leather has attempted to use other properties than the Carbon-14 content. Thus a technique has been developed for determining the shrinkage temperature of ancient leathers and relating it to the age.[B34]

A high content of the imino acid hydroxyproline with a high content of the amino acid glycine is characteristic of animal skin and can be measured in exceedingly small amounts *chromatographically*.[L4] This here involves, in effect, the controlled and special spreading of a spot on blotting paper. An extract of suspected leather residues that have become morphologically unrecognizable can be run on a suitable column or paper in a standard manner, when any hydroxyproline and glycine would separate and move to a definite area. Hydroxyproline has recently been found also in the vegetable cell wall.[L2A]

Although it appears not to be possible to recover vegetable *tanning* residues from buried leather in a firmly identifiable state, inferences can now be drawn with increasing confidence from the manner and products of analytical extraction.[W15] A neolithic sheath seemingly contained three layers of leather each differently tanned.[S26] Alum-tawing apparently confers permanent whiteness —at least to Pre-Dynastic Egyptian material; in addition it automatically mordants dyes (cf. p. 111). Intriguing problems are posed by the detection of possible primitive phosphatide tannage in early times—the result of dressing with brain substance—and by attempts at unscrambling various combination tannages.

Residues of pitch or resin lining may be found in water-bottles and drinking vessels. The two chief characteristics which distinguish *parchment* are a lamellar arrangement of its collagen—instead of the weave in leather—and the presence of calcium salts used in its production which does not involve tanning. Another feature which may remain more clearly in parchment, and has been successfully utilized, is the particular type and grouping of hair-follicles in different animal species.[R21]

Glues and *tempera media* have been obtained from early times by working up animal bones for glue size, using both egg yolk and white, making size from parchment, (true) isinglass and other glues from fish. In suitable circumstances these proteinaceous materials are very resistant indeed to change, and once again they contain characteristic amino acids that can be determined chromatographically.[E1, H12]

Such classified listing is of course merely an organizational means to an end. *Ecological considerations* clearly emerge as pre-eminent once again (p. 48); more than that, they alone are in fact able to make certain kinds of archaeological evidence meaningful at all (p. 210).

During the excavation of some barrows at Snail Down, in Wiltshire, clusters of small mammal bones were found at a number of scattered points. Had it not been for the presence of an ecologist familiar with excavations, one might perhaps not have been so certain of having these bones recovered. But even had they been, in his absence, they might very easily have gone in the normal way for zoological identification and come back described, quite simply and correctly, as the remains of water-voles. No one directly concerned might have thought any more about it, perhaps.

As it happened, the ecologist was particularly interested in wild mammals and their mutual interactions with habitat and predators. It struck him that water-voles would not be expected within some miles or more of the site, at least today. Had the Bronze Age been wetter, or had the status of the water-vole perhaps changed considerably since?

It then became apparent that the groupings of the bone clusters were associated with what were taken to be stake holes, and that they appeared from the original surface, on which the barrow was built, upwards throughout the thickness of the mound. Jewell[J2] describes vividly how he came to be able to suggest that the stakes had in fact been a reality, and that buzzard-like birds had disgorged their pellets while perched intermittently on some of them during lulls in the work.

The *dating* of *human* (and animal) "fossil" *bones*, other than by C–14 has been discussed frequently in recent years.[H7, K5] Important points include its fundamentally relative character, dependence on environment, and the need to use a battery of techniques to complement each other. Fluorine, uranium, nitrogen, carbon, water, ash and iron contents of bones can all help in the interpretation of their status. As the ratio of carbon to nitrogen can here be regarded as constant, the nitrogen test provides an indirect carbon assay. Except the uranium test, which depends on its natural radioactivity and is thus non-destructive (to specimens smaller than 2 in. × 3 in. × 4 in.), all are essentially refined versions of ordinary microchemical tests, specially designed to deal with that very small size of sample which usually can be spared in such cases. Under normal fossilizing conditions of burial, fluorine and uranium increase and nitrogen decreases with age, but so slowly (at least for the two former) that Bronze Age and Saxon material could not be distinguished on that basis alone. Also there are special conditions under which the amounts present may remain virtually the same for thousands of years (K. P. Oakley).

For more recent bones—although fossilization is of course a function of circumstance rather than period of burial—the condition in which the material is found is of interest. It seems to depend mainly on pH (p. 181), although such factors as drainage and microbiological activity must clearly have some effect. The (combinations of) amino acids characteristic of bone, like those in leather, can be separated and detected chromatographically.

For an *anatomical and pathological examination* the whole human skeleton is important, and the larger the number of individuals the more likely is something statistically useful to emerge about the "racial" and ecological status of the group. Care is needed in the selection and cleaning or other treatment of bones in the field and the specialist is best consulted from the start. Apart from the routine "ageing and sexing" of individuals, and the determination of the number represented where this is not plain—as for example in disturbed or communal burials, or in cremations (which have been unjustly neglected)[W8, W9]—there are the standard data such as dimensions of bones and the ratios of these dimensions (J. S. Weiner, J. D. Trevor), any evidence of malformation, disease or surgery,[B30, B31, B32, W10] and recently also blood-grouping.[D5, M6]

It appears that there is often enough dried blood left in the marrow of rib bones, for example, to allow *blood-grouping* tests to be carried out even on the earliest available material—always provided of course that it has been preserved under suitable conditions. At the British Museum (Natural History) large series of datable material of all types and ages are now in the process of being collected, and a serological laboratory has got under way.[S15]

Until suitable standards and techniques have been worked out satisfactorily, and a sufficient number of bones have been tested to make statistical appraisal possible, no one can say what precisely the value of this work will be. It seems likely, however, to provide at least useful corroborative data for the anthropological status of the people whose skeletons we find, almost straightaway; and it is hoped, of course, to establish in this manner patterns of connections not only between tribes and peoples but also between, say, any true (i.e. blood) relations in a communal burial.

Most of the *statements of a general nature* which were made at the C.B.A. Conference[B11] have already come out in the course of this chapter, and indeed also in others, but it is perhaps worth while picking out a few of the most important by way of a brief summary.

By some gentle, unconscious irony—implicit though it be in most scientific work—the first thing the specialists discussing "Archaeology in the laboratory" urged us to do was to get them into the *field*! The closest possible collaboration between them and the excavator, as also between themselves, is necessary, and that links up directly with two other needs—for clear ideas about what he wants, on the part of the digger; and for the use of several techniques, comparatively, wherever possible.

The value of such work, if properly arranged and conducted, is always bound to be mutual, particularly where several specialists are concerned with one set of material evidence; and in such cases it is almost always vital to move quickly, as the evidence may change on exposure, and to proceed in the right order of specialisms. Clearly someone must at all times have an overall picture of developments on the site, and also know scientific potentialities and requirements.

A glance at Table 7 will show what such a first-stage inspector of the evidence must have as his primary tool: a *microscope*—low power and preferably stereoscopic, with as long a working distance as possible. In addition he must have another, for the study of many of the materials involves examination of a sample in thin or polished section at magnifications of up to ×200 and more.

Equally clearly, of course, it is the microscope which makes possible the vertical approach at all. The different specialisms have each settled for their standard magnifications, according to the size of the characteristic units they study. But within every sphere of inspection there is a whole range of ascending magnitudes to which the given material is blown up in turn, and in this way its self-revealing "growth", at a swing of the objective or the turn of a knob, is interpreted at every stage.

A good secondary tool would be a *spectrograph*, preferably—if as yet quite impossibly—of X-ray type, or even a microprobe, with other X-ray units (p. 254).

At least in Britain, perhaps the most precious kinds of *material* are those *of organic origin.* One of those curious twists of inevitable compensation has made it possible here for the scientist, once he accepts the limits valid at any given time, to turn a seeming scourge into a useful tool, and himself from frustration to continuing development. As more comes to be known in greater detail about the fate of such materials during burial, increasing numbers of the jigsaw are found to fit—and in the process, of course, fundamental knowledge of their structure and synthesis is advanced almost by the way. Excellent preservation alone would probably never have provided the stimulus or the information.

Apart from the further refinement of non-destructive, rapid and automatic methods of elemental and structural analysis, as the "Proper Study of Mankind" fans out increasingly to catch the fascinating and valuable reflections from the environment, three of the most recent developments deserve special encouragement. They are the geophysical applications, particularly the magnetic ones; the submicroscopic examination of wood and other vegetable material; and the intensive study of the well-preserved organic complexes found under anaerobic conditions—with co-operative ingenuity and complexity to match.

Having said this much, one is, of course, at once tempted to add that the fundamentals of soil formation and surface geology, metal and pottery technology, and of the degradation and conservation of materials should be made subjects of primary importance in archaeological teaching. But this would start a chain reaction for equality of all the other approaches I have described. All the same, perhaps I may be permitted to dream, for once.

On the ideal excavation of the future, the supervisor is fully aware of the importance of constant and close collaboration with the scientific director. There is a semi-permanent yet mobile laboratory station. Of three assistant scientific directors, one is responsible for routine and continuous scientific surveys in advance of digging: geophysical, geochemical, geomorphological, ecological, soil and possibly others developed in the meantime.

Another supervises scientific examination of all features and finds as they appear and are released by the diggers after recording. He employs continuously a qualified petrologist, metallurgist, pedologist, ceramics specialist, physical anthropologist, general zoologist and general botanist. There are also several "general purpose specialists" covering between them building and decorative materials and techniques, products manufactured from animal and vegetable sources, such as leather and textiles, and writing materials of various kinds.

The analytical section is centred around a field X-ray fluorescence spectrometer, capable of measuring with sufficient accuracy even the fluorine and nitrogen contents of bones, but includes also X-ray apparatus for diffraction, radiological and "flying spot" work. The dating section deals with Carbon-14, archaeomagnetic and other forms of palaeochronometry. There is an all-round physical chemist to provide minor test services and deal with emergencies while machines are out of action.

Not least—if inevitably last in the order of this particular list—the third assistant scientific director is charged with all the conservation work. Suitable facilities, and the information given by the examining department, make it possible for his staff to deal immediately with recognizable objects and to complete work on the vast majority of them before the season's excavation is over—working on beyond when necessary.

In this way, the archaeological supervisor as a matter of routine gets vital information on the spot, as well as before, or at least during, the excavation whose course he is thus able more confidently to control. Furthermore, most of the finds are "revealed" ready for typological appraisal, and where possible and necessary

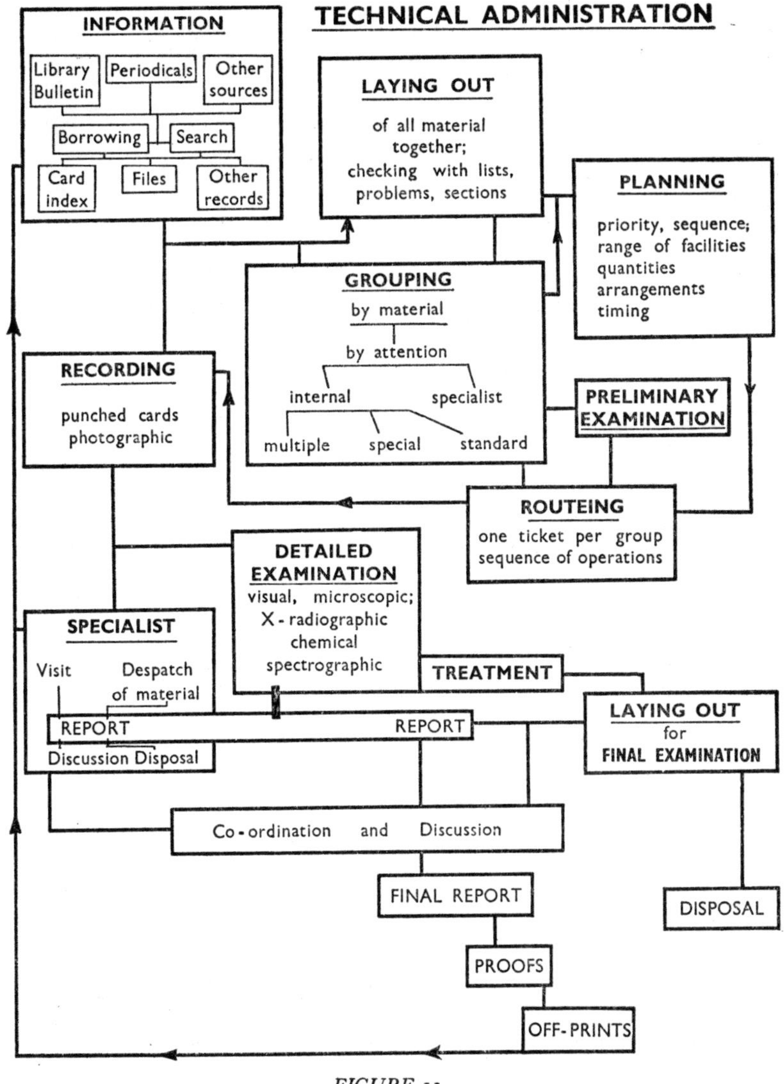

FIGURE 11

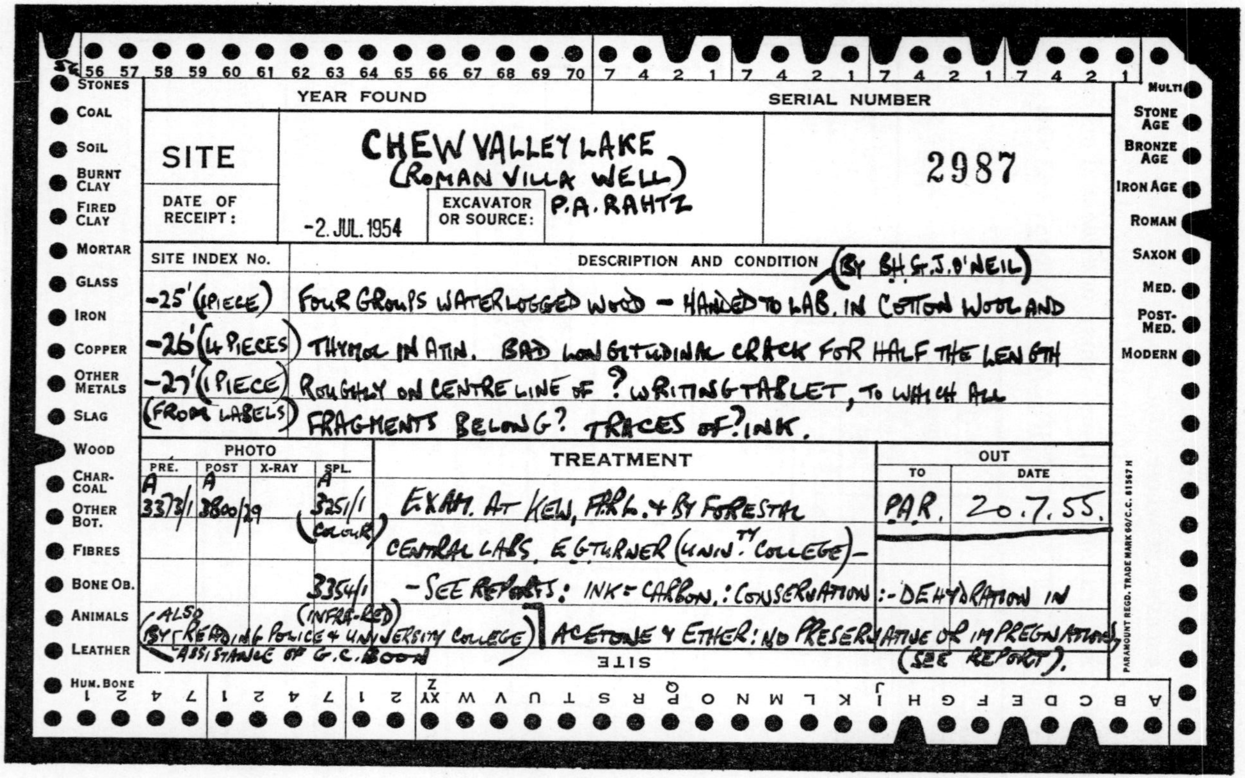

56 57 58 59 60 61 62 63 64 65 66 67 68 69 70 7 4 2 1 7 4 2 1 7 4 2 1 7 4 2 1

STONES · COAL · SOIL · BURNT CLAY · FIRED CLAY · MORTAR · GLASS · IRON · COPPER · OTHER METALS · SLAG · WOOD · CHAR-COAL · OTHER BOT. · FIBRES · BONE OB. · ANIMALS · LEATHER · HUM. BONE

MULTI · STONE AGE · BRONZE AGE · IRON AGE · ROMAN · SAXON · MED. · POST-MED. · MODERN

YEAR FOUND			SERIAL NUMBER
SITE	CHEW VALLEY LAKE (ROMAN VILLA WELL)		2987
DATE OF RECEIPT: -2. JUL. 1954	EXCAVATOR OR SOURCE:	P.A. RAHTZ	

SITE INDEX No.	DESCRIPTION AND CONDITION (BY B.H. ST. J. O'NEIL)
-25' (1 PIECE)	FOUR GROUPS WATERLOGGED WOOD – HANDED TO LAB. IN COTTON WOOL AND
-26' (4 PIECES)	THYMOL IN A TIN. BAD LONGITUDINAL CRACK FOR HALF THE LENGTH
-27' (1 PIECE)	ROUGHLY ON CENTRE LINE OF ? WRITING TABLET, TO WHICH ALL
(FROM LABELS)	FRAGMENTS BELONG? TRACES OF ? INK.

PHOTO PRE.	POST	X-RAY	SPL.	TREATMENT	OUT TO	DATE
A 3373/1	A 3800/29		A 3251/1 (COLOUR)	EXAM. AT KEW, F.P.R.L. & BY FORESTAL	PAR.	20.7.55.
				CENTRAL LABS. E.G. TURNER (UNIV.TY COLLEGE)–		
			3354/1 (INFRA-RED)	– SEE REPORTS: INK = CARBON.: CONSERVATION :- DEHYDRATION IN		
(ALSO BY READING POLICE & UNIVERSITY COLLEGE) (ASSISTANCE OF G.C. BOON)				ACETONE & ETHER: NO PRESERVATIVE OR IMPREGNATION, (SEE REPORT).		

SITE

A B C D E F G H I J K L M N O P Q R S T U V W XY Z 2 1 7 4 2 1 7 4 2 1

PARAMOUNT REGD. TRADE MARK 60/C.C. 81567 H

FIGURE 12. *One of the punched record cards on which all basic information about finds is kept at the Ancient Monuments Laboratory. The system permits one to "needle out" any item or group—whatever the order of cards—according to at least five main criteria: year found, number, period, site (coded, along bottom edge) and material. Further refinements are possible by using "free" holes along right-hand edge.*

suitably cleaned and conserved for exhibition at the same time as the archaeological field notes are complete.

There is no backlog, no delay—what a dream! The time between seasons is spent on staff holidays, research, visits to other similar or very specialized institutions and collections—for the purposes of comparing notes and matching material—and in dealing with the relatively few matters arising from the season's dig that could not be determined or interpreted in the course of it—and of course in preparation for the next.

So much for the dream. In the meantime, interested parties are working towards the short-term ideal of a Central Scientific Institute for Archaeology. Until this has become a reality, however, the work can only be done with the help of specialists who are otherwise committed. The organization at the Ancient Monuments Laboratory is shown in Figures 7, 11, and 12, and Table 8.

This can never be a substitute for an institution where all kinds of specialist, each highly qualified in his own field—from epigraphy *via* archaeology to nucleonics—are working together not only under one roof but also in rooms with interconnecting doors. But we are perhaps not quite ready for such self-sufficiency; isolated research communities seem to lose some vital spark after a generation.[A8]

Ultimately, any specialist must Antaeus-like return to his own deep Gea reservoir, in one way or another, for refreshment in his struggle with the herculean problems that confront him. While we extol the virtues of interdisciplinary mixing, the freshness of approach from every angle must not be forgotten. This can only be maintained if each man's isolated view is securely based on a confidence shared by some others at much the same vantage point.

Possibly the intensive development of a loosely federated collaboration such as I have been describing is still best, at least during our present stage. As long as we accept that specialists must remain professionally faithful in their fashion, whatever the motive in their search for the tangible details, we also retain this most valuable way of getting to know one another. Perhaps in this sense above all, the meticulous salvage and reconstruction of the past is an activity of supreme and universal importance.

TABLE 8

Standard methods in use at the Ancient Monuments Laboratory

(for bulk of treatment and treatment in bulk; for details see relevant table following)

METAL

Condition \ *Material*	*Iron*	*Copper and silver and alloys*	*Lead*
SOUND	Deoxidine (tab. 8.1)	Electrolytic bath (tab. 8.2)	
DOUBTFUL	P.V.A. and soak (tab. 8.4) (?with gas reduction [tab. 8.3])	Gas reduction (tab. 8.3)	P.V.A. and soak (tab. 8.4)
POOR	P.V.A. AND SOAK (tab. 8.4)		

NON-METAL and **MOUNTING**

Siliceous		*Organic*			MOUNTING
Pottery	Glass	Leather (tab. 8.5)	Wood (Waterlogged)		Special presentation, consolidation, etc., using Perspex; all materials, incorporating X-ray evidence and other features Conjectural extrapolation of form
Manual/mechanical cleaning of any			Dehydration[P9]		
decoration	detail		Large	Small and special	
Vacuum impregnation (nitro-cellulose)[B13, B16]			Slowly dried in polythene bags for long period	Acetone for suitable period	
Assembly			If poor, surface sealed at suitable stage (wax; epoxy resin)	Ether for suitable period; removed under vacuum	
Durofix	(No satisfactory and economical permanent adhesive, unless material porous, thin, or impregnated)			If possible, left "thus dry"; otherwise, vacuum impregnation	
Restoration					
Dental plaster	Plastic (sheet or casting)				

TABLE 8

8.1 Deoxidine*

IRON: SOUND

Immersion	Solubilization of corrosion products and (release of) enclosed deposits Relative passivation of metal surface being exposed
Steelwire-brushing (under cold, running water)	Mechanical removal of obstinate residues, but using comparable material (Products of treatment more soluble in the cold)
Repeat until overall metallic surface. If necessary, renew solution	(On exhaustion of acid, at pH 4, excessive concentration of phosphates: white crystalline deposit on objects; separation of lighter, organic phase)
Final brushing (under hot water)	Production of "finished" surface, and final rinse (To assist evaporation of water from "heated" object)
Acetone dip (followed by air-drying under 60 W lamp)	Replacement of water residues by virtually "dry" acetone Prevention of "rust bloom", avoiding need for final dry brush
Molten beeswax (about 70°C)	Continuous water- (and air-) barrier in some depth, especially in pits and crevices, and across jagged edges and sharp points [B12]
Result: (*e.g. pl. 20 and col. pl. I*G)	Metallic, unpolished surface, showing "fibrous drawing" marks typical of wrought iron; bright at first, gradually dulling acceptably. Very stable in dry conditions. Where kept moist, especially where severe condensation, and/or nuclei of corrosion products remain, superficial rusting can occur but is easily removed, e.g., by rubbing over with an eraser which removes the rust film and re-spreads adjacent wax. Wax easily removed by melting or solvents

* A.C.P. Deoxidine 125, ICI Engineering Trades Dept.

8.2 Electrolytic Bath

COPPER, SILVER, TIN, AND LEAD ALLOYS: SOUND

Contents	Approx. 2% solution of caustic soda in distilled water Anode (positive): steel plate (or platinized titanium) Cathode (negative): object (suspended from copper rod in copper wire "stirrup" or "basket")
Operation	Direct current (from mains *via* trickle charger) at about 5 V and 0·1 A for full charge

8.2 Electrolytic Bath—*contd.*

Action First stage:	(Oxygen evolved at anode as soon as current passes)
No bubbling on object	Penetration and reduction of corrosion products and
Darkening, some deposition of black "powder"	"plating" of metallic iron from impurities in solution (caustic soda, "soil" in corrosion products, steel anode), even with titanium anode, on to freshly exposed metal surface. (p. 201.)
Second stage:	End of main reduction
Bubbling on object	Evolution of hydrogen
	Disruption and sloughing of "reduced" corrosion products' skin
Further and increased deposition of black "powder"	Metallic iron "plating" continues and increases
Light glass-brush (under running hot water)	Removal of black deposit loosely adhering to surface; if this is pitted, intensive brushing may be needed, and correct choice of moment important, as any subsequent action will prefer metallic areas and avoid uncleaned pockets
Return to bath and repeat, if necessary, till overall metallic	
Boiling in distilled water	Removal of residual salts, derived mainly from bath itself Carried out in (about 4–5) successive changes until leaching negligible (control by conductivity) Basically like "intensive washing" P9 but simplified, like the whole process, as found adequate for dealing with bulk of British material where chlorides not present in dangerous quantity or depth
Acetone dip to dry	As for iron (tab. 8.1)
Light glass-brushing (dry) (preferably with mounted brush mechanically rotated about its axis)	Production of "bright" metallic finish (no "scratching", or brushing-on of foreign material)
Birlon† *dip*	Protective "lacquer" combining strength and plasticity even in an "invisibly" thin coat
Result: (*e.g. col. pl. I*A, G)	Metallic unpolished surface, more or less rough according to manner and depth of corrosion during burial; bright at first, dulling according to metal: acceptably, except for copper alloys containing much lead (which darken considerably after any treatment); lead itself is more satisfactory, and may be left uncoated to dull "naturally", although attacked by "intensive washing".

8.2 Electrolytic Bath—*contd.*

The bulk of material has been found very stable, though isolated cases may need special re-treatment after periods varying according to conditions of burial and composition. Lacquer film easily removed by solvent supplied as "Thinner", and second (identical) bath treatment takes only fraction of the time. Generally, objects treated in batches of up to twenty or more at a time, provided effective current density is maintained, but individual and manual wet-brushing has so far remained inescapable.

---

† Birlon, and Thinners: Cellon, Ltd.—a vinyl-based copolymer.

8.3 Gas-Reduction**

MAINLY COPPER (ALLOY): DOUBTFUL, OR SOUND WITH DOUBTFUL SURFACE WHICH BATH OR ANY LIQUID MIGHT DISRUPT; ALSO IRON IN SPECIAL CASES, E.G. EXHIBITION: DOUBTFUL OR UNSOUND

Assembly	(Two-piece) metal container with suitable inlet from top, for (coal) gas stream and thermometer, and suitable outlets at side(s) E.g., one (rectangular) baking tin inverted on another, bolted together with asbestos washers between the flanges except for the four corners; asbestos bung with holes for thermometer and gas inlet Objects in depressions on (copper) gauze support to avoid direct contact with base of chamber The whole on a suitable gas-ring with separate supply to inlet
Operation	Chamber filled with gas and issuing streams at corners lit
Heat from below to about 200°C and continue for about ½ hr. or, if flame tinged green, until this tinge disappears	Most copper corrosion products reduced to metallic state *in situ* Lead in corrosion products, though not in metal (alloy), is similarly affected but melts into globules which separate and may be removed on cooling Tin is not reduced Organic matter is charred and may seriously interfere Side reactions may produce ammonium and tin chlorides (vapour) and ? hydrocarbons
If coherence of powdery objects desired, heat to 400–500°C for a short period	Slow growth across crystal boundaries—"sintering" of loose areas

8.3 Gas Reduction—*contd.*

Cooling	Heating gas turned off, and when fall in temperature becomes negligible flames at corners blown out but passage of gas through inlet continued until room temperature reached** Important to prevent reaction between hot, highly reactive (finely divided) reduced copper surface and oxygen in air
Result: (*e.g. col. pl. I*A)	In form, the object is little changed, if at all, depending on porosity of original surface The colour is changed to a more or less bright metallic tone according to amount of organic matter present, efficiency of cooling, and other factors The texture is opened up considerably as a result of removing, in effect, about half the corroded surface by weight Metallographic structure unlikely to be significantly affected

Visual and manual exploration indicates *next step*:
either *BATH* (tab. 8.2)
or *Glass-brushing under acetone* (if water undesirable)
or *Glass-brushing or flaking, dry*
or *Immersion in or impregnation with Birlon* (tab. 8.2)

Iron:	To improve appearance (and, especially, align with other exhibits), objects after *PVA-soak* (tab. 8.4) treatment may be gas-reduced Metallographic structure may be affected The resulting film of (charred PVA) carbon, penetrating to limits of soaking, is also mildly protective and sealed with an additional coat of PVA

** Explosion hazards attend inexpert or careless operation of this (as any other) process involving manipulation of gas–air mixtures.

8.4 "PVA and Soak"††

MAINLY IRON, ALSO COPPER (ALLOY): DOUBTFUL OR UNSOUND
(Not suitable for assemblies, or treatment, of both together)

Immersion in PVA solution (if not possible, brush or flow on) *and air-drying*	Consolidation of friable objects that might otherwise fall apart, especially during the next step; mechanical "cleaning" or other pre-treatment is usually risky or wasteful Production of water-permeable PVA film

8.4 "PVA and Soak"—*contd.*

Suspension (in perforated plastic tray or bag *in distilled or deionized water*, renewed at suitable and increasing intervals—sometimes for weeks or even months—until test reaction negligible)	Elution of water-soluble salts, mainly chlorides, through the partly destroyed, but sufficiently cohesive, "pin-holed" PVA film Control by acid silver nitrate test for chlorides or, preferably, by conductivity meter Number of objects treated at the same time is limited only by size of tank and quantity of water available: ratio $\frac{\text{vol. object}}{\text{vol. water}}$ should = about $\frac{1}{20}$
Air-drying	Effective dehydration to limits of water penetration (not critical)
Re-immersion in PVA solution, and air-drying	Reinforcement of previous PVA film to limits of salt-elution, where not (also beneficially) blocked by "rust" formed in that process
Result:	Chemically and physically, the "object" and thus the evidence remains in effect unchanged Visually, there is saturation or even gloss, depending on porosity and manipulation—gloss may be removed, and saturation controlled to the desired level, by suitable surface treatment with solvent, but this has to be balanced against considerations of stability Like all other ("safe") methods, this cannot ensure complete and permanent stability, but any remaining salts are deep enough to remain largely inactive for long periods, and any action is much restrained by the cohesive effect of the PVA film Fresh outbreaks are easily and similarly treated to the next limit of penetration as extended by the outbreak itself—i.e. the worse the object the more effective the treatment As always, dry storage will much prolong the period of stability—for exhibition, process is combined with gas-reduction (tab. 8.3) in the case of iron

†† 15–20% w/w solution of polyvinyl acetate in toluene; the dry film is soluble in most organic solvents including benzene and acetone. Fire and poisoning hazards attend large-scale operations and adequate ventilation and precautions are essential.

8.5 Leather

MAINLY: WATERLOGGED, SOUND; OFTEN ALSO (BETTER THAN NEAT OIL) FOR MOIST OR DRY, SOUND

Immersion

First stage:

In emulsion of neat's-foot oil in water, 1 : 1, prepared by rapid mechanical mixing with 2–3% Lissapol N§ as emulsifier	Material suspended in perforated plastic tray or bag, exactly at the halfway level Emulsion diffuses into water contained in leather

8.5 Leather—*contd.*

The emulsion is deliberately made to be unstable; as it begins to separate, process reaches

Second stage:

In emulsion auto-dehydrating by gravity at increasing rate, drops coalescing to form larger, heavier units and ultimately complete separation, i.e.	At every level, water drops separate (downwards) from oil (floating) Water appears to come out of the leather while the oil stays in

Third stage:

In "pure" neat's-foot oil (top layer) above water containing "impurities" and salts from leather	More oil enters leather, now holding less water, along pathways "lubricated" by "advance oil" from emulsion This seems to apply also to dry leather which is better wetted by emulsion than neat oil

Sometimes a repetition of stages 1 and 2 improves penetration, before stage 3 is allowed to proceed to completion

Drainage	Tray or bag suspended above container until bulk of excess oil has drained back; if not too contaminated the remaining liquid can be mixed again into an emulsion for use with next batch of leather (stage 1)
Drying	Surfaces of objects are briefly wiped, and objects are wrapped in newspaper or similarly absorbent waste material and left for short period to de-grease the surfaces Objects left for short period to dry in open, protected from dust, and "finished" by thorough wiping or polishing of surfaces
Result:	No change in shape or suppleness, from state in which found Usually lightening of colour, back from "artificial" darkening due to water saturation, and towards "natural" (and probably original) colour Oil or salt "spue" may appear on the surface after some time, especially when dehydration incomplete; but this merely unsightly and may easily be wiped off Objects very stable indeed, and will normally not take up water vapour excessively, even in moist surroundings, unlike most other usual impregnants which are miscible with water and render the leather hygroscopic

§ Lissapol N, ICI Dyestuffs Div.

BIBLIOGRAPHY

AND

AUTHOR INDEX

In some instances up-to-date titles have been inserted at proof stage and are, therefore, not numbered. An asterisk denotes a publication that is of general value even though it may not be specifically referred to in the text.

The figures in bold type at the end of each entry provide the Author Index.

A1 AERO STILLS LTD., London, e.g., *Times*, 14.10.59, p. 22 **32**

A2 AITKEN, M. J. (*a*) Magnetic dating; (*b*) Magnetic prospecting. *Archaeometry*, 1958, *1*, 16–20 (*a*), 24–6 (*b*); 1959, *2*, 17–19 (*a*), 32–42 (*b*, with P. J. Fowler); 1960, *3*, 41–4 (*a*), 38–40 (*b*) **197, 198, 229**

A3 AITKEN, M. J., Magnetic prospecting: an interim assessment. *Antiquity*, 1959, *33*, 205–7 **29, 198, 209**

A4 AITKEN, M. J., *Physics and Archaeology*, 1961, Interscience **72, 198, 208, 229, 231**

A5 ALEXANDER, J., *et al.*, Report on the investigation of a round barrow at Arreton Down, I.o.W. *Proc. prehist. Soc.*, 1960, *XXVI*, 263–302 **125**

A6 ALLEN, J. A., Manganese deposition on shells of living molluscs. *Nature*, 1960, *185*, 336–7 **181**

A7 ANON. (editorials), e.g. (*a*) The impact of science and technology on humanism; (*b*) Science and the humanities. *Nature*, 1959, *184*, 1595 (*a*); 1961, *189*, 695 (*b*); also numerous directly relevant editorials throughout 1961: *191*, 1229; *192*, 1, 95, 195, 387, 587, and reports of addresses by the Minister for Science: 393–8 and 787–91 **16**

A8 ANON. (ed.), Co-operation in research. *Nature*, 1961, *192*, 785–7 **257**

A9 ANON. Agreement to broaden the curriculum. *Head Teachers' Review* (Feb.) 1962, 15. *See also* N.A.T.O. **16**

A10 ANON., Computer shows Babylonian tablet dated precisely 183 B.C. *Illustr. Lond. News*, 1962, *240*, 635 **26**

A11 ANSTEE, J. W., Fragments of Roman "bronze" scale armour from Corbridge. *Mus. J.*, 1953, *53*, 200–2 **121, 163**

A12 ANSTEE, J. W., and BIEK, L., A study in pattern-welding. *Med. Arch.*, 1961, *VI*, 71–93. *See also* B16 **108, 165**

A13 ASHBEE, P., The Great Barrow at Bishops Waltham,

Hampshire. *Proc. prehist. Soc.*, 1957, *XXIII*, 137–66. *See also* p. 124 **122, 125, 180, 187**

A14 ASHBEE, P., The Wilsford Shaft. *Antiquity*, 1961 *XXXVII*, 116–20 **31**

A15 ASHBY, SIR ERIC, Technological humanism. *J. Inst. Met.*, 1956–7, *LXXXV*, 461–7 **16**

*A16 ATKINSON, R. J. C., *Field Archaeology* (2nd edn., revised), 1953, Methuen **28**

A17 ATKINSON, R. J. C., *Stonehenge*, pp. 107–10, 1956, Hamish Hamilton **81**

*A18 ATKINSON, R. J. C., *Archaeology, History and Science*, 1961, Cardiff: University of Wales Press

B1 e.g., BAGBY, P., *Culture and History*, 1958, Longmans, Green **16**

B2 BAILEY, T. A., *The re-erection of fallen stones at Stonehenge, 1958–9* (M.P.B.W. report, unpublished) **32, 192**

B3 BARGHOORN, E. S., Palaeobotanical studies of the fishweir and associated deposits. (In JOHNSON *et al.*, The Boylston Street Fishweir II.) *Pap. Peabody Found. Arch.*, 1949, *4*, 49–83 **149**

B4 BARKER, H., Radiocarbon dating. *Nature*, 1959, *184*, 672–4; *Antiquity*, 1958, *XXXII*, 253–63 **242**

B4A BARRACLOUGH, G., The crisis of historicism. *Listener*, 1956 (2 Feb.) 171–2 **16**

B4B BARTON, K. J., Settlements of the Iron Age and Pagan Saxon periods at Linford, Essex. *Trans. Essex archaeol. Soc.*, 1962, *I* (3rd ser.), 57–104 **44**

BASAK, R. K., *see* S10

B5 BATE-SMITH, E. C. (and METCALFE, C. R. (*a*) only) (*a*) Leucoanthocyanins, 3. The nature and systematic distribution of tannins in dicotyledonous plants; (*b*) The phenolic constituents of plants and their taxonomic significance. *J. Linn. Soc.*, 1957, *LV*, 669–705 (*a*); 1962, *LVIII*, 95–173 (*b*) **152**

B6 BECK, S. D., *The Simplicity of Science*, 1960, Lutterworth Press **23**

B7 BELFORD, D. S., *et al.*, The impregnation of timber by waterborne preservatives. *J. appl. Chem.*, 1959, *9*, 192–200 **126**

B8 BELFORD, D. S., X-ray spectrographic analysis—a new technique in wood preservation research. *Record of Convention*, 1961, British Wood Preserving Association **207**

B9 BELSHÉ, J. C., Conference on geophysical methods, 1961. *Antiquity* (forthcoming). *See also* C16, and REES **29, 207**

B10 BERESFORD, M., *The Lost Villages of England*, 1954, Lutterworth Press **27**

BEVERIDGE, W. I. B., *The Art of Scientific Investigation*, 1961, Mercury Books **89**

B11 BIEK, L., Archaeology in the laboratory. Summary of report of Conference, Council for British Archaeology, 1954 (unpublished). *Nature*, 1954, *174*, 957. *See also* F3 **206, 252**

B12 BIEK, L., CRIPPS, E. S., and THACKER, D. M. D., Some methods for protecting cleaned iron objects. *Mus. J.*, 1954, *54*, 32–6 **160, 259**

B13 BIEK, L., *et al.*, A new impregnating chamber. *Mus. J.*, 1955, *54*, 311–13 **187, 258**

*B14 BIEK, L., Technology of ancient glass and metal; summary of symposium at British Association Meeting, 1956. *Nature*, 1956, *178*, 1430–4. *See also* A12 **165, 237**

B15 BIEK, L., The examination of some copper ores. *Man*, 1957, 84 **221**

B16 BIEK, L., ANSTEE, J. W., and CRIPPS, E. S. A wooden bucket restored. *Mus. J.*, 1958, *57*, 257–61 **161, 258**

B17 BIEK, L., *Studies on Metals in the Electrolysis of Dilute Alkalis. (With particular reference to the anodic behaviour of iron in dilute sodium hydroxide solution during cathodic cleaning of ancient corroded bronze objects.)* M.Sc. Thesis, London University (to be submitted) **201**

B18 BIGGS, H. E. J., Mollusca from prehistoric Jericho. *J. conch.*, 1960, *24*, 379–87 **248**

B19 BIMSON, M., The technique of Greek black and *terra sigillata* red. *Antiq. J.*, 1956 *XXXVI*, 200–4. *See also* HOFMANN **167**

B20 BLIN-STOYLE, A., Spectrographic analysis of British Middle and Late Bronze Age finds. *Archaeometry*, 1959, *2*, 1–24 **239**

B21 BLOOMFIELD, C., Sesquioxide immobilization and clay movement in podzolized soils. *Nature*, 1953, *172*, 958 **151**

B22 BLOOMFIELD, C., Leaf leachates as a factor in pedogenesis. *J. Sci. Food & Agric.*, 1955, *6*, 641–51 **154**

B23 BOOTH, G. H., and TILLER, A. K., Polarization studies of mild steel in cultures of sulphate-reducing bacteria. *Trans. Faraday Soc.*, 1960, *56*, 1689–96 (*a*); 1962, *58*, 110–15 (*b*) **157**

B24 BOOTH, G. H., TILLER, A. K., and WORMWELL, F., A laboratory study of well-preserved ancient iron nails from apparently corrosive soils. *Corrosion Sci.*, 1962, *2*, 197–202 **157**

B24A BOWERS, F., *Textual and Literary Criticism.* 1962, Cambridge University Press **44**

B25 BRADLEY, P. L., An assemblage of arthropod remains from a Roman occupation site at St. Albans. *Nature*, 1958, *181*, 435–6. *See* L8 **248**

B26 BRILL, R. H., and HOOD, H. P., A new method for dating ancient glass. *Nature*, 1961, *189*, 12–14 **237**

B27 BRITISH ASSOCIATION FOR THE ADVANCEMENT OF SCIENCE, e.g. at the Bristol Meeting, 1955. *Advanc. Sci.*, 1955–6, *XII*, 258, 301, 515, 531 **16**

*B28 BRITISH ASSOCIATION FOR THE ADVANCEMENT OF SCIENCE, Section H (Anthropology and archaeology): Sessions at annual meetings on "ancillary aids", in *Advanc. Sci.*, from 1947 (*IV*, 332 ff.) onwards

B29 BRITISH LEATHER MANUFACTURERS' RESEARCH ASSOCIATION, *Hides, Skins and Leathers under the Microscope*, 1957, Egham, Surrey: The Association **249**

B29A BROECKER, W. S., *et al.*, Radiocarbon measurements and annual rings in cave formations. *Nature*, 1960, *185*, 93–4 **242**

B30 BROTHWELL, D., The palaeopathology of early British man. *J. R. anthrop. Inst.*, 1961, *91*, 318–44 **251**

B31 BROTHWELL, D. R., *Digging up Bones*. British Museum (Natural History) Handbook, 1963, H.M.S.O. **251**

*B32 BROTHWELL, D. R., and HIGGS, E. S. (eds.), *Science in Archaeology*, 1963, Thames & Hudson **18, 237, 247, 251**

*B33 BRUCE-MITFORD, R. L. S. (ed.), *Recent Archaeological Excavations in Britain*, 1956, Routledge & Kegan Paul **27, 28, 182**

B34 BURTON, D., POOLE, J. B., and REED, R., A new approach to the dating of the Dead Sea Scrolls. *Nature*, 1959, *184*, 533–534. *See also* POOLE and REED **249**

B35 BUTTERFIELD, H., *Man on his Past—the History of Historiography*. Wiles Trust Lectures, Queen's University, Belfast, 1955, Cambridge University Press **40**

B36 BUTTERWORTH, B., and HONEYBORNE, D. B., Bricks and clays of the Hastings Beds. *Trans. Brit. ceram. Soc.*, 1952. *LI*, 211–59 **228**

B37 BUTTERWORTH, M. A., Examination of microspores in coal (in WEBSTER, A note on the use of coal in Roman Britain). *Antiq. J.*, 1955, *XXXV*, 216–17 **220**

*C1 CALEY, E. R. (ed.), Symposium on archaeological chemistry, Philadelphia, April 1950. *J. chem. Educ.*, 1951, *28*, 63–96. Also Symposium in 1962 (forthcoming) **111, 245**

C1A CALEY, E. R., *Analyses of Ancient Glasses, 1790–1957*. Corning Museum of Glass Monographs, Vol. I, 1962, New York: The Museum **135, 237**

C2 CAMBI, L., Sul metallo dei monili delle tombe del sepolcreto di Ponte S. Pietro, Castro d'Ischia, Viterbo. *Istituto Lombardo Accademia di Scienza e Lettere*, 1958, *92*, 169–72 **136**

C3 CAMPBELL, H. S., The influence of the composition of supply waters, and especially of traces of natural inhibitor, on corrosion of copper water pipes. *Proc. Soc. Water Treat. Exam.*, 1954, *3*, 100–15 **130**

CARTER, G. F., *see* S21

CASE, H., *see* C11

C4 CHADWICK, S., Finglesham—a re-appraisal. *Med. Arch.*, 1958, *2*, 1–71 **127**

CHATTERJEE, A. K., *see* T6

C5 CHEVREUL, M. E., Sur la composition chimique des statuettes de bronze trouvées par M. Mariette (Louvre). *Compt. rend.*, 1856, *XLIII*, 735 **140**

C6 CHILDE, V. G., The significance of the lake dwellings in the history of prehistory. *Sibrium*, 1955, *II*, 87–91 **88**

C7 CHILDE, V. G., *Piecing Together the Past*, 1956, Routledge & Kegan Paul **93, 120, 165**

*C8 CLARK, J. G. D. *Prehistoric Europe; the economic basis*—e.g., Pls. II, XII and XVI (2nd edn.) 1952, Methuen **211**

C9 CLARK, J. G. D., *The Study of Prehistory*. Disney professorship inaugural address, 1954, Cambridge University Press **17**

C10 CLAYTON, K. M. (ed.), *Geomorphological Abstracts*, from 1960, The Editor, c/o London School of Economics **209**

C11 COGHLAN, H. H., and CASE, H.,

Early metallurgy of copper in Ireland and Britain. *Proc. prehist. Soc.*, 1957, *XXIII*, 91–123 **238**

C12 COGHLAN, H. H., *Early History of Iron in Northwest Europe*, 1954, Oxford: Pitt Rivers Museum. Also in H7 **136, 239**

C13 COGHLAN, H. H., Etruscan and Spanish swords of iron. *Sibrium*, 1956–7, *III*, 167–74 **134**

C14 COGHLAN, H. H., *Notes on the Prehistoric Metallurgy of Copper and Bronze in the Old World*, 1951, Oxford: Pitt Rivers Museum. Also in H7 **81, 136, 165**

C15 COOK, M., and RICHARDS, T. LL., The self-annealing of copper. *J. Inst. Met.*, 1944, *70*, 159 **162**

C16 COOK, R. M., and BELSHÉ, J. C., Archaeomagnetism: A preliminary report on Britain. *Antiquity*, 1958, *XXXII*, 167–78 **231**

COOK, S. F., *see* H7

C17 COOKSON, M. B., *Photography for Archaeologists*, 1954, Max Parrish **33**

C18 COOMBE, D. E., On the interpretation of the discontinuous distributions shown by certain British species of open habitats. *J. Ecol.*, 1954, *42*, 95. Note on *Carex humilis* Leyss **90**

C19 CORNWALL, I. W., *Bones for the Archaeologist*, 1956, Phoenix House. Contains many useful drawings and suggestions, and notes on packing **247**

C20 COULSON, C. B., *et al.*, Polyphenols in plant, humus and soil. *J. Soil Sci.*, 1960, *11*, 20–44 **156**

C21 CRAWFORD, O. G. S., *Air-photography for Archaeologists*, 1929, H.M.S.O. For contrasts see especially Pls. III and IV (due to types of cropmark and cover), X and XI (type of cover) and XVII and XIX (time of year) **28**

CRIPPS, E. S., *see* B12 and B16

C22 CRISP, D. J., JONES, L. W. G., and WATSON, W., Use of x-ray stereoscopy for examining shipworm infestation *in vivo*. *Nature*, 1953, *172*, 408 **244**

C23 CUTLER, H. C., *History of Maize* (forthcoming) **244**

D1 DAUNCEY, K., Ancillary aids to archaeology. *Advanc. Sci.*, 1952, *IX*, 33–6 **63**

D2 DAVEY, N., *A History of Building Materials*, 1961, Phoenix House **52, 232, 233**

D3 DAVIDSON, H. R. ELLIS, *The Sword in Anglo-Saxon England*, e.g., pp. 156–7; also Appendix, 1961, Oxford: Clarendon Press **108, 165**

D4 DAVY, C., *Towards a Third Culture*, 1962, Faber **14**

D5 DE BEER, SIR GAVIN, *Reflections of a Darwinian*, 1962, Thomas Nelson **251**

D6 DENNINGER, E., and EBINGER, H., Versuche über die Rekonstruktion der "Terra Nigra". *Germania*, 1953, *31*, 67–8 **167**

D6A DE GEER, G., A geochronology of the last 12,000 years. *C. R. XI Congr. Geol. Inst. Stockholm*, 1910; Geochronologia Suecica Principles. *K. Svensk Vet. Akad. Handl. Stockholm*, 1940, 18 (3rd. ser.), no. 6 **225**

D7 DE VRIES, H., Variation in concentration of radiocarbon with time and location on earth. *Koninkl. Nederlandse Akad. Wetensh. Proc.*, 1958, Ser. B, *61*, 1–9 **243**

D8 DICKSON, T. E., "Pure" art. *Studio*, 1961, *162*, 42–7, 76–7 **68**

D9 DIMBLEBY, G. W., Pollen analysis as an aid to the dating of prehistoric monuments. *Proc. prehist. Soc.*, 1954, *XX*, 231–6. *See also* T7 **49, 246**

D10 DIMBLEBY, G. W., *The development of British heathlands and their soils*, 1962, Oxford University Press **52, 155, 221, 246**

D11 DOBSON, R. M., and SATCHELL, J. E., *Eophila oculata* at Verulamium: a Roman earthworm population. *Nature*, 1956, *177*, 796–7. *See* L8 **52**

D11A DOLLEY, R. H., Explanatory note on the coins, medals, dies and seals, pp. 66–71, in *Kings and Queens A.D. 653–1953*, catalogue of exhibition (3rd edn.), 1953, Royal Academy of Arts **86**

DRAKE, R. J. (ed.), *Molluscs in Archaeology and the Recent.* Quarterly from August 1960 (I.), Vancouver: Department of Zoology, University of British Columbia **248**

D12 DUMAS, F., *Deep Water Archaeology*, 1962, Routledge & Kegan Paul **32**

D13 DUNCUMB, P. Improved resolution with the X-ray scanning microanalyser, in *Proceedings of the Second International Symposium on X-ray microscopy and X-ray microanalysis, Stockholm*, 1960, Amsterdam: Elsevier **238**

D14 DURY, G. H., *The face of the earth*, 1959, Penguin Books **209**

E1 EASTOE, J. E., A semi-micro method for the detection of amino acids by ion exchange chromatography. *Biochem. J.*, 1961, *79*, 652–6 **250**

EBINGER, H., *see* D6

E2 ELAM, C. F., Some bronze specimens from the royal graves at Ur. *J. Inst. Met.*, 1932, *XLVIII*, 97–108 **136**

ELDRIDGE, C. H., *see* F4

E3 ELLWOOD, E. C., Reports TE/18,943 and 19,597 (unpub.), Tin Research Institute **138**

E4 EL SHAZLY, E. M., WEBB, J. S., and WILLIAMS, D., Trace elements in sphalerite, galena and associated minerals from the British Isles. *Trans. Inst. Min. Metall.*, 1956–7, *66*, 241–71 and 478–90 **221**

E5 EMELEUS, V. M., The technique of neutron activation analysis as applied to trace element determination in pottery and coins. *Archaeometry*, 1958, *1*, 6–15 **117, 228, 238**

E6 EMELEUS, V. M. (*b* with SIMPSON, G.), (*a*) Neutron activation analysis of Samian ware sherds, *Archaeometry*, 1960, *3*, 16–19; (*b*) Neutron activation analysis of ancient Roman pot sherds, *Nature*, 1960, *185*, 196. *See also* R14 **91, 220**

E7 EVANS, J. V., Bloodgrouping in ruminants and human migration. *Advanc. Sci.*, 1956, *XIII*, 198–200 **247**

E8 EVISON, V. I., An Anglo-Saxon cemetery at Holborough, Kent. *Arch. Cantiana*, 1956, *LXX*, 84–141 **106**

E9 EVISON, V. I., *Excavations at Buckland, Dover*, 1951–2 (forthcoming) **118**

F1 FAEGRI, K., and IVERSEN, J., *Textbook of Modern Pollen Analysis*, 1950, Copenhagen: Ejnar Munksgaard **247**

F2 FAGAN, B. M., Cropmarks in

antiquity. *Antiquity*, 1959, *XXXIII*, 279–81 **28**

F3 FARRER, T. W., BIEK, L., and WORMWELL, F., The role of tannates and phosphates in the preservation of ancient buried iron objects. *J. appl. Chem.*, 1953, *3*, 80–4. *See also* H16 **143**

F4 FINK, C. G., and ELDRIDGE, C. H., *The Restoration of Ancient Bronzes and other Alloys*, 1925, New York: Metropolitan Museum of Art **141, 201**

F5 FISHER, R. A., *The Design of Experiments* (4th edn.), 1947. Oliver & Boyd. *See also* BEVERIDGE **89**

F6 FOX, LADY A., Excavations on Dean Moor, in the Avon Valley, 1954–6. The Late Bronze Age settlement. *Trans. Devon. Ass. Advance. Sci.*, 1957, *89*, 73–5 (analysis, by Brown-Firth Research Labs., Sheffield); 33 (interpretation) **165**

F7 FOX, SIR CYRIL, *A Find of the Early Iron Age from Llyn Cerrig Bach, Anglesey*, 1945, Cardiff: National Museum of Wales **143**

FRANCE-LANORD, A., *see* S3

F8 FRANKFORTER, G. B., The occurrence of copper in the plant world. *Chem. News*, 1899, *79*, 44–5 **127**

FRYD, C. F. M., *see* H18

F9 FURUSAKA, C., Sulphate transport and metabolism by *D. desulphuricans*. *Nature*, 1961, *192*, 427–9 **157**

G1 GARBER, S., Structure of scale on plain carbon steels. *Nature*, 1959, *183*, 1387–8 **134**

GARINO, C., *see* R11

G2 GEIJER, A., (*a*) The conservation of textile objects. *Museum*, 1961, *XIV*, 161–7 (*see* Pl. 39 for "preservation" of silk by gold); (*b*) *Birka III, Die Textilfunde aus den Gräbern*, 1938, Uppsala (pp. 80–1; Pl. 21.1 especially, for reconstruction of weave from pressure points left on gold brocading by textile yarns, here decayed but *in situ* on other fragments). *See also* B32 **123**

*G3 GETTENS, R. J., and USILTON, B. M. (eds.), *Abstracts of Technical Studies in Art and Archaeology 1943–1952*, 1955, Washington: Smithsonian Institution. (This was succeeded by I1) **109**

G4 GETTINS, G. L., TAYLOR, H., and GRINSELL, L. V., The Marshfield barrows. *Trans. Brist. Glos. archaeol. Soc.*, 1953, *72*, 23–44 **137**

G5 GILYARD-BEER, R., *Excavations of six barrows of the Devil's Ring Group, Brightwell Heath, Suffolk* (forthcoming) **104**

G6 GILYARD-BEER, R., and KNOCKER, G. M., *Excavations on the site of Chertsey Abbey, 1954* (forthcoming) **106**

G7 GLOCK, W. S., *Principles and Methods of Tree-ring Analysis*, 1937, Washington: Carnegie Institute. *See also* KOLCHIN **241**

G8 GODWIN, H., *The History of the British Flora*, 1956, Cambridge University Press **100**

G9 GODWIN, H., History of weeds in Britain, in HARPER (ed.) *The Biology of Plantains*, 1960, Oxford: Blackwell Scientific Publications **246**

G10 GODWIN, H., e.g., in GREENFIELD, A neolithic pit and other finds from Wingham, East Kent. *Arch. Cantiana*, 1960, *LXXIV*, 58–72 **222**

G11 e.g., GODWIN, H., SUGGATE,

R. P., and WILLIS, E. H., Radiocarbon dating of the eustatic rise in ocean level. *Nature*, 1958, *181*, 1518–19 **27**

G12 GREENFIELD, E., Excavation of Barrow 4 at Swarkeston, Derbyshire. *J. Derbysh. archaeol. nat. Hist. Soc.*, 1960, *LXXX*, 1–48 **74**

G13 GREENFIELD, E., *Excavations at High Cross, Leicestershire, 1955* (forthcoming) **240**

G14 GREENFIELD, E., *The Roman bath house and well at Denton, Harlaxton, Lincs.* (forthcoming) **164**

G15 GREENFIELD, E., *Excavations at Thistleton, Site 3, Rutland, 1958–61* (forthcoming) **164**

GREENFIELD, E., *see* R7

*G16 GRIFFIN, J. B. (ed.), *Essays on Archaeological Methods*, 1951, Ann Arbor: University of Michigan Press

G17 GRIMES, W. F., Early man and the soils of Anglesey. *Antiquity*, 1945, *XIX*, 169–74 **211**

GRIMSHAW, R. W., *see* S8

GRINSELL, L. V., *see* G4

H1 HALL, E. T., Chemical investigation of museum objects. *Archaeometry*, 1959, *2*, 43–52 (incl. table) **211**

H2 HANDLEY, W. R. C., (*a*) *Mull and Mor Formation in Relation to Forest Soils*, 1954, Forestry Commission (Bulletin No. 23); (*b*) Further evidence for the importance of residual leaf protein complexes in litter decomposition and the supply of nitrogen for plant growth. *Plant and soil*, 1961, *XV*, 37–73 **152, 154**

H3 HANSON, D., and PELL-WALPOLE, W. T., *Chill-cast Tin Bronzes*, pp. 4–5, 1951, Edward Arnold **164**

HARTLEY, K. F., *see* R14

H4 HATHWAY, D. E., (*a*) Oak bark tannins. *Biochem. J.*, 1958, *70*, 34–42; (*b*) Experiments on the origin of oak-bark tannin. *Biochem. J.*, 1959, *71*, 533–7 **154**

H5 HATLEY, A. J., *Excavations at Salisbury Hall, Walthamstow, 1955* (forthcoming) **139**

*H6 HAWKES, C. F. C., Archaeology as science. *Advanc. Sci.*, 1957, *XIV*, 92–102

HAYES, R. J., *see* W14

*H7 HEIZER, R. F., and COOK, S. F. (eds.), *Application of Quantitative Methods in Archaeology*, 1960, Tavistock Publications **227, 250**

H8 HELBAEK, H., Early crops in Southern England. *Proc. prehist. Soc.* 1952, *XVIII*, 194–233; Domestication of food plants in the Old World. *Science*, 1959, *130*, 365; Preserved apples and *panicum* in the prehistoric site at Nørre Sandegaard in Bornholm. *Acta Archaeologica* (København), 1952, *XXIII*, 107–15; La recherche paletnobotanique. *Sibrium*, 1955, *II*, 225–31 **244**

H9 HELBAEK, H., Notes on the evolution and history of *Linum*. *KUML*, 1959, 103–20 **244**

H10 HENRIKSSON, S. T., Some experiments with oscillating pressures in wood impregnation. *Record of convention*, 1961, British Wood Preserving Association **161**

H11 HERITAGE, G. H. R., *The lifting and mounting of the mosaic floor found at Downton Roman Villa, 1957* (M.P.B.W. report, unpublished) **34**

HIGGS, E. S., *see* B32

H12 HEY. M., Chromatographic analysis of paint media. *Studies in Conservation*, 1958, *3*, 183–93 **244, 250**

H13 HILLIS, W. E. (ed.), *Wood Extractives*, 1962, Academic Press **154**

H14 HINSHELWOOD, SIR CYRIL, Address of the President at the formal opening ceremony of the Tercentenary Celebrations (of the Royal Society). *Proc. roy. Soc. A*, 1960, *257*, 421–30. Summary in *Nature*, 1960, *188*, 345–6 **16**

H15 HINSLEY, J. F., *Non-destructive Testing*, pp. 408–9, 1959, Macdonald & Evans. *See also* LAMBLE **192**

H16 HOAR, T. P., and FARRER, T. W., The anodic characteristics of mild steel in dilute aqueous soil electrolytes. *Corros. Sci.*, 1961, *1*, 49–61; Table 2 **184**

HOFMANN, U., The chemical basis of ancient Greek vase painting. *Angew. Chem.* (Intern. edn.), 1962, *I*, 341–50 **167**

H17 HOLDEN, E. W., Excavations at Hangleton, 1952–3. *Sussex Arch. Coll.*, 1963, *CI* (forthcoming) **129**

HONEYBORNE, D. B., *see* B36

HOOD, H. P., *see* B26

H18 HOSKINS, C. R., and FRYD, C. F. M., The determination of fluorine in Piltdown and related fossils. *J. appl. Chem.*, 1955, *5*, 85–7. A very sensitive method now available is due to BELCHER *et al.*, *J. chem. Soc.*, 1959, 3577 **90**

H19 HUXLEY, SIR JULIAN (ed.), *The humanist frame*, 1961, Allen & Unwin **16**

*I1 INTERNATIONAL INSTITUTE FOR CONSERVATION OF HISTORIC AND ARTISTIC WORKS, *Abstracts of the Technical Literature on Archaeology and the Fine Arts*. From 1955. (This was preceded by G3.) **109**

*I2 INTERNATIONAL CENTRE FOR THE STUDY OF THE PRESERVATION AND THE RESTORATION OF CULTURAL PROPERTY, *International Inventory of the Museum Laboratories and Restoration Workshops*, 1960, Rome: The Centre

*I3 INTERNATIONAL CENTRE FOR THE STUDY OF THE PRESERVATION AND THE RESTORATION OF CULTURAL PROPERTY, *Climatology and Conservation in Museums*, 1961, Rome: The Centre; also *Museum*, 1960, *13* (4). *See* critical comment by REES JONES in *Nature*, 1961, *191*, 1050–1

IVERSEN, J., *see* F1

JAHN, E. C., *see* W16

J1 JEDRZEJEWSKA, H., Old mortars in Poland. *Studies in Conservation*, 1960, *5*, 132–8 **236**

J2 JEWELL, P. A., Buzzards and barrows. *Listener*, 1958 (13 Feb.); *The South African Archaeological Bulletin*, 1958, *XIII*, 153–5 **250**

J3 JEWELL, P. A. (ed. of *c*), (*a*) Natural history and experiment in archaeology; (*b*) An experiment in field archaeology. *Advanc. Sci.*, 1958, XV, 165–72 (*a*); 1961, XVIII, 106–9(*b*); (*c*) *The Experimental Earthwork on Overton Down, Wilts.*, *1960* (forthcoming), British Association **48, 226**

J4 JEWELL, P. A., Changes in size and type of cattle from prehistoric to medieval times in Britain. *Zeitschr. f. Tierzücht. u. Züchtungsbiol.*, 1962, *77*, 159–67 **247**

J5 JOHNSON, A. H. (in PIGGOTT, Excavation in passage graves and ring-cairns of the Clava Group, 1952–3). *Proc. Soc. Antiqs. Scot.*, 1954, *LXXXVIII*, 200–4 **181**

J6 JOHNSTON, D. E., *Excavations at Chalk, Gravesend, Kent, 1961* (forthcoming) **164**

JONES, L. W. G., *see* C22

K1 e.g., KARAGEORGHIS, V., A "Homeric" burial discovered in a royal tomb of the seventh century B.C.: excavations at Salamis in Cyprus. *Illustr. Lond. News*, 1962, *240*, 894–6 **44**

K2 KNOCKER, G. M., *The Saxon Town of Thetford* (forthcoming), H.M.S.O. *See also* G6 **105**

K3 KNOWLES, E., and WHITE, T., The protection of metals with tannins. *J. Oil Col. Chem. Ass.*, 1958, *41*, 10–23 **151**

K3A KØIE, M., Tøj fra Yngre Bronzealderfremstillet afNælde. *Aarbøger*, 1943, 98–102 **89**

KOLCHIN, B., Dendrochronological method in archaeology. *Sixth International Congress of Prehistoric and Protohistoric Sciences, Rome, 1962*, forthcoming in *Atti* (*see* U1) **241**

K4 KONONOVA, M. M., *Soil Organic Matter*, 1961, Pergamon Press **156**

*K5 KROEBER, A. L. (ed.), *Anthropology Today*, 1953, Chicago: University Press **54, 88, 227, 250**

K6 e.g., KUBIENA, W. L., *The Soils of Europe*, 1953, Murby **155, 225**

L1 LAL, B. B., Excavations at Kalibungan. *Illustr. Lond. News*, 1962, *240*, 455 **64**

*L2 LAMING, A. (ed.), *La Découverte du Passé*, 1952, Paris: Editions Picard **28**

L2A LAMPORT, D. T. A., and NORTHCOTE, D. H., Hydroxyproline in primary cell walls of higher plants. *Nature*, 1960, *188*, 665–6 **249**

L3 LE BORGNE, E., Susceptibilité magnétique anormale du sol superficiel. *Ann. Géophys.*, 1955, *11*, 399–419 **208**

L4 LEDERER, E. and M., *Chromatography—a Review of Principles and Applications* (2nd ed.), 1957, Amsterdam: Elsevier **249**

L5 LEVI, D., (*a*) Excavations at Gortyna. *Illustr. Lond. News*, 1960, *236*, 16, Fig. 3; (*b*) A museum amid the ruins of a Minoan villa. *Museum*, 1960, *XIII*, 130–2 **31**

LOWTHER, A. W. G., *see* S7

L6 LUCAS, A., *Ancient Egyptian Materials and Industries*, e.g., p. 46 (3rd edn.), 1948, Edward Arnold **245**

L7 LUCAS, A., *M/s notebook in Griffith Institute:* "black material looking like pitch . . . is leather (actually, rawhide) decomposed by damp". Information kindly communicated by J. W. Waterer, who also refers me to Carter, H., *The Tomb of Tut-ankh-amun, I*, 132–3 **249**

L8 LUNN, J., *Excavations on the site of the car park, Verulamium, St. Albans, 1955* (forthcoming) **167**

L9 LUTZ, H. G., Concentration of certain chemical elements in soils of Alaskan archaeological sites. *Amer. J. Sci.*, 1951, *249*, 925–8 **63**

M1 MACKAY, R. R., *Excavations at Winklebury Camp, 1959* (forthcoming) **122, 240**

M2 MACKERETH, F. J. H., A portable core sampler for lake deposits. *Limnol. Oceanog.*, 1958, *3* (2), 181–91 **32**

M2A MAYES P., *et al.* The firing of a pottery kiln of a Romano–British type at Boston, Lincs. *Archaeometry*, 1961, *4*, 4–30 **228**

M3 MEDAWAR, P. B., *The two heredities*. The B.B.C. Reith Lectures, 1959, 1960, Methuen **16**

METCALFE, C. R., *see* B5

M4 MINISSI, F., (*a*) Sicily. Piazza Armerina under "Perspex": how the great mosaics are being protected. *Illustr. Lond. News*, 1960, *236*, 129; (*b*) Protection of the mosaic pavements of the Roman villa at Piazza Armerina (Sicily). *Museum*, 1961, *XIV*, 128–32 **31**

MOREY, J. E., *see* S1

M5 MOSS, A. A., Niello. *Studies in Conservation*, *1953*, *1*, 49–61 **117**

M6 MOURANT, A. E., Blood groups and human evolution. *Advanc. Sci.*, 1956, *XIII*, 91–103 **251**

MUSTY, J. W. G., *see* T3A

N1 NASH & THOMPSON, LTD., *The Tellohm Soil Resistance Meters—Geophysical Model* (with bibliography), 1957, Chessington, Surrey: The Company **207**

NATO, *An International Institute of Science and Technology*, 1962, Paris: NATO. Provision for interdisciplinary studies. **16**

N2 e.g., NEWMAN, J. R. (ed.), *What is Science?* 1956, Gollancz **16**

*N3 NICKOLLS, L. C., *The Scientific Investigation of Crime*, 1956, Butterworth **66**

N4 NORTH, A. A., and WELLS, R. A., Analytical methods for geochemical prospecting. *Symposium de Exploración Geoquimica*, 1959, *II*, 347–62. *See also*, e.g., *Analyst*, 1956, *81*, 660–8 (tungsten and molybdenum); *Trans. Instn. Min. Metall.*, 1960, *69*, 361–9 (beryllium) **207**

N5 NORTH, F. J., *Geology in the museum*, pp. 66ff., 1941, Oxford University Press. *See also* C19 **35**

N6 NORTHCOTE, D. H., The cell walls of higher plants: their composition, structure and growth. *Biolog. Rev.*, 1958, *33*, 53–102. *See also* L2A **59, 244**

O1 OAKLEY, K. P., Fire as palaeolithic tool and weapon. *Proc. prehist. Soc.*, 1955, *XXI*, 36–48 **134**

O2 OHRELIUS, B., *Vasa, the King's Ship*, 1962, Cassell **34**

O3 ORGAN, R. M., (*a*) Carbowax and other materials in the treatment of waterlogged palaeolithic wood; (*b*) Polyethylene glycols in the treatment of waterlogged wood—some precautions. *Studies in Conservation*, 1959, *4*, 96–105 (*a*); 1960, *5*, 161–2 (*b*) **161**

P1 PANSERI, C., (*a*) *Richerche metallografiche sopra una spada da guerra del XII secolo* (Quaderno I), 1954; (*b*) (ed.) *La tecnica di fabricazione delle lame di Acciaio presso gli antichi* (Quaderno II), 1955, Milan: Associazione Italiana di Metallurgia **136, 166, 239**

*P2 PARTINGTON, J. R., *The Origins and Development of Applied Chemistry*, 1935, Longmans, Green

PELL-WALPOLE, W. T., *see* H3

P3 PERRIN, R. M. S., Nature of

"chalk heath" soils. *Nature*, 1956, *178*, 31–2 **87, 225**

P4 PHILLIPS, H., The chemistry of leather. *J. R. Soc. Arts*, 1954, *CII*, 824–75 **248**

P5 PIGGOTT, C. M., Excavation of fifteen barrows in the New Forest, 1941–2. *Proc. prehist. Soc.*, 1943, *IX*, 1–28 **181**

P6 PITTIONI, R., Urzeitlicher Bergbau auf Kupfererz und Spurenanalyse. *Archaeologia Austriaca*, 1957, Beiheft 1. *See also* 1954, Heft 15; 1958, Beiheft 3; 1959, *26*; 1960, Beiheft 5; and *Sibrium*, 1958–9, *IV* **238**

P7 PLANT PHENOLICS GROUP, Monographs: Fairbairn (ed.)—*Pharmacology of Plant Phenolics*, 1958, Academic Press; Ollis (ed.)—*Recent Developments in the Chemistry of Natural Phenolic Compounds*, 1961, Pergamon Press; Anon.—*The Chemistry of Cocoa*, 1961: Brit. Food Man. Ind. Res. Assoc. *See also* P8 and P12 **153**

P8 PLANT PHENOLICS GROUP, Symposium on humic acid, Dublin, 1959. *Proc. roy. Dublin Soc.*, 1960, Ser. A, *1*, 53–195 **65**

*P9 PLENDERLEITH, H. J., *The Conservation of Antiquities and Works of Art*, 1956, Oxford Univ. Press **141, 201, 258, 260**

P10 PLESTERS, J., (*a*) The examination of paint films in micro-section, *Mus. J.*, 1954, *54*, 97–101; (*b*) Cross-section and chemical analysis of paint samples, *Studies in Conservation*, 1956, *2*, 110–57 **236**

POOLE, J. B., and REED, R., The preparation of leather and parchment by the Dead Sea Scrolls Community. *Technol. and Cult.*, 1962, *III*, 1–26. The "tannery" of 'Ain Feshkha. *Palest. Explor. Quart.*, 1961, July–Dec., 114–23 **249**

P11 PRESTON, R. D., The fine structure of wood with special reference to timber impregnation. *Record of convention*, 1959, British Wood Preserving Association **59, 126, 241**

P12 PRIDHAM, J. B. (ed.), *Polyphenols in Plants in Health and disease*, 1960, Pergamon Press **154**

P13 PYKE, M., *Automation: its Future and Purpose*, p. 9, 1956, Hutchinson **97**

Q1 QUENOUILLE, M. H., *The Design and Analysis of Experiment*, 1953, Charles Griffin **89**

R1 RAHTZ, P. A., Shearplace Hill, Sydling St. Nicholas, Dorset. *Proc. prehist. Soc.*, 1962, *XXVIII*, 289–328 **186**

R2 RAHTZ, P. A., Excavations on Farncombe Down, Berks. *Berks. Arch. J.*, 1963, 60, 1–24 **74, 183, 186, 247**

R3 RAHTZ, P. A., Excavation of two mounds on Row Down, Berks. *Berks. Arch. J.*, 1960, *58*, 20–32 and 1963, *60*, 25–9 **183**

R4 RAHTZ, P. A., Excavations at Downton, Salisbury, 1955/7. *Wiltsh. archaeol. & nat. Hist. Mag.* I (Prehistoric): 1962, *LVIII*, 116–41; II (Roman): (forthcoming) **34**

R5 RAHTZ, P. A., *Excavations at Little Ouseburn, nr. Boroughbridge, Yorks., 1958* (forthcoming) **181**

R6 RAHTZ, P. A., *King John's Hunting Lodge at Writtle, Essex* (forthcoming) **176**

R7 RAHTZ, P. A., and GREENFIELD, E., *Excavations on the Site of the*

Chew Valley Lake, near Bristol (forthcoming), H.M.S.O. **144, 189, 220, 239**

R8 RANKE, L. von, *Zur Kritik neuerer Geschichtsschreiber*, 1824, Berlin: Reiler **40**

R9 RAW, F., e.g., in "Soil as environment for animal life"—symposium at British Association Meeting. *Nature*, 1961, *192*, 315–17 **155**

R10 READ, SIR HERBERT, Baudelaire as art critic. *Listener*, 1955 (20 Oct.) 665 **41**

R11 REGGIORI, A., and GARINO, C., Esame tecnologico di un gruppo di spade galliche della Lombardia nord-occidentale. *Sibrium*, 1955, *II*, 43–55 **136, 166, 239**

REED, R., *see* B34 and POOLE

REES, A. I., Electrical prospecting methods in archaeology, *Antiquity*, 1962, *XXXVI*, 131–4 **29, 207**

R12 REYNOLDS, L., *The Manufacture of Wood Charcoal in Great Britain*, 1962, H.M.S.O. **134**

R13 REYNOLDS, S. H., *The Vertebrate Skeleton* (2nd edn.), 1913, Cambridge University Press **247**

R14 RICHARDS, E., and HARTLEY, K. F., Spectrographic analysis of Romano-British pottery. *Nature*, 1960, *185*, 194–6 **91, 229**

RICHARDS, T. LL., *see* C15

R15 RICHARDSON, K. M., Excavations in Hungate, York. *Archaeol. J.*, 1959, *CXVI*, 51–114 **142, 163**

R16 e.g., RICHMOND, I. A., in JOPE (ed.), *Studies in Building History*, Pl. II, 1962, Odhams. *See also* B32

R17 ROMANOFF, M., *Underground Corrosion*. National Bureau of Standards, U.S.A., Circular 579, 1957, Washington, D.C.: Government Printing Office **51, 239**

R18 ROYAL COMMISSION FOR HISTORIC MONUMENTS, ENGLAND, *A Matter of Time*, 1961, H.M.S.O. **15, 28**

R19 ROYAL SCHOOL OF MINES, (*a*) Autoradiographic indication of surface movement on cobalt pellet during destructive oxidation; (*b*) Geochemical prospecting. *Research Report for 1950–3*, 1954, 6 and Fig. 3 (*a*); 23–5, Figs. 12 and 13 (*b*) **130, 207**

R20 RUSSELL, LORD (BERTRAND), *The impact of science on society*, 1952, Allen & Unwin **16**

R21 RYDER, M. L., (*a*) Follicle arrangement in skin from wild sheep, primitive sheep and in parchment; (*b*) Follicle remains in some British parchments. *Nature*, 1958, *182*, 781–3 (*a*); 1960, *187*, 130–2 (*b*) **249**

R22 RYDER, M. L., (*a*) Sheep of the ancient civilisations; (*b*) The domestication of the sheep. *Wool Knowl.* 1959 (Winter), *4* (12), 10–14 (*a*); (Summer), *4* (10), 19–23 (*b*) **247**

S1 SABINE, P. A., and MOREY, E., A petrographical review of the porcellanite axes of Northern Ireland. *Ulster J. Arch.*, 1952, *15*, 56–60 **92**

S2 ST. JOSEPH, J. K. S., Air reconnaissance in Britain: (*a*) 1951–5; (*b*) 1955–7. *J. Roman Stud.*, 1955, 82–91 (*a*); 1958, 86–101 (*b*). *See also* B33 **28**

S3 SALIN, E., and FRANCE-LANORD, A., A laboratory for archaeological research. *Museum*, 1951, *4*, 190–1 **117, 165**

S4 SAUNDERS, A. D., Excavations at Park Street, 1954–7. *Archaeol. J.*, 1961, *CXVIII*, 100–35. **133**

S5 SAVORY, J. G., Damage to wood caused by micro-organisms. *J. appl. Bacteriol.*, 1954, *17*, 213–18 **59**

S6 SCHMALZ, R. F., Flint and the patination of flint artifacts. *Proc. prehist. Soc.*, 1960, *XXVI*, 44–9 **220**

S7 SCHOVE, D. J., and LOWTHER, A. W. G., Tree-rings and medieval archaeology. *Med. Arch.*, 1957, *1*, 78–95 **241**

S8 SEARLE, A. B. (*b* with GRIMSHAW, R. W.), (*a*) quoted in *Report of Natural Sciences Committee* (1944–6), Council for British Archaeology (unpublished); (*b*) *The Chemistry and Physics of Clays* (3rd edn. entirely revised and enlarged) 1959, Ernest Benn **91, 166**

S9 SEMENOV, S. A., *Pervobytnaya tekhnika* (*Prehistoric technology*), Vol. I, 1957, Moscow: Academya Nauk. Reviewed at length in *Antiquity*, 1961, *XXXV*, 161–3 **13, 56, 211**

S10 SEN, J., and BASAK, R. K., The chemistry of ancient buried wood. *Geol. Fören. Stockh. Förh.*, 1957, *79*, 737–58 **149**

S11 SHEPARD, A. O., *Ceramics for the Archaeologist*, 1956, Washington: Carnegie Institution **166, 228**

S12 SHOTTON, F. W., New petrological groups based on axes from the West Midlands. *Proc. prehist. Soc.*, 1959, *25*, 135–43 **92, 220**

SIMPSON, G., *see* E6

*S13 SINGER, C., *et al.* (eds.), *A History of Technology*, 5 vols., 1954–8, Oxford: Clarendon Press

S14 SMITH, C. S., *A History of Metallography*, 1960, Cambridge University Press **136**

S15 SMITH, M., Blood-grouping of the remains of Swedenborg. *Nature*, 1959, *184*, 867–9 **252**

S16 SMITH, M. A., The limitations of inference in archaeology. *Archaeol. News Letter*, 1955, 3–7 **17**

S17 SMYTHE, J. A., in HARTLEY, Bronze-worker's hearth. *Chester arch. Soc. J.*, 1954, *41*, 7–9 **240**

S18 SOCIETY OF LEATHER TRADES CHEMISTS, *The Chemistry of Vegetable Tannins*, 1956, Croydon: The Society **153, 248**

S19 SNELL, F. D. and C. T., *Colorimetric Methods of Analysis* (3rd edn.), Vol. II, p. 750, 1949, New York: Van Nostrand **140**

S20 e.g., SNOW, C. P., *The Two Cultures and the Scientific Revolution.* The Rede Lecture, 1959, Cambridge University Press **14**

S21 SOKOLOFF, V. P., and CARTER, G. F., Time and trace metals in archaeological sites. *Science*, 1952, *116*, 1–5. *See also* B32

S22 SPARKS, B. W., *Geomorphology*, 1960, Longmans, Green **209**

S23 SPARKS, B. W., Appendix II: Land mollusca, pp. 299–301, in A6. *See also* B32 and DRAKE **248**

S24 STEAD, I. M., Excavations at the South Corner Tower of the Roman fortress at York, 1956. *Yorks. archaeol. J.*, 1958, *XXXIX*, 515–38 **188**

S25 STEERS, J. A., *Sea Coast*, 1953, Collins **27**

S26 STOKAR, W. VON, Vorgeschichtliche Lederfunde und Lederverwendung. *Collegium*, 1936, No. 796, 433–7 **249**

S27 STONE, J. F. S., and WALLIS, F. S., Reports by Stone Axe

Subcommittee of the South-Western Group of Museums. *Proc. prehist. Soc.* 1941, *VII*, 50 First Report; 1947, *XIII*, 47–55 Second Report; 1951, *XVII*, 99–158 Third Report **92, 220**

S28 STOVES, J. L., *Fibre Microscopy: its Technique and Application*, 1957, National Trade Press **245, 248**

SUGGATE, R. P., *see* G11

S29 SUTHERLAND, C. H. V., and HAROLD, M. R., Silver content of Diocletian's early post-reform copper coins. *Archaeometry*, 1961, *4*, 56–61 **238**

TAUBER, H., *see* W17

TAYLOR, H., *see* G4

*T1 TAYLOR, W. W. (ed.), *The Identification of Non-artifactual Archaeological Materials*—Report of conference in Chicago, 1956. 1957, Washington, D.C.: National Research Council of the National Academy of Sciences **90**

THACKER, D. M. D., *see* B12

T2 THELLIER, E., Thése Fac. Sc., Paris; *Ann. Inst. Phys. Globe*, 1938, *XVI*, 157–302; also with Thellier, O.: *C. R. Acad. Sci. Paris*, 1937, *204*, 184; 1941, *212*, 281; 1942, *214*, 382; 1946, *222*, 905; 1951, *223*, 1476; 1952, *234*, 1464 **230**

T3 THOMAS, H. H., The source of the stones of Stonehenge. *Antiqs. J.*, 1923, *III*, 239–60 **92**

T3A THOMAS, L. C., and MUSTY, J. W. G., A spectroscopic survey of English and Continental medieval glazed pottery. *Nature*, 1961, *192*, 1143–4 **48, 169**

T4 THOMPSON, F. C., The early metallurgy of copper and bronze. *Man*, 1958, *LVIII*, 1 and Pl. B*a* **136, 162**

T5 THOMPSON, F. C., The use of the microscope in numismatic studies. *Numism. Chron.*, 1956, *XVI*, 329–39 **117**

T6 THOMPSON, F. C., and CHATTERJEE, A. K., The age-embrittlement of silver coins. *Studies in Conservation*, 1952–4, *I*, 115–26 **135, 162**

T7 THOMPSON, M. W., DIMBLEBY, G. W., and ASHBEE, P., Excavation of a barrow near the Hardy Monument, Black Down, Portesham, Dorset. *Proc. prehist. Soc.*, 1957, *XXIII*, 124–36 **151, 181**

*T8 THOMSON, G., *Recent Advances in Conservation—The I.I.C. Rome Conference, 1961*, 1963, Butterworth

T9 THORNBURY, W. D., *Principles of Geomorphology*, 1954, Chapman & Hall **209**

TILLER, A. K., *see* B23 and B24

T10 TOYNBEE, A., *A Study of History*, 1951–61, Oxford University Press **16**

T11 TURNER, E. G., A Roman writing tablet from Somerset. *J. Roman Stud.*, 1956, *XLVI*, 115–18 **147**

T12 TURNER, W. E. S., Studies of ancient glass and glassmaking processes. *J. Soc. Glass Tech.*, 1954, *XXXVIII*, 436–56T—I, II; 1956, *XL*, 39–52T—III; 162–186T—IV; 277–300T—V **135, 237**

T13 TYLECOTE, R. F., *Archaeology and Metallurgy*, 1962, Edward Arnold. *See also* W20 **239**

*U1 UNION INTERNATIONALE DES SCIENCES PRÉHISTORIQUES ET PROTOHISTORIQUES, *Atti del VI*

Congresso Internazionale delle Scienze Preistoriche e Protoistoriche, 1962, Florence: G. C. Sansoni **207**

USILTON, B. M., *see* G3

V1 VAN GIFFEN, A. E., Twee samengestelde palissade-heuvels (I en II) bij Nijlande, Gem. Rolde. *Nieuwe Drentsche Volksalmanak*, 1941, *59*, 7–12, Pl. 5 **180**

V2 VAN ZEIST, W., *Pollenanalytical Investigations in the Northern Netherlands, with Special Reference to Archaeology*, 1955, Amsterdam: North-Holland Publ. Co. **246**

V3 VAROSSIEAU, W. W., Ancient buried and decayed wood seen from a biological point of view, in BEEKMAN, *Hout in alle tijden*, 1949, *1*, 331–87 **148**

V4 VERNON, W. H. J., The open-air corrosion of copper. *J. Inst. Met.*, 1929, *XLII*, 181–202 **129, 176**

V5 *cf.* VERNON, W. H. J., (on the related study of) The atmospheric corrosion of copper, II (The mineralogical relationships . . .). *J. Inst. Met.*, 1930, *XLIV*, 389–408 **119**

V6 VON ENGELN, O. D., *Geomorphology*, pp. 524, 540. 1942, New York: Macmillan **27, 209**

W1 WACHER, J. S., Excavations at Calke Wood, Wattisfield, 1956. *Proc. Suffolk Inst. Archaeol. nat. Hist.*, 1958, *XXVIII*, 1–28 **168**

W2 WACHER, J. S., Litton Cheney Excavations, 1956. *Proc. Dorset nat. Hist. Fld. Cl.*, 1958, *80*, 160–77 **75, 181, 186**

W3 WACHER, J. S., Interim report on excavations at Cirencester, 1960. *Antiqs. J.*, 1961, *XLI*, 64; *also* 1963, *XLIII* (forthcoming) **25**

W4 WACHER, J. S., *Excavations at Southampton, 1955* (forthcoming) **131**

WALLIS, F. S., *see* S27

W5 WATERBOLK, H. T., *De Praehistorische Mens en zijn Milieu* (English summary) 1957, Assen, Netherlands: Van Gorcum **246**

W6 WATSON, F. J., Romano-British kiln: building and firing a replica. *Pottery Quarterly*, 1958, *5*, 72–5 **169, 228**

WATSON, W., *see* C22

WEBB, J. S., *see* E4

W7 WEBSTER, G., *et al.*, *Waternewton, 1958* (forthcoming) **196**

W8 WEINER, J. S., Skeletons: some remarks on their value to the human biologist. *Antiquity*, 1954, *XXVIII*, 197–200 **251**

W9 WELLS, C. P. B., A study of cremation. *Antiquity*, 1960, *XXXIV*, 29–37 **251**

W10 WELLS, C. P. B., A new approach to ancient disease. *Discovery*, 1961, *22*, 526–31 **251**

WELLS, R. A., *see* N4

W10A WENHAM, L. P., Excavations–York College for Girls, Low Petergate, 1957–8. *Yorks. Arch. J.* (forthcoming) **51, 188**

*W11 WHEELER, SIR MORTIMER, *Archaeology from the earth*, 1954, Oxford: Clarendon Press **23**

W12 WHEELER, SIR MORTIMER, *The Stanwick fortifications, North Riding of Yorkshire*, p. 58, 1954, Society of Antiquaries **52**

*W13 WHEELER, SIR MORTIMER, Science in archaeology. *J. R. Soc. Arts*, 1957, *105*, 860–70 **242**

W13A WHEELER, SIR MORTIMER, Size and Baalbek. *Antiquity*, 1962, *XXXVI*, 6–9 **60**

W14 WHITE, E. E., and HAYES,

R. J., The use of stereo-colour photography for soil profile studies. *Photogr. J.*, 1961, 101, 211–15 **34**

W15 WHITE, T., The chemistry of the vegetable tannins. Chapter 18 (pp. 98–160) in O'FLAHERTY: *Chemistry and Technology of leather*, Vol. II. American Chemical Society Monograph, 1960, New York: Reinhold. *See also* K3 **153, 248, 249**

WILLIAMS, D., *see* E4

W16 WILLIS, E. H., and TAUBER, H., Variations in the atmospheric radiocarbon concentration over the past 1300 years. *Amer. J. Sci., Radiocarbon Suppl.*, 1960, *2*, 1–4., *see also* G11 **94, 243**

W17 WISE, L. E., and JAHN, E. C. (eds.), *Wood Chemistry* (2nd edn.), 1954, New York: Reinhold Publishing Corporation **149**

W18 WOOLDRIDGE, S. W., *The Geographer as Scientist*, 1956, Thomas Nelson **209**

W19 WOOLLEY, SIR LEONARD, *Ur of the Chaldees*, pp. 50 and 55, 1929, Ernest Benn. I am grateful to Mr. J. W. Waterer for drawing my attention to this reference and allowing me to use his interpretation of the evidence described **65**

WORMWELL, F., *see* B24 and F3

W20 WYNNE, E. J. and TYLECOTE, R. F., An experimental investigation into primitive iron-smelting technique. *J. Iron St. Inst.*, 1958, *191*, 339–48 **81, 239**

Y1 YOUNG, J. Z., *Doubt and Certainty in Science: A Biologist's Reflections on the Human Brain.* The Reith Lectures, 1950. 1951, Oxford: Clarendon Press **16**

Y2 YOUNG, S., An analysis of Chinese blue-and-white. *Oriental Art*, 1956, *II*, 43–7 **237**

*Y3 YOUNG, W. J. (ed.), *Application of Science in Examination of Works of Art.* Proceedings of a Seminar, Sept. 1958. 1959, Boston (U.S.A.): Research Laboratory, Museum of Fine Arts **228, 236, 237, 238, 245**

Z1 ZEUNER, F. E., Geological report on the excavation of the Saxon burial ship at Sutton Hoo. *Antiqs. J.*, 1940, *XX*, 201–2. Amplified at a subsequent (unpublished) lecture and by private communication **182**

Subject Index